Deirdre

DEIRDRE

and Other Great Stories from Celtic Mythology

EOIN NEESON

MAINSTREAM
PUBLISHING

EDINBURGH AND LONDON

First published in Great Britain in 1997 by
MAINSTREAM PUBLISHING COMPANY (EDINBURGH) LTD
7 Albany Street
Edinburgh EH1 3UG

ISBN 1 85158 992 9

A catalogue record for this book is available from the British Library

Typeset in 11 on 13pt Garamond
Printed and bound in Finland by WSOY

Contents

Short Glossary

a chróidhe	a cree	my heart, an endearment
brúden	brooden	a hostelry; see below
brúdenach	broodunuck	two meanings: 1, having many mansions; 2, wealthy owner of an important hostelry, non-aristocratic
crann tamall	crown tomal	a 'tree' of bells rung for silence
Emhain Macha	Owin Mocka	the capital city of Ulster, Anglicised as Armagh
éric (eiric)	ayrick	Anglicisation, blood-fine
faitche	fwatche	sward or plain
geasa (pl. geise)	gassa (geishe)	a solemn injunction, a personal taboo
gríanán	gree-ah-nawn	a garden suntrap
kern	kern	English; also kirn, origin unknown
leabhar	lyower	A book
Leabharcam	Lyowercum	Proper name
nemheidh	nemy-nevy	sanctuary; a sacred or privileged person or place
ollagoning (olagón)	ullagohning	Anglicisation, lamenting, keening
ollamh	ullav	professor
sídh(e)	shee	people of the 'other world'; fairy, though the English meaning of the word is inappropriate
tathlum	tahlum	a stick sling

Introduction

Nowadays the word 'myth' is generally used to suggest one of three things, all of them inaccurate. These are: (1) an arena the exclusive province of scholars; (2) fairy tales for children; (3) a synonym for what is untrue.

The phrase 'it's only a myth' usually means that something is fallacious. This gives an inaccurate and pejorative meaning to the word. The usage seems to be based on the idea that since mythology is imaginative, it must also be false, or at least so imprecise as to be irrelevant. But the truth is that if myth is based on anything at all, it is on reasoning. The second common error is to dismiss myths as stories fit only for children. It is, of course, true that mythological stories appeal to children. After all they are meant to impress and be awe-inspiring. But – appalling 'fairy-tale' versions notwithstanding – any suggestion that myths are suitable only for children is a nonsense. The mythologies, demonstrating man's awe before the 'unknown and the supernatural', are themselves evidence of that. Kees W. Bolle writes:

Myth is a collective term used for one kind of symbolic communication and specifically indicates one basic form of religious symbolism, as distinguished from symbolic behaviour (cult, ritual) and symbolic places such as temples and icons. Myths in the plural are specific accounts concerning gods or superhuman beings and extraordinary events in circumstances and in a time that is altogether different from that of ordinary experience.

In fact mythology is a key to the self-image of a people, providing a revealing, often authoritative, blueprint of past human outlook. Hence the efforts made to determine its real meaning. Myths relate events and states of affairs basic to, yet surpassing, both the mortal world and its people. And as Bolle says: 'present extraordinary events without trying to justify them'. Here is their importance as repositories of self-image. Eoin MacNeill, another authority on ancient literature and customs, makes the point that: 'In . . . ancient Ireland, perhaps more truly than in the Homeric age of Greece, one may look for the European *juventus mundi* . . .'

There's no simple definition of mythology. It is something of fact and something of fiction, but entirely of neither. It has been created by man to give shape and definition to otherwise inexplicable wonders and unseen gods.

But then there is the doctrine that nothing has validity that cannot be scientifically proven (which, from about the mid-fifteenth century onwards would become a rigid axiom of many disciplines so that much accumulated folk wisdom, some of it doubtless contaminated, was jettisoned for centuries and is only now in the process of being re-examined). In relation to mythology this inflexible doctrine would prove very hostile. While it did much good – in medicine, for instance – that was not always the case. When also (later) applied to history – as when one brigade of historians sought to encase the subject in a straitjacket of 'scientific revision' – it occasionally produced some very peculiar results[1]. Mythology, like superstition, came to be lumped with lack of sophistication and became a casualty, so that those who took it seriously had, like Macauley, often to 'cheerfully bear the reproach of having descended below the dignity of history'. In reality it is absurd to exclude oral tradition on the grounds that it is irrelevant to historical knowledge – particularly concerning belief. To suppose that it was of interest only to children and old people before verifiable written documentation became common is ludicrous, but not unknown.

It is patent nonsense to assert that countless generations responded to the fundamental mysteries of life and death with what they perceived as essentially false. Their myths enshrined what they believed and what they believed was, for them, the truth. Accordingly we may infer – even if we cannot prove – the validity and veracity of myths and that, however dressed up, mythology is based on a perception of truth and not on a perception of falsehood.

In a letter to the *Irish Times* (5.1.94), Donal O'Driscoll, PP, Cloyne, Co. Cork, wrote: 'Myths . . . are of value because they embody underlying states of mind, distillations of human experience illustrating human nature in its universal aspects, and so are ideal vehicles for the communication of fundamental truths.'

Mythology is universally evident in human communities – except the most modern (in which it is being formulated) – and is, like religion, a basic constituent of human culture. It is a repository of old truths and beliefs and, so, contains – even if only in symbolic form – the history, records and beliefs of the ancients. Accordingly the functions of the mythologist and the historian are far from being mutually exclusive.

In fact myths present a model for man's behaviour from prehistoric times. Some of the 'cult' syndromes of some of the newer nations, such as those which seem to proliferate in California, may be examples of the innate drive, or instinct, concerned with the superhuman and the spiritual, to which people can relate. Mythology, by describing what can never be determined by reason and observation alone, offered an explanation for what was otherwise inexplicable.

Myth and social development combined provide clues to students of history and anthropology. As with overlapping cultures, such as the neolithic and later civilisations, overlapping clearly also occurs in documented mythology.

In his *Theogony*, Hesiod offers an account of the creation of the universe and the generation of the gods which emphasises that mythology is man's attempt to answer the questions – whence the world, the sky, the gods that fill them, mankind himself, and why. And if, today, the word 'myth' is corrupted it is because it concerns patterns of belief so ancient that we lack the appropriate means to discern them; which is not to say that such patterns – even beliefs – may not have been misconceived, but that is a different question.

Mythology expresses the anxiety of man through the ages to define and understand perceived mysteries. It cannot, therefore, be said to be either wholly fact or wholly fancy. It can be said to represent elusive truths envisaged by societies – usually remote in time – and perhaps, but not necessarily, in thinking.

Of course, unlike what history purports to do, mythology does not provide concrete answers. On the other hand where else should one look to know what the peoples of past civilisations believed?

*　　　*　　　*

A function of myths is to provide answers to natural, social, cultural and biological phenomena. They help illuminate the nature of ancient ritual and religious custom. Of course this can sometimes be circular and self-validating, the myths authenticating the rituals and customs occurring in them. But, even so, they provide a pattern for what can never be determined by reason alone.

It seems to be generally accepted that mythology originates as an imaginative interaction between man, his nature and his spirit, fuelled by his hopes, fears, experiences, conditioning and . . . who knows . . . the Hand of God? Mythology is really a term used to indicate a form of religious symbolism, and is an indication of the self-image of a people in a given civilisation.

Like all religious symbolisation myths lie outside normal requirements of justification. They concern gods and extraordinary events or circumstances in a time outside ordinary human experience. They are a source for knowledge of problems of existence and their definition, and they have an authoritative, revelatory function in respect of human existence. Hence they are understood both as religious phenomena and as narrative literature.

As with religious ideas, those of mythology seek both to surpass and at the same time be basic to the known world. It is therefore argued that myths should be understood as being both religious phenomena and narrative literature. In that case is not the time overdue when mythology was restored to a place of dignity and is no longer an adulterated province of childhood, a remote one of scholars, or, worst of all, a mere synonym for falsehood?

Gods and sacrifice are concomitant. The concept of gods, from whatever Pantheon, living in the heavens or in some equally remote, but glorious place, is universal. The idea exists in different cultures throughout the world, too numerous and too frequent to be coincidental. The question arises whether this is the result of cross-fertilisation of ideas or is the natural spontaneous thrust of man's hope and expectancy towards another, supernatural, world?

The thrust of mythology is towards enlightenment. The profoundest mystery is death and the association between it and religion is clear. Death remains as much a mystery to us as it was to our primitive ancestors. Evidence of religious activity, belief in the supernatural and awe before death is everywhere evident in prehistoric tombs. Communication between man and his gods cannot be a one-way process.

Again like religion, myths, being concerned with the suprahuman and the spiritual, offer explanations for the otherwise inexplicable from the world of the supernatural, with which, through mythology and various phenomena, men are familiar and to which they are sometimes transported. If, then, myths are criteria for falsehood, religion must be in a very bad way.

Today many of us have powerful, institutionalised, religious doctrine and faith to assist us. Surely these occupy a place similar to that of mythology for the ancients? Or are we expected to assume that people down through the ages were not moved by hopes, fears and faiths of their own? Are we to assume, as in spite of all our assembled wisdom we so often seem to be instructed, that man's soul leaped into his body only when he learned to write? How awesome and powerful in early nomadic man must have been the fear of death and the aspiration to overcome it! Surely he lived in a world peopled with vast numbers of spirits, and brought these spirits and their worlds with him down through the ages?

It cannot be accidental that religion and mythology provide the ligaments and tendons that held together many of the magnificent cultures and civilisations of history. The concept of justice, perhaps consequent on the idea of gods, enters into mythology early on. With that idea the needs of the helpless reached towards heaven to change the god of the strong into the protector of the helpless and the weak.

*   *   *

Although many of the great influences affecting mankind have altered through the millennia (especially in the last few centuries), so far as we know the nature of man himself has changed very little. Neolithic peoples of today and the recent past, such as the African bushmen and Australian aboriginals, differ from the rest of us only in conditioning. It is reasonable to assume that the outlook and behaviour of the druids and their peoples were influenced by the laws, rituals and prohibitions of the religions they practised, obscure though these may be, in much the same way as we today are influenced by the taboos and totems of our own time. Since it would be totally fallacious to suppose that people are other than children of their age, we may also infer that early people and their druids reacted to their total environment much as we do to ours. It is virtually certain that they practised a religion containing elements already very old. Thus we may reasonably assume that some traditions and characteristics still surviving are rooted in older patterns which were, in turn, the inheritors of traditions going back thousand of years.

In Ireland early waves of immigration – from various but, in the main, probably related sources – contributed to the matrix of Celtic homogeneity. The early Celtic settlers were the inheritors of Indo-European traditions already very ancient. Behind them, as Stuart Pigot points out, lay the wholly obscure religions of neolithic agriculturalists; finally, underlying all were the beliefs and rites of the hunting people . . . a pedigree which could be 20,000 or more years long. Blinded by science or not, we are an extension of that pedigree.

Throughout recorded history a noticeable characteristic of the Irish has been a belief that the next world is more important than this one. At the same time a distinction has always been made between the two, thus ensuring that enjoyment in this life is enhanced, not diminished, by the promise of the next. This balance of the spiritual and material (by no means exclusively Hibernian) is less common in a Western society dominated by materialism. Ironically peoples who have not developed, or have rejected, a mythological Pantheon of their own to explain the dark recesses of the mind and the gleaming virtues of aspiration, sometimes do not possess this balance, and seem instead to attend the golden calf, reborn, and a curious devotion to superstition, a compensatory theology, perhaps; the myth validating the belief?

It is unlikely that this double-worldly characteristic was instantly acquired by the Irish on their conversion to Christianity. As the only Celtic people not conquered by Rome, it is reasonable to suppose that they preserved a Celtic tradition more or less intact, and that, therefore, such ideas were also part of the Celtic heritage. This may have helped ease the path of Christianity. There was undoubtedly a virtually bloodless acceptance of it by a people who, in an enduring *bouleversement du mystique*, evidently welcomed a new spiritual and intellectual dynamic.

Perhaps because it is so difficult to interpret that mythology that it is so often dismissed as unworthy of serious historical consideration. Yet it is against the same criteria as history, namely religion, politics and a record of events – common to all societies at all times – that mythology should be considered in order to be understood. Of these the spiritual is probably the most tantalising aspect. Where there is a spiritual concept there are inevitably gods, a religion and priests . . . what, in Ireland, was synthesised in so-called druidism and druids.

The extent that a society moulds its mythology, and vice versa, is a variation on the old chestnut 'if God had not made man, man would have had to invent God'. Since, in the main, mythology deals with relationships between man and the supernatural and not with concrete matters, the question 'Is myth fact or fancy?' is meaningless except in a relative and comparative sense. No sensible person believes in euhemerism – attributing to a myth a factual, historically accurate basis, or to mythological gods a magnification of real people. But neither is it sensible to reject mythology holus-bolus simply because we don't understand it and because those who did or who developed it are beyond reach. The questions involved may not be capable of a full, clear and complete answer. But that is a fault of time and our inability to penetrate it. It does not invalidate the perceptions and the trust of countless dead generations. There is no doubt that mythologies, diminished and debased by time or not, represent a vast accumulation of religious significance and perceived belief.

When more than one community vies for the same distinct territory (as happened in both Japan and Ireland during the neolithic period and also later on), or where two or more ideologies vie for control of a community, the dominant usually endures. But aspects of the subordinate culture will also survive and, so, become sources of minor tradition. Professor Pigot observed: 'We . . . see that . . . druids are particular instances of a general problem, the limitations of human knowledge of the past.'

In heroic Ireland and Shogunate Japan, society contained a developed sense of justice, both worldly and unworldly. The Brehon law, the legal tracts of the Gaelic Celts, deals with criminal and civil law and endeavours to legislate for all circumstances and situations. Like the Japanese system it 'was essentially administrative rather than court-based'.[2] There was no lawyer class, as such, but there were brehons whose function was to advise the king who administered the law. The law governing religion and worship in pre-Christian Ireland is, for the obvious reason – the clerical 'clean-up' between the sixth and twelfth centuries – less well known, but the indications are that it was similarly institutional and comprehensive.

*   *   *

The description of 'facts' is 'particular observational data relating to the past or present'. However, when it is a question of considering the past in human terms this rigid formula proves inadequate, either excluding more than might be included, or encouraging dogmatic conclusions that sometimes verge on the ludicrous. W.G. Aston puts it (*Nihongi, Chronicles of Japan from the Earliest Times to AD 697*): 'the confirmed habit of throwing back, no doubt more or less unconsciously, to more ancient times the ideas of their own age' is misleading; and results in mythological, even historical, facts being interpreted according to much later principles, so that more recent values are attributed to the older tradition. But 'even the large untrue element is not without its value. Bad history may be good mythology – statements at variance with fact often throw a useful light on the beliefs or institutions of the age when they became current'(Terence Barrow, Introduction to Aston's *Nihongi*). For instance Heinrich Schliemann's conviction and determination led him to successfully establish the reality behind one of the greatest so-called 'myths' in the world, Troy. And if he stretched matters to include the 'discovery' of Priam's treasure (which is the subject of doubt) that is another matter and neither invalidates the superior discovery, nor justifies those who ridicule it. Nor is there much doubt about the 'myth' of the Minoan labyrinth of Crete.

So far as we can tell the Irish Celts were a pastoral/agricultural homogeneous people, distinct in language and custom from their British and European counterparts. They had a well-developed social order and a complex and extensive legal system purporting to govern all aspects of life (and death). Contrary to popular opinion there is little evidence that they were an unusually militaristic race for the period or their state of development, but the 'warrior' cult and associated sense of honour were highly developed, and were similar to those of the samurai class of Japan and the Bushido code during the Shogunate. Indeed there are pronounced cultural similarities in the development of these two homogeneous island peoples who were cut off for centuries from outside influence, one of them in the self-styled Land of the Rising Sun, the other in the equally self-styled Land of the Setting Sun, which is one of the oldest names for Ireland.

Parallels may be seen in their island development in relative isolation. It happened in Ireland for about a thousand years, from 500 or 600 BC to the coming of Christianity about AD 400–500, and in Japan for about the same sort of time, from about AD 600 to 1853. Could it be the case that homogenous peoples with a certain advanced level of cultural development will, if allowed to develop on islands small enough to be conceptual and in the absence of any external or alien dynamic, tend to progress along similar lines? Here may lie an explanation for the similarities in the use of colour, form, manners, custom, poetry, warrior cult and code of honour between, for instance, the Tokugawa period in Japan and the Gaelic Order at the time of Patrick.

Many so-called enlightened people would think it absurd that a leading world nation in the twentieth century would consider its leader to be a god descended from gods. Yet until at least the middle of the Showa period Emperor Hirohito was considered by most of the intelligent, civilised, cultured population of Japan to be just such. Why then should there be incredulity at similar beliefs thousands of years ago, or doubt about the processes that gave rise to them? Why should we now think that people who lived with and believed in such 'myths' were somehow different because of that, or dismiss the traditions of their mythology as trivial?

In the case of Japan the historical explanation lies in Japanese tradition and mythology as enshrined in the *Nihongi* and the *Kojiki*, the seventh- and eighth-century principal sources for Japanese mythology, which bear a comparative relationship to the Irish *Leabhar Gabhala* (*Book of Invasions*) and the *Lebor na hUidhri* (modern spelling, Leabhar na hUidhre – Lyower nuh Hyree) more familiarly known in translation, from the vellum on which it was written, as the Book of the Dun Cow.

While these throw light on what are thought to be the superstitions of uncivilised peoples, in the other case we have a perfect contemporary example of precisely just such a 'myth' flourishing in what is, paradoxically, one of the most civilised, scientifically and technologically advanced societies of our time.

In both the Irish and Japanese Pantheons gods and goddesses had incestuous relationships (how else were they to populate an empty world?) that resulted both in children of unusual powers and in associated guilt: outstanding Celtic offspring of such relationships have their counterparts in the Japanese chronicles. For example Lugh Lamh Fada,[3] the Ildanach or IL-Dana, who was destined to kill his grandfather, the one-eyed demi-god Balor (a smith, like the one-eyed smith-god, Ma-Hitotsu-no-Kami, also called Ama-tsu Mara in the *Kojiki*). 'Thus,' as the Rees brothers put it, 'the incestuous birth of the hero again symbolises the presence in the child of a universal, the beginning and the end, which recognises neither brother nor sister, father nor mother – and in the last synthesis, neither species nor gender nor element.'

*   *   *

The people who first reached the island of Ireland already had a long tradition behind them. By becoming an island people they also became essentially homogeneous and provided the critical circumstances enabling the development of cultural characteristics that, because of their isolation in contrast to that of their intermingling continental cousins, endured.

Irish literature, based on myth and legend is, apart from that of Greece and Rome, by far the oldest in Europe. The earliest surviving copies of chronicles from Ireland date from between the sixth and eighth centuries AD. The impact of the Christian dynamic in the fifth century was revolutionary, and it is to Christianity that the impetus to write them down is often attributed. Before that there were older – possibly, but by no means certainly, oral – chronologies from which these later models were drawn. Written under the influence of Christian morality – perhaps even by Christian monks – they were, not surprisingly, almost certainly modified to some extent. They tended to be written in both Latin and Old Irish, and may not have been the first recensions. Whether the use of Latin and Old Irish followed the coming of Christianity or not, is not known. But, interestingly, even the prehistoric linear carved script – ogham – found mainly on Irish mesoliths, is in alphabetical form.

The remarkable thing is not that the 'cleaning-up' occurred, but that so much of the original vitality and psychological insight survived. For this we are in debt to those early clerics and scribes who recognised the importance of what they dealt with and preserved it for posterity.

The heroic period, as it is called, in Ireland, illustrated through the annals and such accounts as those of the *Leabhar Gabhala* and the *Book of Invasions* (copies dating only from the eighth century onwards), have been dated with reasonable accuracy to between 200 BC and 250–350 AD.

In ancient Ireland alone we find the autobiography of a people of European white men who came into history not moulded into the mould of the complex East – nor forced to accept the law of Imperial Rome; Christian indeed already when that record comes first to be written down, yet accepting Christianity freely with all the freedom that is possible to men; retaining at the same time all of their own tradition . . . the laws, the local histories and genealogies, the heroic legends of the Irish nation, are copiously recorded in writing within a period covering portions of the seventh and eighth centuries, wrote MacNeill.

Much of the rediscovery work of Celtic pre-history that occurred towards the end of the last century, native traditional lore and mythology having been virtually lost under alien rule since 1601, was undertaken by – mainly German – scholars steeped in the philosophy of the Greek and Roman world (and, to a considerable extent, in nineteenth-century romanticism). They may, for such reasons, have further excluded much of what remained of, for instance, the phallicism and animism that was fundamental to the Irish Celtic system, the curious awe surrounding the product of incestuous relationships (a feature of the cosmogonies of both Japan and Ireland), and so on and that was shocking or immoral to Victorian eyes. Their view of the Celts would also, no doubt, have been coloured by such dubious authorities as Julius Caesar and would, in any case, tend to have been influenced by their knowledge of the Celts of northern Europe rather than by those of Ireland or Scotland, who, ironically, were the purest reservoirs of surviving Celtic folklore, culture and tradition, though differing in many important respects from northern European Celticism.

The 'heroic age' even has some influence on Irish people to this day. For instance that of more than 2,000 years of the spoken Irish language, the oldest vernacular in Europe, but now in decline.

In early Ireland and Scotland poets, scholars, lawyers and druids occupied exceptionally high positions in society. Indeed, poets were men of such distinction and power that they stood second only to kings. But they became so arrogant and powerful and so abused their privileges – for instance, the right to visit a nobleman with all their retinues, sometimes numbering in the hundreds, and stay, on full board so to speak, for as long as they chose – that in 574 AD a National Council at Drum Ceat in County Antrim was convened solely to consider two questions: the first was whether to permit a form of home rule or self-government to the Irish colony of Scotland; and the second was to consider the abolition of the Order of Poets. (These, with the help and guidance of the great saint Columba, or Colm Cille, were decided by granting home rule on terms of a tribute and help in time of war and by retaining the Order of Poets, but with drastically reduced rights.)

Amongst the personas attributed to Ireland by the early Celts two were basic, and both were female. One was that of a beautiful, fecund princess, the other that of an ancient, infertile and malevolent hag, the Cailleach. As an agricultural/pastoral people the Celts depended on crops and fodder and were, therefore, very aware of rotation and of cyclic events. So significant was this idea that the king, in an important ritual 'married' the earth (in what form it is now impossible to say, but presumably as a young queen). Presumably also it was believed that as the king grew old and less potent his consort, too, would age, progressing from being the young queen to becoming the old, barren – and therefore infructuous Cailleach. Moreover, so long as the old king lived the infertile Cailleach would reign as queen, with consequent risk to general fecundity and prosperity. According to cyclic theogony *she* might be rejuvenated or retain her youth and remain fit for marriage; but for a mortal king that was impossible. Hence the idea of ritual murder/sacrifice of the king at an appropriate juncture and the vast mythology fabricated around that event – and which may remain in what Jung called the (racial) collective unconscious. There is no doubt that the Irish Celts practised this ritual.

If this theory has substance it might help explain why the Celts, like some of the Hellenes with whom they had much in common, practised ritual murder of their kings, rejuvenating and making once again nubile the very land itself. It is possible to make the not unreasonable assumption that prior to the marriage of a rejuvenated earth to a new (young) king both the ritual murder of the old king *and* the ritual 'birth' of a new required to be accomplished.

Over the entrance to the Newgrange tumulus there is a small aperture that, in and around the winter and summer solstices, admits the sun's rays to penetrate the long passageway and illuminate the chamber deep within the interior in a marvellous and uncanny fashion – a construction duplicated in some of the Egyptian temples, as, indeed, are many of the hieroglyph and other carvings at Newgrange and elsewhere.

Here are many mysteries in one. What of Newgrange itself and its prehistoric builders? This aperture may explain the tradition that Newgrange, Brugh na Boinne, is the home of Aengus Óg, the love/sun god, otherwise hardly consonant with its being solely a necropolis. Complicating the mystery is the fact that the people with whose active mythology Newgrange is most associated – the Celts under one name or another – did not come to Ireland until almost three thousand years after Newgrange had been built, though it features so profoundly in their mythology, accounts of which were, themselves, modified by Christian thinking a thousand years later again! On what repository of belief and tradition did the Celts superimpose or build their own? Or have we contradictory traditions and rituals interred at Newgrange?

It is held that the Newgrange complex is (primarily) a ritual burial ground. The assumption that sometimes follows is that these huge, abiding and spectacular monuments constitute some kind of vast mausoleum in which multitudes of people were cremated and buried from time to time. Of course nothing could be more illogical. If they were ritual burial chambers – and there is little doubt about this – they were clearly and primarily the temples of whatever ritual was involved. If only because of limitations of space such a ritual cannot have included large numbers of people, although many who were not directly involved may have been, and probably were, outside onlookers, even participants, as was certainly the case in later years with early Christian churches. It is otherwise difficult to explain satisfactorily how such rituals might be accommodated in, or close to, these monuments, which took immense organisation and innumerable man-hours to build. They were not mere burial chambers, like the pyramids of Egypt (which they pre-date) and which were constructed to commemorate individual kings; but were used over and over again, presumably for the same, or a derived or substituted ritual. This can only have involved their being the focus of some kind of spiritual activity or cult which, it may be reasonably inferred, clearly had both an élite priesthood and the participation (willing or otherwise) of a substantial population.

The tumuli were not, therefore, like the pyramids, monumental crypts and ends in themselves. They were demonstrably places of living and longstanding ritual. The question that arises is what kind (or kinds) of ritual might have been involved? Much speculation, some of it highly imaginative and some of it circumstantially alluring, has been put forward from time to time, but seldom takes into account the great imponderable itself – human nature, which probably has not changed all that much.

There is at the outset the apparent contradiction of Newgrange being, on the one hand, a mausoleum (necropolis, some would have it), and, on the other, the traditional home of the young sun/love god Aengus Óg. Significantly enough his home was, according to tradition, 'forever open to everyone' – a phrase which is itself open to several interpretations, ranging from that of 'Death the leveller' to a popular centre for communal worship and festivity.

The apparent stratification of cultures involved complicates the problem. But even with overlapping cultures and contradictory rituals, it is not unreasonable to assume that the essence of these survived as long as the rituals themselves. Tara – Cathair Cro-Fhind, the Crimson City, to the Tuatha de Danaan – is close to Newgrange. It was, from beyond the mists of time, both the real and 'mystical fifth' centre of Ireland and the seat of its kings. The standing pillar-stone known as the Bud Fhearghus, or the Standing Member of Fergus (now moved from its original position), was alleged to have shrieked when the true (and new) king drove his chariot round it. It still bears scars held to be from chariot bosses.

Looking at the Newgrange complex from the air it is apparent that the mounds, Knowth, Dowth and Newgrange, form a triangle of three hemispheres on the face of the flat countryside. Two are about the same size and the third is larger. They are reminiscent of an outsize representation of a pregnant Mediterranean fertility goddess. Moreover, the Newgrange chamber is shaped precisely like a womb. And, wonder of wonders, what happens on the solstice? The life-giving rays of the sun penetrate this 'womb'. And for what conceivable purpose other than to fertilise the earth and bring forth a new, vital king?

Is it too far-fetched to suggest that we are here looking at the womb of the world? That the old king was brought to Newgrange where he was ritually murdered[4] and cremated and that the new king sprang forth from this womb, perhaps even smeared with the blood of his predecessor, leaped on a chariot, drove to Tara and whirled round the 'Standing Member' so that it screamed, and that the mystical and cyclic ritual was completed when he 'married' the earth? The thesis is perhaps fanciful. It cannot be proved. But it makes considerable sense.

*   *   *

Mythology may not be a precise record, but it is a record. The relatively homogenous Irish Celts, distinct in language and customs from their British and European counterparts (both of whom have largely disappeared), possessed a developed social order and a complex and extensive legal codex. Far from being mutually exclusive, mythology and history are interdependent to a considerable extent. To try to study ancient peoples and their customs seriously, but exclude from consideration what influenced much of their behaviour and attitudes, would be a bit like trying to study the history of Christendom without reference to the Old Testament.

This influence may be observed in Ireland, for instance, in the identification of the heathen goddess, Brigit, with Saint Brigit, and the adaptation by Christianity of the heathen feast of Imbolc, dedicated to the goddess Brigit, as the saint's feast-day. Brigit was the popular goddess of early spring and lambing and, consequently, of slaves and fudirs who were essentially responsible for lambs and lambing in the Celtic world. A similar process occurred with the adaptation of heathen places of veneration, often wells, which were absorbed in large numbers into forms of Christian worship.

The difference between myth and legend is sometimes simplified along the lines of 'a myth is an invented story, while a legend is not wholly an invented story – it is a kind of history', as Anne Terry happily claims in the introduction to her book *Myths and Legends*. This statement is all the more lamentable because it is directed at children. In fact the situation is almost precisely the reverse. There is some truth, somewhere, in mythology; but a legend is essentially an invented story about a real place or person. Terry compounds the matter by stating: 'Of course, there may be plenty of invention and myth wrapped around a legend, but always at its heart there is a kernel of historical truth.' This is also wrong. It would be more accurate to say that, in general, while there *may* be truth in mythology it is unproved and unverifiable; but legends tend to be fictions about people known to have existed. The following oversimplification illustrates the point: the *Iliad* is – or was – a myth; Homer is a legendary figure.

In her book, *Mythology*, Edith Hamilton says: 'The Greeks did not believe that the gods created the universe. It was the other way about; the universe created the gods. Heaven and earth had been formed before the gods and were the first parents. The Titans were their children and the gods were their grandchildren.' The accumulation of fear, struggle, conditioning, adaptation and assimilation, over countless thousands of years, prior to the emergence of this concept may only be guessed at. It is equally so for every mythology. The old mythologies, often now reduced to tales for children, were once the repositories of the spirit.

In *The Irish Landscape*, Frank Mitchell points out that:

Like all primitive folk they (the early inhabitants of Ireland) will have seen their surroundings as peopled, not only by the living community, but also by potentially beneficial deities who had to be propitiated, by hostile demons who had to be avoided or exorcised and by the spirits of the former members of the community.

Regrettably a dismissive attitude discredits the evidence, circumstantial though it may be, about the origin of the earliest Irish Celts, the Firbolgs, Nemedians and Tuatha de Danaan. Schliemann's discovery of the site of so-called 'mythical' Troy at the beginning of the century upset the conventional wisdom that it was only a figment of Homer's imagination. (Paradoxically, those who held the conventional view were in no doubt of the reality of Homer, which is now in question.) It is unlikely that over a period of more than a thousand years generations continued to give shape, substance and form to imaginary peoples called Tuatha de Danaan, Nemedian and Firbolg. It is more credible to assume that there was some basis in fact. There are many possibilities and, no doubt, theories to go along with these – for instance that they were peoples whose cultures were absorbed by the dominant Milesian Celts; that they were anthropomorphosised Celtic god-figures, either of which might explain the central role played by Brugh na Boinne and other pre-Celtic sites in Celtic mythology. But that the idea of these peoples being simultaneously imaginary and ageless is less than credible.

In spite of her location Irish mythology is closer to the sunlit mythology of the Mediterranean and central Eurasia than to the gloomy ones of Northern Europe and Scandinavia, and shares with the Mediterranean tradition a similarity of brightness, feeling and comparable incidents, style and characters.[5] Newgrange, the massive neolithic monument in the Boyne valley, is the oldest stone building in Europe, rivalling in size, awesomeness and function, the Egyptian pyramids which it pre-dates. It also long pre-dates the later Celtic culture in whose mythology it, nevertheless, so significantly features. It existed long before the Celts came to Ireland, which was not before 800 BC and was probably later. They designated it Brugh na Boinne, the Hostel on the Boyne, and allotted it to their sun/love god, Aengus Óg – Young Aengus – either by adopting the established rituals of an older people or because it was the most imposing monument in the country and is in the east where the sun rises. MacNeill states: 'All the Mediterranean lands are permeated even in their prehistoric times by the influence of the East.' There is constant reiteration in Irish mythological tales of association and connection with the Greeks and with the Scythians, who inhabited the Ukraine and Russian steppe contiguous to the Celtic heartland.

There are three main streams of European mythology, two of them subdivided. They are the dark, brooding mythological cycles of Northern Europe, the sun-filled (irrespective of the blood spilled) Mediterranean tradition and the Celtic, the last two being much older than the first. Recalling the proposition that in mythology lies the essential self-image of a people, these links are probably the strongest evidence of the Mediterranean origin of the dominant Irish Celts.

Isolated on the fringe of Europe and lapped by the nethermost ocean of the time; a good deal closer geographically to the primitives of Britain and northern Europe who later developed their bloody sagas of immolation and despair, why and how did the ancient Irish (evidently) reach a more advanced level of social and cultural development, and why is their mythology permeated with an ambience closer to that of the distant Mediterranean and the Persian/Indian tradition than to that of northern Europe? Surely the answer lies in tradition itself – which maintains that the dominant Irish Celts came via the Mediterranean bringing with them aspects of the cultures they had experienced *en route?*

It is also possible that incoming Christian priests of the fifth century, perhaps some of them of Mediterranean origin and influence, introduced such characteristics when committing the mythologies to writing. But if that happened one would expect, after any initial effect, that the influence would have quickly corrected itself. The bulk of available recensions date from the tenth and eleventh centuries, which is more than ample time for natural readjustment. The characteristic is evidently deeper and more enduring.

From as early as 1000 BC a race called the Milesians, allegedly skilled mathematicians and philosophers, lived in Ionia (part of modern Turkey), having come there via Macedon from the region where the Celtic heartland bordered Scythia. According to Herodotus, who thought they had Scythian connections, they were an Hellenic (that is non-Greek, but within the loose Hellenic hegemony) and Phoenician people, who spoke a distinct language of their own.[6] (In this time and context 'Phoenician' should not be confused with the later citizens of North Africa. Like Philistine it was a word loosely applied to sea-nomads, rather as the word 'Viking' later came to be used to describe all Norsemen.) According to Irish tradition Milesius, the forbear of the Irish Milesians, was a Scythian who came with his people from Spain which he reached via Egypt. The Ionian Milesians were a strong, independent people, the only ones in the region from whom neither Croesus, the Lydian, nor Cyrus, the Persian, exacted tribute when they overran the area. Both Herodotus and Zenophon mention the later Milesians as being good at commerce, war and colonisation. (For what it is worth consider the aural similarity of Ionia, an Hellenic placename, And Cliona, one of the names allegedly given to Ireland by her Milesian settlers and later transmuted into the eponymous name of a 'mythical' queen.) The Milesians lived in three cities in Ionia, the chief of which was called Miletus. They represented a portion of the race only, the remainder being nomads and settlers. It was the Milesian command of the seas that enabled them to survive when their neighbours were overwhelmed by the Lydians, the Medes and the Persians; and it was their command of the sea that enabled them to establish trading colonies in Sicily, Sardinia, Italy and Spain – and, finally, to reach Ireland.

Although like the Macedonians the Milesians were Hellenes, they lived in Asia and, in the pantheistic climate of the period, would have been familiar with, and possibly influenced by, Asiatic mystical beliefs. After the battle of Mycale, in which the confederated Hellenic states defeated the invading armies of Xerxes, the Milesians (who *had* been under Persian domination at this time, approximately 500 BC), according to Herodotus attacked their enemies from the rear during the battle and were instrumental in the Hellenic victory.

Subsequently the Hellenes held a council to decide the future of the people of Ionia and decided to abandon the indefensible coast to the Persians and remove for resettlement elsewhere. The plan was abandoned (after pressure from the Athenian Greeks who had no wish to see this forward area of defence fall into Persian hands), but not before many of the Milesians decided, notwithstanding, to ship westward and settle elsewhere.

So there is, at least, a *prima facie* case in support of the *Leabhar Gabhala* theory that a people called the Milesians could have come to Ireland via Spain about this time, which is roughly consonant with Milesian migrations from Ionia to Tartessia, that is between 800 and 500 BC.

The *Book of Invasions* tells us that the Milesians followed the Tuatha de Danaan to Ireland and that the Tuatha de Danaan had followed the Nemedians (allegedly Celts from northern Spain) and the Firbolgs. The Milesians either conquered or absorbed the earlier inhabitants. We are also told that before these Celtic peoples the earlier dominant inhabitants were Fomorians – said to have been from Lochlann, southern Scandinavia (or who may have been Picts, who survived until much later in Britain).[7] However, as we have seen, the idea that the Irish Celts or Gaels might have come from the Mediterranean is contested – mainly on the grounds that it cannot be proved. Neither, of course, can it be disproved. Leaving tradition aside if one must, the circumstantial evidence is still heavily in favour of the former hypothesis.

There are numerous references in Irish mythological tradition to Scythia and Scythian relatives. While these references are held by some scholars to be no more than embellishments or the lacunae of later scribes, others take such references seriously and hold that the Celts and the Scythians may have been related. There is no argument that they were contiguous in the Eurasian heartland. And it is very likely that they intermingled. *The Annals of the Four Masters* (a sixteenth-century Irish historical compilation by four scholars, similar to the compilation of the *Nihongi*) relies heavily on the *Book of Invasions*, in which the mystic significance and inter-relationships of the personalities depicted in it is that of classical mythology. It states that the Gaels, the specific name for the Irish Celts, arrived in Spain from Scythia and from there proceeded to Ireland. To the sixteenth-century compilers Scythia may have meant anywhere in eastern Europe or the Middle East. But it is an historic fact that the Galatians of Asia Minor – like *Gael* and the *Galicians* of Spain evidently of common derivation – who lived close to the site of old Miletus, retained a Celtic language down to the fourth century AD.

References to Scythia in Irish mythology may be just an extravagant way of saying, for instance, that a skilled warrior learned his craft from experts overseas.

According to Hutton the version of Cuchulain's training contained in the *Foghlaimh Conchulaind*, an unedited tract at the time, gives in detail the story of his training by Scathach, or Scatha, in Scythia and Great Greece, Scythia being, she says, 'a vague term for a region extending from what is now Hungary eastward far into Asia'. In other words what was – at least in part – the Celtic heartland. That there was frequent intercourse between the Celts of Ireland and the Celts of Europe is not disputed, nor is the fact that down to the fifth century AD fighting men from Ireland went to assist their European cousins against the Greeks, Romans and Egyptians. That young Irish nobles should have gone from Ireland to get warlike training among the Celts of the Continent is, therefore, not unlikely.

In Kuno Meyer's edited version of the Wooing of Emer (by Cuchulain) one finds that Cuchulain went to Scatha '*fri Alpi allaanoir*'. This has been argued as meaning that he went to Albyn, in fact to the Isle of Skye, and that it was there that Scatha had her war-school. Presumably the reasoning was that, being closer, a journey to Scotland was not an unreasonable undertaking for the ancient Irish, but a journey to Scythia was. But why, for a people whose homeland was in that region and who were much travelled in a period of much travel, a journey to Scythia might seem unreasonable, is not explained. As Hutton points out, eastward from Alpi would not answer the position of Skye relative to Scotland; but it does answer the position of Scythia relative to the Alps. Furthermore, the *Book of Leinster* refers to Cuchulain's training in Armenia and to his wars – significantly, perhaps, in the light of the fact that Scatha, his teacher, was a woman – with the *Cichloiste*, or Amazons. There appears to be no other reason why Amazons should find themselves in an Irish mythological story than that there was some basis for it.

The convenient argument is sometimes advanced that all the Celts who came to these islands came north-west across Europe. It is far more probable that they came by several routes. Certainly it is likely that the preponderance of those who came to Britain did so via northern Europe. Equally the probability is that the preponderance of those who came to Ireland came south-about via Spain; certainly it is probable that the dominant ones did. That is not to say that of all the Celts who came to Ireland none came via Britain. Such an assertion would be as preposterous as that none came from Spain. But that the dominant group came from Spain is difficult to dispute. The meeting of the two streams might, for instance, explain the Tuatha de Danaan clash with the Firbolg. That a group of Celts who reached the Atlantic seaboard overland should speak one dialect, while another coming via Macedonia, Ionia, Italy, Spain to Ireland should speak another is logical. But that a dominant group came overland to Brittany, thence to England and Wales and from there to Ireland where they not only significantly altered their speech, but also infused their traditions with some migrant vitality so as to produce a culture and sophistication significantly different to, superior and more enduring than that it left behind in Britain, is far from logical.

Traditionally the Gaels (Celts), like the Ionian Milesians and the Scythians, were colonisers. They, too, colonised Ionia (Galatia), Spain (Galicia) and other places along the Mediterranean, as well as Gaul. They participated in several Mediterranean battles, against, for example, Ramses III of Egypt (c. 1125 BC), and as allies of Alexander the Great (c. 330 BC). The circumstantial evidence that they and the Milesians were kith and kin is powerful. The Celtic heartland lay in the Danube basin. It is ludicrous to suppose that the Celts who eventually reached the Atlantic moved westward by land only and that they ignored the most obvious and attractive route, down the Danube. Or that, having crossed forested north Europe, the sea to Britain and Wales and then the sea to Ireland, they adopted the name Milesian, but left no trace of Milesian connections on their considerable journey; on the contrary, leaving instead a tradition that maintains that they came from Spain where the Milesians had settlements. Those who followed the migratory paths north-west and south-west, would have developed, and picked up over the centuries from the peoples with whom they had contact and amongst whom they settled, distinctive characteristics of their own – thus accounting for the many differences in character, behaviour, outlook and speech that were so obvious when these two streams of Celtic migrants met again on the distant islands of western Europe.

The territory of the Celts in the European heartland marched in the east with that of the Scythians. Again it is stretching credibility beyond acceptable limits to assume an absence of intercourse between them. To additionally assume, as is sometimes done, that the Celts of central Europe who moved to the rich south-east lost their migratory spirit in Ionia and ignored the movements that were taking place from there along the Mediterranean, also strains credibility. The Celts who went south-east to Ionia are very likely to have migrated west along the Mediterranean trade routes.

The likelihood is that the dominant Celts who came to Ireland in successive waves of migration did so from a common source and that that source was the Mediterranean, whence they migrated from the Celtic/Scythian steppe region of central Europe via Macedonia and Ionia. These peoples brought with them the benefits of the advanced civilisations of Persia and the Mediterranean, with which they had contact, thereby distinguishing them from the more barbaric Celtic peoples of Britain and northern Europe. They spoke a language so modified as to be substantially different. (One of the differences was similar to that pointed out by Herodotus referring to certain Ionian settlers in Italy. Within a few centuries their native tongue differed from that of later waves of Ionian colonists, particularly in the pronunciation of G, K, P and Q – which is also one of the principal ways in which the language spoken by the Gaels, or Goidels, differed from the Celtic Welsh and Breton, hence the cognomen 'P Celts' and 'Q Celts'.)[8]

Although there are references to small colonies such as those of the Pretani (the original name for the Britani) in parts of Wexford and elsewhere on the east coast of Ireland, one does not hear of corresponding offshoots of Milesians, Tuatha de Danaan and so on in Britain as one would expect if that had been their route to Ireland. But we do know of invasions and the conquering of parts of Britain by the dominant Irish Celts over a long period. The impelling factor that might have precipitated a major invasion of Ireland by a people called the Milesian and led by one named Miletus was war and famine in Miletus and a mass migration from its population westwards to Spain in the eighth century BC before the rise of Miletus as an established Hellenic city circa 500 BC.

While no intelligent person nowadays takes literally racial names such as Slav, Anglo-Saxon, Latin, Celt, Japanese and so on as an index of (sole) origin, the dilution is, in some cases, much greater than in others. More polygenic races such as the English, the Americans and the Chinese, are clearly more hybrid than the Irish and the Japanese, who resided in island countries where the admixture of foreign blood has been very small for a very long time. It is fairly clear that what is true of today was even more true three thousand years ago when vast migrant bodies of people, apart from the intermingling races of Asia Minor and the Mediterranean, crossed and recrossed the known and penetrated the unknown . . . unless, of course, human nature has changed a great deal in the interim.

There is no doubt that a people called the Milesians and a Celtic people lived in Asia Minor, Italy and Spain simultaneously. The questions are: could they have intermingled, been the same or been related? Did the dominant Celtic people who came to Ireland come from Spain? And were the Milesians who according to tradition came to Ireland those (or the descendants of those) who went to Tartessia from Miletus? In each case the answers could be 'Possibly'.

The (Miletus) Milesians could have been of Celtic origin and have spoken a Celtic tongue. They were certainly thought by the Greeks to have been Scythian, but that might just as easily have meant Celt. Their language was Indo-European and common in an area in Ionia Celts are known to have colonised. The Scythians entered Asia in pursuit of the Cimmerians *whom they expelled from Europe* . . . in other words the Scythians drove these Cimmerians, as the Greeks called them, eastward from an area dominated by the Celts, who also moved eastward and are known to have established at least one colony on the Caspian Sea. There was tremendous migratory movement at the time and that there were links between the Celts and the Scythians is hardly arguable. Having dealt with the Cimmerians and established themselves on the shores of the Caspian, where the Milesians also had colonies, the Scythians drove southwards and subjugated the Medes, dominating the territory where the Milesians and Lydians had earlier settled. The Scythians maintained supremacy in that part of Asia for 28 years, until the Medes expelled them. But surely during that time Scythian customs, manners, traditions, not to mention blood, were established? Are all these parallels coincidences? The vast tract of land known as Scythia was just north of Macedonia and its neighbour in Asia Minor, Ionia. And the Scythians were also known to the Greeks as the Scoloti; not too far removed from Scotii, the name by which the Irish became known.

The tradition of the *Leabhar Gabhala* is that Nemed and his followers hailed from the region of the Caspian Sea, where the Scythians and the Milesians had settlements. It is there, too, that Xenophon places a people named the Dana. One cannot avoid the connection with Tuatha de Danaan, literally People of Dana(n). One of the names for the Greeks, Danaos, may not be without significance. Xenophon's description of the Dana who lived by the Caspian closely resembles the classical image of the Tuatha de Danaan. He says that they possessed awe-inspiring wizard-like characteristics. And in that context the proper title of Lugh Lamh Fada, the demi-god son of a Tuatha de Danaan father, Cian, and a Fomorian mother, Eithlenn, was the Ildanach (pronounced Ill-Dawnuck, Man of Enlightenment). The Ildanach is said to have brought with him to Ireland a light, generally supposed to have come from this forehead. Was it the brightness of fire? Of intellect? Of knowledge and technology? An early bronze or iron helmet, perhaps? Was the 'lamh-fada' – the long hand – a spear thrower (as was used most exclusively, according to Xenophon, by the Asiatic communities of which the Dana were one), like a thong-wrapped javelin – the 'weaver's beam' of the Phoenicians – such as was used exclusively in western Europe by the Irish from the earliest times until the seventeenth century?

In all the Irish legends the heroes are accustomed to rely on their spears as their principal weapons, usually described as 'great and small'. This, presumably, refers to a heavy hand spear for close combat of the type universally used in Mediterranean regions since the fourth millennium, and a form of javelin (carried, by the way, in a quiver attached to chariots, which is also the custom in Asia Minor). *Always* the method of throwing is described as being done by fitting the (fore)finger into a cord or loop to hurl the spear. Some authorities have, ludicrously, asserted that this was a method of retrieving the spear after it was thrown – a perfect example of how the simple can be distorted by straining after a solution at the expense of common sense and common knowledge. The purpose of the cord was one of elementary ballistics. It provided greater velocity, spin, accuracy and a lower trajectory. Professor Yigael Yadin, Professor of Archaeology in the Hebrew University of Jerusalem (who was responsible for the partial excavation of Masada), writes in *The Art of Warfare in Biblical Lands*:

The Bible likens the shaft of Goliath's javelin to a 'weaver's beam', for this type had not been seen in Israel and had no name in Hebrew. What was meant by a 'weaver's beam' is the leash rod of a loom. This is a block of wood which separates the threads of the warp to offer passage for the threads to the weft. The characteristic feature was the loop or leashes of cord attached to it . . . a typical Aegean javelin had a loop and a cord wound round the shaft so that the weapon could be hurled a greater distance with greater stability by virtue of the resultant spin. The Greeks called such a javelin 'the loop'.

Interestingly, a 1594 portrait of Captain Thomas Henry Lee, an Irish soldier from the period of the Tudor Conquest (he was of mixed parentage, born in Carlow it is thought), shows him holding what appears to be a javelin in his right hand with the index finger inserted through such a loop. The Gaelic tradition (of which the myths and legends, the Brehon law and the social system were the most tenacious aspects) still survived, even if debased and in a period of transition. The portrait also shows that in the matter of dress (which is elaborate and extravagantly decorated in the manner of the period), Irish tradition was still strong. The gallant captain also wears at his belt a contemporary snaphaunce pistol.

Tradition also maintains that the Tuatha de Danaan came to Ireland from the north. This, if it were true, would appear to end the hypothesis that they came from the Mediterranean since it would be difficult and unconvincing to attempt to prove that Spain, Persia and Greece lie north of Ireland. But the ancient Celts were nothing if not devious and mischievous. Riddles, puzzles, inversions and, in important and spiritually profound matters such as the origin and coming of their ancestors, reversions played a very big part in their approach to life. This is well demonstrated by the Rees brothers in their seminal work on Celtic beliefs, *Celtic Heritage*. If, therefore, we adopt their insight and read *south* for *north* the dilemma not only resolves itself, it supports the hypothesis.

Structurally the story of the battles of Moytura between the Tuatha de Danaan and, respectively, the earlier Fomorians and the Firbolgs – the motives, the actions and the outcome – is typically classical. It all begins with a prophecy that the Fomorian leader, the demi-god Balor (colloquially, 'Balor of the Evil-Eye'; consider Baal etc.) is warned that his grandson will kill him. To prevent this Balor locked his only child, the beautiful Eithlenn, in a tower so that she would never conceive. But the Tuatha de Danaan, Cian (later killed by the Sons of Tuireann), heard of her beauty, reached her with magical assistance, spent a night with her and Lugh was born nine months later. Balor immediately sent the child to be drowned. He was saved and in due time, as Lugh Lamh-Fada, the Ildanach, sided with his father's people and killed Balor at the First Battle of Moytura. It is reminiscent of the story of Astyages, the Median king who tried to kill his grandson, Cyrus, in much the same way, and with similar results.

One also sometimes hears that even if the Nemedians, the Tuatha de Danaan and the Firbolgs – even the Milesians – existed they had different and separate origins. There is no evidence for such an assumption. All (with the possible exception of the Firbolgs) are said to have come to Ireland from Spain, there from Asia Minor and there from the Celtic heartland. There is some circumstantial evidence to suggest that the Celtic Firbolg may have reached Ireland by the northern route, but from the same source as the others. All are said to have been related. It is an indisputable fact of history that colonisation from one source tends to attract successive waves of colonisation from the *same* source rather than from other sources.

Nevertheless, tradition also holds that during the supremacy of the Milesians the Tuatha de Danaan vanished, with their mysteries, under the earth where they still survive (or did at the time of earliest recorded history) in the form of Sídhe (pronounced Shee), or other-world people. Here is additional room for speculation about the place of the (then) 2,500-years-old Newgrange. What did the Tuatha de Danaan and the Milesians make of these awesome monuments, the origins of which were further removed in time from them than they are from us? It is not hard to imagine the gradual absorption of the de Danaan by a more vigorous and pragmatic wave of migrants who, in turn, benefited from the established culture of their forerunners. It has happened repeatedly in historic times.

The Milesians survived. They were the dominant Celts or Gaels who set their seal on Ireland between 800 and 500 BC. On the balance of probabilities the first waves of Celtic migrants – Nemedians, Tuatha de Danaan, Firbolg and Milesian – had a common origin, perhaps a common tongue and were kith if not kin. It was normal for migrant waves of people to take the names of their leaders as well as of their origins. Even if the Nemedians, the Tuatha de Danaan and the Milesians had, as is sometimes argued, different characteristics it does not mean that they had separate origins. Time, local conditions and influences would in a few hundred years produce such differences in people of similar background and language, and still does.

The suggestion has been made that the name Ireland – or Eire – derives from Piera, a name with an Indo-European root expressing fecundity. The fertile soil of Ireland, as well as her abundant gold, was regarded with awe by the Greeks. The Greek home of the Muses is also Piera. It is argued that the names Eriu (from which Eire derives), Hibernia and Juvernia, all alternative names for Ireland, derive from this word.

According to tradition the Milesian newcomers defeated the Tuatha de Danaan at the Battle of Tailteann in Meath, where Lugh is said to have instituted a series of games on the Hellene model in honour of his Tuatha de Danaan foster-mother, Taillte. It is conceivable, and to some extent in accordance with what we know of the relationship between them, that the Milesian victory was a bloodless one on the sportsfield. Such would, perhaps, contribute to the recognition the Milesians subsequently accorded the Tuatha de Danaan. Of course it may have been a bloody battle, but what seems important is that the Tailteann games, which survived for centuries (and were revived, briefly, within living memory), were similar to the games of Lydia, a settlement close to the Ionians in Asia Minor.

*   *   *

There is no precise evidence that there was a native script or form of writing in Ireland prior to the arrival of Christianity in the mid-fifth century. If it was possible for earlier records to be made and narratives or accounts kept, they have not survived. So it is claimed that the Irish myths were entirely oral and not written down until after the coming of Christianity, the argument being that writing did not exist in Ireland before introduction by Christian missionaries. It is an inference which may be challenged. There was continuous known contact over a long period with Rome and Roman Britain. The Irish Celts seem an unlikely people to ignore and forego the evident benefits of available literacy, even if they did not develop it themselves. Sedulius (Saigheal), contemporary of Patrick and writer of the first great Christian poem, was Irish; as was his other contemporary, the notorious heretic, Pelagius. Aethius came to Ireland before Patrick, seeking books to replenish the restored library at Alexandria, and the druids are said to have had a secret writing made on books of thin, wedge-shaped palettes of wood, held together at the bottom by a peg so that they could be spread like a fan. Because no examples survive does not mean that they never existed. For all we know myths were written down in some form. It might be borne in mind that the earliest written versions available are from the tenth and eleventh centuries, and are themselves copies of earlier examples. Where, now, are those earlier writings? The methods of the time and the perishable materials that were almost certainly used are more likely to account for their non-existence today, rather than the non-literacy of the peoples concerned. It stretches credibility very considerably to argue that intelligent people capable of formulating a complex legal and civil codex, who, for hundreds of years, traded with literate and powerful neighbouring nations, and who possessed a well-developed social order, would reject, and not have used, the benefits of a facility as fundamentally important as writing, if only for recording transactions and heredity.

By definition the social importance of mythology lies in the period before recorded history began. And in Ireland, so far as we know, written records came quite late. If this is so mythological influences may also have lingered quite late.

Certainly Ireland produced an explosion of written literature from the sixth century onwards which long pre-dates that of anything else in western Europe.

So, as far as we can tell in the absence of concrete proof to the contrary, Irish myths were first committed to writing after Christianity reached her shores, but when the literatures of modern Europe had not yet begun and the literary energies of the ancient world were past. Irish literature is, therefore, the oldest of the western world and is a direct literary link between later European and classical literature. And it was from newly Christianised Ireland that emerged the first classical scholars of the so-called Dark Ages.

When western civilisation was devastated after the fall of the Roman Empire learning, literature and religion went into decline everywhere in Europe except in Ireland, the only European nation-state of the period which was not part of the Empire. Christianity was not established in Ireland until about the middle of the fifth century, just when the Roman Empire had begun to founder. Within 80 years schools of learning – the monasteries, roughly the equivalent of later university townships, with up to 3,000 students exclusive of servants, retainers and other support – had sprung up and missionaries were going from Ireland to Europe bringing with them not only their new-found faith to re-illumine the darkness there, but also the literature of Ireland. (It is to this period that the saying – Isles of Saints and Scholars – refers.)

It is said that thanks are due to Patrick himself for having the ancient literature committed to writing and preserving it, and for not having it destroyed as heathen teaching, the somewhat doubtful presumption being that they were not written down before that. But, written *ab initio* or not, it is certainly held that one of Patrick's three great achievement was the preservation of the ancient Irish literary tradition. The other two traditional legs on which this great cauldron of a man stood – and the word cauldron is used here in the magisterial and praiseworthy sense, for the great cauldrons of the Celts were awe-inspiring items of surpassing merit and value (indeed, according to tradition, Patrick himself, as a slave, was paid for by one such); these other two legs were his Christian conquest of Ireland and the fact that, within eight years of his coming, he had been invited to sit on a royal commission to codify the law of the land. All of this is tradition only and part of the mystique of Patrick.

Irish peregrini of the sixth to tenth centuries brought with them the literature of Ireland and, so, influenced the development of the literatures of France, Germany, Italy and England. The very form of the twelfth-century French romance *Aucassin y Nicolette* is, according to A.H. Leahy, that of the chief Irish romances and may have been suggested by them. He writes:

It is as hard to suppose that the beautiful literature of Ireland had absolutely no influence upon nations known to be in contact with it, as it would be to hold the belief that the ancient Cretan civilisation had no effect upon the literary development that culminated in the poems of Homer.

Is it to be supposed that the Gaelic tradition that lasted for over fifteen hundred years materialised from nothing, out of nowhere, matured and fully sophisticated? Or that it was solely the product of unknown imaginations boiling on the westernmost island of Europe when the Continent slept after the fall of Rome? Hardly. In broad outline the hypothesis proposed is that mythology – the Irish no less than any other – however modulated it may become in the process of verbal and literal passage through time, is rooted in the facts of aspiration, mystery, hope and – perhaps – event. The scholar and writer C.S. Lewis wrote: '. . . myths become past refractions of God through the imagination penetrating to reality.'

FOOTNOTES

1   See *Ideology and the Historians*, ed. Ciaran Brady (Lilliput Press, Dublin, 1981), for a stimulating presentation of respective arguments between the Hungarian historians John Lukacs and Ivan Bertend on history as a 'scientifically useful' discipline.
2   Louis M. Cullen, The Hosei Ireland–Japan papers, Paper No. 22.
3   Lugh Lamh-Fada (Lawve-fodda, Long-handed; cognate with Lug, Lieu, Lugos – also the origin, by corruption and detraction, of leprechaun) was also known as the Il-Dana or Ildanach, the Enlightened One. He was the anthropomorphic sun-god of science and of accumulated wisdom of the Tuatha de Danaan. But he also had the status of a real person and became the father of Cuchulain. The sobriquet Long-handed relates to his ability to kill at a distance. It was characteristic of the Irish Celts down to the seventeenth century (also to the biblical Philistines) to wrap a cord round the shaft of a javelin, put a loop for the forefinger, thus providing greater velocity and lower trajectory. Lugh killed the Fomorian King, Balor, who was his grandfather, from a distance. Is it too speculative to suggest that the event and the name Long-handed commemorate the introduction of some new weapon technology?
4   One of the important archaeological 'finds' at the Newgrange complex is a carved stone mace-head, clearly of ritualistic significance.
5   A view not shared by all mythologists. All the evidence to the contrary notwithstanding, some – in the main, and characteristically, English – persist in the xenophobic idea that Ireland shares the polygenic British tradition, see, for instance, Berresford Ellis's *A Dictionary of Irish Mythology*. An appalling insert has been introduced into a modern American edition of Thomas Bullfinch's classical *Mythology*, called *Bullfinch's Mythology* (Gramercy, New

York), which includes not only a bowdlerised version of the Cuchulain story from the Tain Bo Cuailgne, but it is listed under the heading 'Hero Myths of the British Race', itself an extraordinary anachronism in a book purporting to be concerned seriously about mythology.

6 A fact easily overstressed. An Indo-European root simply means that it was one of a group of languages with a common origin, the relationship between them being, perhaps, more accurately compared to the relationship between Portuguese, Italian, Rumanian and even Finnish. It does not suggest common identity or homogeneity.

7 Archaeological evidence is that the earliest peoples in Ireland, about 10,000–8000 BC were hunter-fisher people of the mid-Stone (mesolithic) Age. Later, about 5000 BC, they were superseded by neolithic farmers. Presumably it was the latter, or their descendants (or possibly some other migrants) who built Newgrange, which dates from about 3000 BC.

8 See Rees brothers, op. cit.

The Stories

The stories are usually categorised in four groups:
(1) the Mythological Cycle, which deals with the earliest stories, mainly from the *Book of Invasions* and concerning the Tuatha de Danaan in particular;
(2) the Ultonian Cycle, or Red Branch Tales, dealing with Conor Mac Nessa's court at Emhain Macha and of which Cuchulain is the archetypical hero;
(3) the Fianna Cycle, which deals with Fionn Mac Cumhail and the Fianna;
(4) the so-called Cycle of Kings, which is concerned with legendary figures from the proto-historic period.

Since this book is not concerned with legend in the strict sense I have not included any stories from the last group, and simply use First Period, Second Period and Third Period to indicate which category the stories in this book are in: the First Period being in general stories about the Tuatha de Danaan; the Second Period relating to stories from the Ultonian Cycle; and the Third Period to those from the Fianna Cycle.

One is accustomed since childhood to a 'fairy-tale' approach to mythology. This is possibly due as much to the fact that the stories in their early written forms tend to be cryptic and unelaborated as to the fact that they have often been deliberately written, and sometimes debased, in the fairy-tale manner for children. Regrettably, most people seem to carry with them for the rest of their lives the fairy-tale view of mythology and thereby deprive themselves of one of the richest veins of literature and of story-telling available. Occasionally too we come across scholarly, or quasi-scholarly, versions only. In addition, since Irish mythology was largely 'rediscovered' in the nineteenth century when 'heroic romanticism' was all the rage in England, it was almost inevitable that those who translated them into English did so under that influence and gave to the Irish stories an entirely uncharacteristic and improper phoney Tennysonian status they have often been lumbered with ever since. Only very seldom have they been written or rewritten by adults for an adult audience.

33

We know some important facts. Firstly that written down or not, the stories were intended to be spoken to an audience. We may assume that they were recounted in public performances of greater or lesser magnitude, ranging from the fireside level to that of major public entertainments; and we may further assume, also with reasonable confidence, that the audiences, belonging to an illiterate (or largely illiterate) community in which absolute recall, as in most such communities, would have been common, were thoroughly familiar with the minutiae of character and event in the stories. Secondly, while we cannot be certain what the actual manner of recounting might have been, we can be sure of two things: (1) that it was not that of nineteenth-century heroic romanticism, and (2) as we may infer from the old records, that it was stylised in some way – perhaps in different forms and styles of delivery, depending on the teller and the audience.

In general, and in order to present the modern adult reader with an appropriate written version of any of these stories, the characters require to be fleshed out. In general, too, this can only be done with accuracy by cross-referencing from story to story, source to source. The cryptic stories also require appropriate elaboration in respect of topography, background, behaviour and so on. The language, while retaining an intrinsic dignity appropriate to a pastoral and stratified society, should, nevertheless, not be too high-flown and at times, particularly where humour is involved – and it may be taken that there is much humour involved, bawdy, boisterous and tongue-in-cheek – it should be downright earthy. The *seanachie* or traditional story-tellers of my youth seemed to offer the nearest appropriate style, which I have modified according to the Cycles, and adopted. Recent emphasis on folklore and parody have tended to underrate the importance of the *seanachie* somewhat, which is a pity. But I have included an example of the genre – admittedly adapted for reading – to indicate the essential differences between folklore and myth.

Where I felt it necessary to do so I have extended the narrative by filling in the background of events and characters as appropriate by cross-referencing to other sources. And I have tried to give the right mix of sophisticated and vernacular styles to the stories. I can only hope that in doing so I have not spoiled the telling for those who expected something more 'heroic' and that I may have helped in a small way to rescue some of these great stories from the fate of becoming children's 'fairy-tales' only.

E.N.

Saint Patrick's Breastplate

This prayer is ascribed to Saint Patrick. It is not known if in fact he wrote it.[1] The two documents more generally attributed to Patrick (whose own existence is questioned), are the 'Letter to Coroticus' and his 'Confessio'. The poem, with its blending of styles, is redolent of the Christian dynamic in fifth-century Ireland, and seems a suitable item with which to begin this book.

Saint Patrick's Breastplate

I arise today through a mighty strength, the
Invocation of the Trinity;
Through belief in Threeness,
Through Confession of the Oneness
Of the Creator of Creation.
Christ shield me today
Against poison, against burning,
Against drowning, against wounding,
That I may receive abundance of reward.
Christ with me, Christ before me, Christ behind me,
Christ in me, Christ beneath me, Christ above me,
Christ on my right hand, Christ on my left,
Christ where I lie, Christ where I sit, Christ where I rise,
Christ in the heart of every man who thinks of me,
Christ in the mouth of every man who speaks to me,
Christ in every eye that sees me,
Christ in every ear that hears me.

I arise today through the strength of heaven;

Light of Sun,
Radiance of Moon,
Splendour of Fire,
Speed of Lightning,
Swiftness of Wind,
Depth of Sea,
Stability of Earth,
Firmness of Rock.
I arise through God's strength to pilot me,
God's might to uphold me;
God's wisdom to lead me;
God's eye to look before me;
God's ear to hear me;
God's word to speak for me;
God's hand to guard me;
God's way to lie before me;
God's shield to protect me;
God's host to defend me.

FOOTNOTES

1 See *Crucible*, Donal O'Neill (Macdonald/Futura, London, 1986)

The Three Tragedies of the Gael

1. Deirdre and the Sons of Usna
(SECOND PERIOD: ULTONIAN CYCLE)

2. The Sons of Tuireann
(FIRST PERIOD: MYTHOLOGICAL CYCLE)

3. The Children of Lír
(FIRST PERIOD: MYTHOLOGICAL CYCLE)

It is not known when this title, sometimes given as 'The Three Sorrows of the Gael', was conferred on the three stories in question, but they were certainly linked together as representative tragedies during the nineteenth-century Celtic revival. The stories are from the first two cycles which is another indication – if one were needed – of the later and derivative aspect of some of the Fianna tales. Significantly the great tragedy of that cycle, the story of 'Diarmuid and Grainne', is not included in the collective title, presumably because it so resembles the story of 'Deirdre'.

The story of 'Deirdre and the Sons of Usna' is one of the many that, collectively, comprise the *Tain Bo Cuailgne*, or the *Cattle Raid of Cooley*, the great Irish epic set in the Ultonian period, about the first century AD. Since each episode of the *Tain* has a unity and validity of its own it may, without doing violence to the integrity either of individual stories or to the comprehensive schema of the *Tain*, be narrated independently. This was, in any case, almost certainly what happened in the oral tradition, whether it relied on memory or on some early written form, as the whole (a bit like the Wagnerian 'ring') is too long for a single sitting and would also, presumably, depend to a considerable extent on the virtuosity of the performing story-teller.

The story is well integrated and the characterisation exceptionally well drawn. It is the most complete and perfect story in the whole Celtic mythology, demonstrating, perhaps more than any other story from Irish mythology, a fine classical construction; it is in its own way as great and moving in concept, incident and character, as the *Iliad*. The story is fast-moving and is told with a great deal of deliberate art, for instance in the restraint shown in the tragic death of Deirdre.

The second tragedy, 'The Sons of Tuireann', is a tale of vengeance, triumph and adversity, extraordinary voyages and inexorable destiny – four subjects dear to the hearts of the ancient Irish if one is to judge from the frequency with which they appear.

The third tragedy of the Gael, 'The Children of Lír', is so well known as to hardly need comment. It contains the archetypal wicked stepmother whose jealous triumph ends in a hideous personal tragedy and is the first story in which the hand of later Christian 'laundering' may be seen. Happily the results not only marry successfully with the story, but, unless the original had an unsuspected power and authority now lost, also give a strength and purpose to a satisfactory ending.

Deirdre and the Sons of Usna

Second Period: Ultonian Cycle

The greatest king that Ulster ever had was Conor Mac Nessa, and he became king by a ruse. That may seem strange to those unacquainted with the ways of kings, but when I tell you that there was a beautiful woman involved and that the ways of kings in such matters are not so very different from the ways of ordinary men, it becomes easier to understand. In this case the woman was Conor's mother, a beautiful widow called Ness. Like many such women she was as ambitious as she was beautiful and as unscrupulous as she seemed innocent and guileless. And, as she would have been the first to point out herself, I needn't tell you, all she was doing was looking after her own and her son's interests, of course. And that was the truth! The king at the time was Fergus Mac Ri, that is Fergus, son of the king, which goes to show that even though primogeniture was not the system for acquiring a king in ancient Ireland, it sometimes happened that the son of a king was elected king after him (even twice; for Fergus's brother, Fachtna, had been king before him. What's more, he'd been married to Ness). Anyway, Fergus was a powerful and noble ruler and well loved by his people. But he was afflicted with a weakness not all that uncommon in kings and, no more than in the other and related matter referred to above, not unknown amongst commoners either. The fact of the matter is that he was woefully attracted by, susceptible, you might say, to women. If they were good-looking the weakness was very strong in him. And if they had brains as well as beauty – a condition not as rare as you might think – his resistance was very low altogether.

Accordingly, when his eye chanced on his brother's widow (or, to be truthful, was encouraged to fall, for ''twas Ness's doing, of course', and, as the woman once admitted in a moment of aberration, 'no man ever seduced a woman. 'Tis the other way round, as every woman knows. But why should we tell 'um, God

39

'um?' Anyway, when he looked at his attractive young widowed sister-in-law with the intelligence shining out of her eyes and the bright words of her quick wit dancing on her pink tongue, he fell, as he had so often done before (and would frequently do again) straightaway in love, for he was a man for whom being in love was a necessary condition of life. What made it complicated was that he didn't always manage to point his ardour in the same direction. Indeed, and to be truthful about it, it wasn't unknown for him to point it with remarkable generosity in several directions at once.

As if that wasn't enough, beautiful and all as she was, Ness was also – as Fergus was going to find out pretty quick – a strong-willed woman. She was more than that, too, for it was whispered – and maybe 'twas no lie – that she was of noted misbehaviour herself and that Conor wasn't Fachtna's son at all, but the son of the druid, Catha (which might explain why Conor put so much trust in him, as we'll find out in a minute).

Ness, being no angel herself, knew all about Fergus's little ways and she made her plans accordingly. She was highborn enough, and her late husband having been king, to want Conor to be one too, but she didn't have enough influence in the *derbfine*[1] or among the other voting nobles to ensure Conor would make it. So she set out to do two things: firstly, to win Fergus's heart; and secondly, having done that, to deny him what he most desired. She was so successful in both of these undertakings that Fergus developed a consuming passion for her, and, king and all though he was and unprotected widow though she was (though, as you may see, none better able to protect herself and look after her interests), she refused to give in to his pressure and played with him and tantalised him until he was ready to accede to any request she made, and only then did she agree to marry him. And at that she did it on a condition. That condition was that if she married Fergus he must surrender the sovereignty and let Connor take his place as king for one whole year.

> 'So I might have it said, *a grádh mo cróidhe* – love of my heart – that my little son sat on the throne and that his children should be called the descendants of a king, and him so small and helpless, *mo tairbhín-beag-tána-rua*, le 'na tarbh-slíasta – my small-little red leader of the herd, with the bull's thighs on him.'

And since Fergus and Conor, her 'little son' (who was twenty-three at the time), both had copper hair, 'twas up to Fergus to guess who she meant by that remark; which was how she planned it.

Like many another man both before and since, the predicament she'd put him in tore Fergus between two desires. He was distressed by the demand she was making, but he was also tormented by longing. But, as many did before and after him, he consoled himself with comforting thoughts. 'It's only for a year,' he argued. Well, that was the piece of wishful thinking that betrayed him, as wishful thinking often does, for, far from being a consolation to him, it was the beginning of his downfall. In spite of the advice and warnings of his advisers and wise men, Fergus agreed to hand over to Conor the kingship of Ulster for a year the day Ness became his wife. Well, if he did, 'twas no sooner done than Ness, with all her wiles, set out to beguile the minds and hearts of the people for Conor. And that was no easy task for Fergus was a good king – if a bit foolish about women now and then – and popular. But, with Ness's help and advice – and she hadn't kept her eyes and her ears closed when she was married to Fachtna – Conor proved a better king. So that at the end of the year when Fergus went to look for his kingship back, the chiefs and nobles weren't too willing to make the second transfer. Apart from the favours and tokens Ness and Conor had dispensed lavishly amongst the nobility of the province, Conor had become their friend and protector while Fergus had been lost to them with his blind and besotted behaviour, so they were not at all inclined to listen when he tried to persuade them to vote for his kingship to be returned to him. Indeed one of his friends, by the name of Donal Lacha, told him to his face that since he had given up the kingdom in favour of a woman, he cared more for her than it, so he had no right to get it back. They told him he could keep Ness if he wanted her, but they'd keep Conor as king.

I needn't tell you that didn't please Fergus one bit. And to make it worse Ness only sneered at him when he complained to her. Fergus put up with this treatment for a while, but, as we will see, it wasn't for good and in a year, or two, or three – I forget! – with all his family and followers – and between one thing and another and his little ways there were very few of them – he packed up and went to Connacht where he found refuge with Queen Maeve and her God-help-us of a husband, King Ailill. He left Ness behind in Ulster with her son, King Conor.

Time rolled on and the passing years and their cooling hand assuaged the bitter memory of old quarrels between Fergus and Conor. Mind you the fact might have had something to do with it too that Maeve had started to give Fergus the raw edge of her tongue now that he was getting increasingly slower and stiffer where she didn't want him to be, and not where she did. Anyway a yearning home-sickness finally tugged away at the heartstrings of Fergus and the combination was too much for him in the long run, and what did he do but secretly send envoys to Conor? The upshot was that Fergus returned to Ulster with all his followers – and there were a share more of them now. In a public gesture that received much acclaim Conor received him with great honour and placed him next to himself in the land and sometimes on the throne too. But, if he did, didn't he keep a close eye on him as well, for the older Conor became the more acutely he was aware of the fact that there were, among the chiefs and nobles of the province, not a few who would like to see Fergus resume the kingship again even after all that time, especially after what had happened and we'll come to that in a moment. But Conor put the face of friendship on their relationship (but that's all another story). The story we're going to hear now was the reason for Fergus's going in the first place. And, again, there was a woman involved. Only this time it was Conor who was besotted.

For all his good, kingly qualities Conor was a brooding sort of man – and perhaps that's the way of kings, who never know where the next threat will come from, or around what corner stands the next enemy; perhaps that's the way kings have to be. Whether or which, if he could he would have hidden Fergus away in some hole or dungeon until he rotted, or disposed of him outright, but he knew he could not, for the nobles of Ulster would have risen against him if he had. Bad and all as was what Fergus had done, he was still one of their own. And so it was that the fear and suspicion festered away in Conor so that he changed. Men began to fear and dread him and the respect and admiration and liking that had been there gave way to these uneasy and unsettling feelings. And so it went. Old nobles and chiefs died and were succeeded by younger ones for whom the events of the past, what had happened between Fergus and Conor long ago, were hearsay or history, if they had heard them at all. The great deeds of Fergus were part of the legend that surrounded the mighty hero but, like himself, belonged to the past.

Now, all during this time there was peace and tranquillity in Ulster – and that was another reason why stories of times gone by had little meaning or relevance for active young people. For in such times of sunshine and plenty, when the granaries are full and the cattle fat, it was trade and not war that filled the minds of the people; games on the playing field and not battle on the fields of war that occupied the youth of both sexes. And the young women, especially, looked eagerly forward to marriage with a warrior and not to his death – at least not for a while. Old customs were revived and enriched. And these were often encouraged by the king, especially when, as with that of the nobles' banquet, there was a place for him in it where he could relax and receive the acknowledgements he felt were his due and not be always looking over his shoulder for intrigue and conspiracy. The time was approaching when it was the turn of Felim, Conor's chief story-teller, to give such a feast and it was one that Conor looked forward to particularly, for Felim always told a good story and always told the best at his own fireside.

Felim had been preparing for this feast – which would last for eight or, maybe, ten days – for more than a year. Even a rich man, such as himself, was hard put to it to survive a visit by the king with all his retinue and many would have gone under if it wasn't for the fact that the king never forgot and made it up in other ways later on. For a man who was not rich it would have been impossible; but then there were few men who were not rich amongst the nobility, and who else mattered?

Close to his castle Felim caused an enormous hall to be built. This would provide the dining hall and the sleeping quarters for the king and all his retinue, so it contained many beams and oaken sleeping compartments and four great places for fires, one at each point of the compass. Hazel wands had been cropped for miles around to make wattle and hundreds of oak trees felled and trimmed for the beams of the wall and the ceiling. The walls were woven from the hazel and willow wattling, a handspan apart, and the space between filled with mud and moss and then the walls sealed with clay and painted with scenes from the life of the king in glowing colours. The doorways and lintels shone with white marble and the flagstones beneath them in black basalt. Beyond this great hall stretched other buildings in rows; stables and sleeping quarters; kitchens and steam rooms for the hundreds of guests of different status.

In from the surrounding country began to come the provisions, with those that were perishable arriving last: cheese and curds, butter and cream, bread and cake; and meat (sheep and swine, hare and deer, salmon for the multitude); beer, wine, fruit of all kinds, from Ireland and by sea from Spain and elsewhere, with great quantities of mead and honey and the wine of Greece and Rome. Entertainers came: harpists, lutists, pipers and players on the drum and tambourine, both men and women; gleemen and jokers and grave performers from far away; and story-tellers besides himself (though he had no fear of them for he knew he could out-tell any of them). Until, finally, all was ready. And when it was and when Felim had looked over it all with a critical eye (and it took him a whole day to check everything), he swore that it would be such a feast as would go down in history for men to talk about forever. And so it was. But not for the reason he had hoped.

On the day appointed for Felim's feast, Conor set out in state from Emhain Macha accompanied by the champions and nobles of the Red Branch. It was one of those days in which the sun wheels overhead like a golden chariot in a blue plain. Below, the splendour of the king all but matched its own. An emblazoned banner spanned the highway like an arch billowing in a gentle breeze, and he passed under that. A hundred knights in scarlet cloaks embroidered in gold and riding black horses pranced at the head of the column; then came a hundred more in green on white horses; and yet another hundred in blue cloaks with silver fringes who rode on chestnut steeds; and then five hundred knights in saffron yellow cloaks appeared, tall and proud in war-chariots, light and airy with panels of beaten bronze, and drawn by well-matched pairs driven by charioteers in white tunics, the scythes and armour of the chariots flashing in the sun. But the scythes were folded up on the hubs of the war-chariots. There was a noble throb on their passing, with no element of war or foreboding. Before

Conor, as he left the great gate of Emhain Macha and turned his face eastward on the road to Felim's country, marched twenty drummers, and behind them twenty trumpeters with small trumpets, and another twenty behind them with great, curving, polished, bell-mouthed bronze trumpets that blared royal music under the sun.

And then, in all his magnificence, came Conor himself. He looked round gravely, not smiling as might a younger man, but neither sternly, and acknowledged the cheering people with a wave of his hand and it was – and all knew it – benign. He travelled in a great four-wheeled chariot spanned with a waving canopy of purple. Before and behind him stretched the lords and nobles and the army; and the glitter and twinkle of the sun on the helmets and the armour, the spear-points and the shields of the knights, was like starlight by day. In all, a thousand or more marched that day with Conor to Felim's feast; but, as Conor, who knew the uneasiness of kings, looked from under his hooded eyes, no smile touched his lips.

As the cavalcade moved slowly along the great highway it threw up clouds of dust so that Conor decided to switch to horseback for part of the journey. And this pleased him, for he was less morose in the *dilat* or saddle cloth; and he felt closer to his entourage, receiving at the same time praise and admiration wherever he rode. But, as the day declined, so too did the sunlight, the great king of the heavens becoming obscured by some dark-bellied clouds that rolled in from the sea behind them, low and brooding, until the sky was covered. They still had some way to go and, before the night slid silently above those clouds to mask the world still more, a wind pushed in on them telling of rain to follow, and swirling the dust of their passage around the members of the cavalcade, so that it clung to their clothes and skin and filled their eyes with grit.

The storm, for such it was that was coming, held off until they reached the great hall and castle of Felim. But, even as Conor dismounted and entered to the warm light from within where, besides the fires, there burned three king's candles as thick as a man's waist, there was a crack from above as if the heavens had split, and a flash of white lightning illuminated everything; then another and another the likes of which no man had heard before and a fear came over them that the sky was, at last, going to fall. But it did not. The lightning and thunder receded towards the hills a little as the bowels of the sundered clouds opened and a tumultuous rain fell.

Felim took the king by the elbow to bring him inside; but Conor, fascinated by this natural display which exceeded anything he had ever seen so that he knew it was no normal phenomenon, stood in the doorway of the castle his cloak flapping like the wing of an ocean sailing ship. 'Welcome, Conor,' said Felim, urging him with his hand. Eventually the king turned to him, realising that his followers would not disperse in the rain until he entered.

'That is a right royal welcome, Felim,' he said, 'even for you.' But it was a false humour, although he smiled and Felim smiled back. But Conor soon settled into a glowering mood which all Felim's goodwill and entertainment was unable to dispel. It seemed as if the first evening of his feast was going to be a disaster both from the storm and the king's ill-humour. Felim was in despair. As the night wore on the intensity of the storm increased again as if, having retreated with the first assault, it had renewed itself, and was now returning to attack the castle directly again. It was obvious that everyone in the great hall was uneasy, even Conor. He looked at those in the smoke-filled hall and nodded. There was a wave in the air and it was caused by fear of the unknown, for there were few men amongst them who feared anything known.

'It is no common storm,' Conor muttered, turning to Felim. 'It has the air of an omen. There is some catastrophe brooding this night.'

Felim went pale. 'Not the sky,' he said. ''Tis not going to fall and crush and darken us forever.'[2]

Slowly Conor shook his head. 'I don't think so,' he said. 'If it were, it would have happened by now. But it is something. And it is not good.'

He lifted the haunch of a young, roasted deer calf and bit into it. As he raised his knife to sever the leg from the bite a fearful scream, loud above even the turmoil of the storm, came from within the castle itself. Many men jumped – pale – to their feet while others reached behind them to their hanging weapons.

'What is that?' asked Conor, turning to Felim.

Felim knew well what it was and threw a curse behind him at the night nine months back that was the cause of it. 'It is nothing, Conor,' he said. 'My wife . . . she is having a child!' He threw up his arms helplessly as if he had nothing to do with the matter.

Conor leaned back, relieved, and waved at the hall so that the men began to relax and sit down. But he could see that they were still jumpy, as he was himself. 'It sounded like no woman's scream to me,' said Conor. 'Is it that she is not all right? Bring her here so that we can see for ourselves.' He leaned towards Felim. 'It would be well,' he said, looking sideways at the uneasy hall, and nodding a small nod. 'Remember what I said. There is a strangeness about tonight. Bring her if she is able.'

So messengers were sent and after a short while Felim's wife came into the hall, big, and supported by two other women. She was brought to Conor who looked at her for a moment without speaking. Then he asked: 'Who, or what, made that scream we heard? It was you, perhaps?'

Felim's wife lowered her head, but when she raised it again and Conor could see that her eyes were filled with tears (though whether they were tears of pain, or of courage, or of fear itself, he was not to know), and she said: 'It was not I who screamed, Conor, but the very child in my womb.'

When he heard this, Catha, the king's druid, rose to his feet and going towards the woman put his hand on her great belly. Bending down he listened through his hand for a moment and then straightened and turned to the king. 'This is a girl-child here,' he nodded. 'Aye,' he continued before anyone could question him, 'and her name will be Deirdre – which means "alarm" – and I must tell you that it is a well-chosen name. For this Deirdre will bring with her to Ulster evil and misery and war.'

When Catha said this the woman all but fell to the floor only she was supported by her companions, who brought her out with comforting words. The company returned to their tables, but without appetite. Conor had fallen deep into thought and none would interrupt him.

Conor remained like that, dark and brooding, at the head of the table, eating little and drinking less, his brows drawn together, shooting little sideways glances here and there around the room, but saying nothing. His manner conveyed itself to all those there so that if there was nervousness of the storm that crashed and thundered about outside, it was nothing to fear that they had of the storm that might break inside if Conor's bad mood took a turn for the worse. The company spoke in whispers; and when a servant dropped a spoon and it clattered on the table, every eye swung in his direction with accumulated anger and hostility, and the poor man slunk away to the servants' quarters (wherever they were) where he got a beating from Felim's major domo so that he passed blood in the night and died the next morning without being noticed for three days. Just when the atmosphere in the banqueting hall had reached the point where everybody expected something dreadful to happen, a messenger came to say that Felim's wife had given birth and that it was indeed a girl who had been born. Conor glared at the messenger and nodded sharply. Then he looked long and silently at Catha while stroking his lower lip with the edge of his thumb.

'What's that you said about this child?'

'She will bring evil and woe and war to Ulster,' said Catha.

At which there was a murmur from the assembly and a voice from the depths, perhaps expressing more the mood that had developed because of the king's manner than any thoughtful opinion, cried: 'Let her be killed!'

But Conor continued to look at Catha and stroke his lip. And when Catha nodded as it were in agreement with the voice from the body of the hall, the king quietly said 'No!' And then, because he was a king, he stated that no one else there would dare to say in such circumstances when the decision was between principle and expediency. 'We will not commit an evil deed to avoid the course of a prophecy' – though it might truthfully be said that, while he was a good king and a great king and man of principle in many things, it was not necessarily the fear of doing evil that prevented him, or had ever prevented him in the past; or, indeed, would prevent him in the future from doing what he wanted.

It is a strange thing, but the storm had fallen silent while the woman was with them and the clouds were gone, though the wind still sang in the turrets and the trees. 'Catha will go out,' said Conor, 'and let him consult the stars to discover her destiny. We owe Felim no less than that.'

Catha went out to the place that surrounded the hall, away from the huts and the fires, and from there he went to the ramparts of the castle to look up and read the immeasurable stars. He did everything with the greatest care. He had with him his starry charts and signs and, by the light of the sailing moon, studied them, switching his gaze from them to the unreachable sky. He knew that what was about to be revealed would be of the greatest importance to Ulster.

Back in the banqueting hall the atmosphere improved following the king's lead, and there were celebrations for the birth of the child. The place was as merry as it had been gloomy not long before. When, however, Catha re-entered and stood silently in the doorway, a silence, like an invisible breeze rippling the surface of a lake, came with him, chill, the length of the room. The laughter stopped and everyone turned to look at the druid. Conor eyed him as he walked towards him. But then, before the druid could reach where he sat, he laughed – too loudly – and said: 'Well, Catha. What do the omens say? Good luck and happiness to her and her parents?' Without waiting for an answer – it was strange; there seemed to be a compulsion about him – he raised his goblet and drank as if to a toast.

And yet, who is man, even a king, to taunt the ways of Fate? As he swallowed the draught his throat constricted and something gripped him by the chest so that he could not swallow. He all but choked, but waved away those who tried to help him. Then he looked at Catha, who stood silently in front of him, with watered, but questioning, eyes.

Catha met the king's eye firmly. After a moment he spoke: 'It isn't only to her parents that this child will bring misfortune,' he said slowly, 'but to all of Ulster . . .' and he looked round, catching an eye here and an eye there, but seeming to catch every eye; he turned back to Conor, '– and to its king –' His voice was hard as he eyed Conor a moment; he swung his eye again around the hall, 'and to the nobles of Ulster,' he ended. There was silence in the hall and Catha continued. 'This child will grow to be so beautiful that she will be the envy of queens and rise up the jealousy of all beautiful women. Kings will go to war for her,' he went on. Turning back to Conor he said with great emphasis: 'Understand me well, Conor; she is born for the misfortune of Ulster and for the downfall of the knights of the Red Branch.'

Conor looked back at him with a baleful and unresponsive eye, but consternation broke out in the hall. The knights and nobles sprang to their feet and almost with one voice shouted that if such evil were going to follow the child then it would be far better to avert it now when she was still an infant and kill her rather than let it begin to accumulate and the evil of the deed along with it. But, out of perversity or what strange motive it is hard to say, Conor quietened them and refused to sanction this course of action. He threw out an arm. 'Let us see her,' he cried. 'Let's see this monster who threatens Ulster. Bring in the child!'

Then the little infant was brought in from where she lay with her mother. When it felt the warmth and the light of the hall and looked up at the faces gazing at her, she, wonderful to relate, as the Romans say (only in Latin), opened her eyes, and smiled, and gurgled at the king. And this moved the great Conor as he had not been moved for a long time. Gently he reached out and lifted the baby from her nurse's arms and held her in his own. Then, still looking at the child, he raised his voice and addressed the company, still holding the baby in his arms. (And not only was she quiet for the first time since she was born as she lay there, the more surprising thing is that, loud and all as he spoke, she raised never a cry nor a whimper while she lay in his arms, but settled in and looked up at him and waved her little fists in the air in a sort of contented fashion. Which only goes to show, of course, how even the mightiest can be misled and seduced by the power of a babe-in-arms.)

This, then, is what Conor said: 'I have no reason to doubt what Catha has said or what the omens he has told us about indicate. But on the other hand I don't see what good can come of killing this innocent child. Therefore if what is to come is to come, let us try to make it come in the best possible way and see if we can't adjust matters to suit ourselves. So I'll make one part of this cold prophecy come true and it is this: when this child grows to the edge of womanhood and is of marriageable age I will myself take her to wife and make a queen of her.'

A gasp wafted through the hall when Conor said this, and Catha looked at him the way he might look at a man who had lost his wits altogether. But Conor went on: 'From this moment on she is under my special protection and I am responsible for her. She will be reared by my direction in a secret place and any man who lifts his voice or his hand against her must reckon with me. And that is how I will guard against this prophecy.'

There was silence. Conor looked round the great, smoky hall, trying to pierce the gloom if not with his eyes, then with his will. But the assembled knights and lords were silent, except for here a cough, there a shuffle of feet and, in the shadows, a soft whisper or two. But if they said nothing in response to Conor's statement, Catha could not keep silent.

'Conor, listen to me,' he said. 'Your intention is noble and generous, but all the signs are against you in this. Consider well what you intend for I tell you solemnly that if it is your will that she live, then she will be a child of sorrow, and "Deirdre of the Sorrows" is what she will be called.'

But Conor was determined and would not listen to Catha. 'Deirdre of the

Sorrows,' he mused. 'It is a nice name. I like it. And I will protect both her and my kingdom; and, when she is old enough to nurse, let her be brought to me and I will attend to her myself.'

And that is what was done. When Deirdre was old enough to be taken from her parents Conor had her brought to one of his hidden castles deep in his own place and private to him, where she was reared and looked after by a wise and skilled nurse named Leabharcam. Here she grew from toddler to childhood in the beautiful gardens surrounding the castle. But she never saw a soul except for Leabharcam – and the king when he came to see her – for the garden surrounded the castle, and the garden was surrounded by a wall and that by a moat. Great wolfhounds guarded the castle by night and Conor was satisfied that his ward was secure and safe in this retreat and that the fate Catha had foretold was offset. For ten years Deirdre lived there with Leabharcam. Catha too was allowed to visit now and then. And as she grew into beautiful maidenhood, Conor's interest in her developed in ways he had not anticipated; for not only would she make an old man a young queen, she'd be for him an ornament in her beauty and learning.

In spite of the fact that she saw no men but Conor and Catha, nor any child except herself when she looked in a mirror or the wandering surface of the stilly ponds that lurked in the shaded parts of the stream that ran through the garden, Deirdre was joyous and happy most of the time. Leabharcam loved her greatly and taught her what she knew, which was a store of great, and often secret, knowledge. And she taught her the motion of the stars and planets so that Deirdre understood time and the changes of the year.

Deirdre grew tall and lissom and flawless in both body and mind until she was by far the most beautiful woman in all Ireland. And she was kept apart in case any of the men of Ulster – or anywhere else for that matter – would see her before she was to sleep with Conor. No one was allowed near her save her foster-father and her foster-mother, Catha and his wife, and Leabharcam, who was a satirist as well as a poet and a nurse. Of Deirdre it was said:

> From the cradle of the womb the cries
> Of Deirdre of the grey-green eyes
> Tormented Ulster. Deirdre's braided golden
> Tresses her gentle, curved cheeks embolden.
> Bright as snow her flawless teeth;
> Two lips that red and smiling meet
> And linger on the world. Dearest daughter!
> Over her there'll be great slaughter.
> Queens envy her her faultless shape.
> From the roaring womb there's no escape.

As Deirdre grew older and more beautiful so did the ageing King Conor's visits become more numerous.

And then – it was winter, because a white carpet of snow lay on everything so that the buds and seeds stirred beneath – Deirdre looked from a window at the white garden beneath, the bare branches and the globules of snow hanging from them like blanched fruits, and she sighed. She saw where Catha had killed a calf for their meal, and she sighed again. Leabharcam, who was behind her near the fire, heard her sigh, a thing she had never heard before. 'What ails you, child?' she asked with a small concern.

'Nothing,' said Deirdre, and then, quickly, 'I don't know.'

'Whisht, child,' said Leabharcam, "tis nothing. Is it a headache you have?'

'No, Leabhar,' said Deirdre (*Leabhar*, which means 'book', being her pet-name for Leabharcam both because of her love for her and because of her knowledge). 'I have no headache. I don't know.' She turned round and looked at her nurse. 'I just feel sad.'

Leabharcam was more than concerned now. She had long dreaded the day when Deirdre would say that, or something like it, for she knew what it meant. But, for the king's sake – and her own – she pretended otherwise.; 'Sad,' she asked, 'for what?'

'And lonely too,' said Deirdre. 'Sad and lonely. That's how I feel.'

Then Leabharcam knew it was serious. 'Sad?' she asked.

Deirdre nodded.

'And lonely?' went on the nurse.

'Yes,' said Deirdre.

'Sure, child dear, how could you be lonely with me here and the king and Catha below to visit you every so often? Hush now,' she added as Deirdre's eyes filled with tears.

'I – I –' stammered Deirdre.

'What is it, *alanna* (my child)?' asked Leabharcam, knowing well the answer.

'It – it's –' said Deirdre.

'Yes, *a críodhe* (my heart)?' said Leabharcam.

'Everyone is so old,' said Deirdre in a rush. And then stopped suddenly.

Leabharcam shuddered. 'Hush, child,' she said. 'You don't know what you're saying. The king isn't old, just . . . just mature; in the prime of life, many would say. There's many a young woman would be proud to be in your shoes. And he's coming today.' She looked round, just in case, for Conor was a silent man.

'But, Leabharcam,' cried Deirdre, 'he *is* old.' She turned away to the window again and was silent for a moment, the tears welling up inside her, but not bursting forth. So she sighed again. Then, as if she were speaking to herself but half over her shoulder so that Leabharcam could hear: 'How I wish I could meet someone who is young.' She looked at where Catha had killed the calf. 'A young man,' she said, 'with those three colours in him.' She pointed to where a raven stood, black in the snow, dipping its great beak in the calf's blood; and Leabharcam, who had come up beside her looked, her heart pounding. 'His hair,' said Deirdre, 'as black as that raven; his cheeks as red as the blood on the snow; and his body as white as that snow itself.'

Leabharcam's hand flew to her mouth so that she spoke from behind it with wide, frightened eyes. 'Whisht, child,' she whispered, 'for the love of God, so that he mightn't hear you; for if he did he would have him killed for sure.'

'Who?' cried Deirdre. 'Who would he' – and she knew Leabharcam meant Conor – 'have killed?'

'No one,' snapped Leabharcam, annoyed with herself. 'I don't know. Never mind me.' Then in a sort of anguish over the look in Deirdre's face, and her plight, 'Sure, there's only one man the like of that.'

Deirdre wasn't listening.

'Last night,' she said, 'I saw him in a dream.'

'The gods between us and all harm,' cried Leabharcam. 'You did not!'

'I did surely,' said Deirdre. 'And that is the man I would like to meet, and to marry, and to live my life with – and not Conor,' she cried, turning on Leabharcam. 'He is old and – and he's ugly and he's not nice . . .'

But now Leabharcam had her by the shoulders and was holding her firmly. 'Hush,' she said. 'Deirdre, listen to me. Forget about this – this dream. That's all it is. If the king knew what you've just said, Naisi's life wouldn't be worth that.' She snapped her crooked fingers with a crack.

'Is that his name?' asked Deirdre. 'Naisi. It's a nice name.'

'Naisi is the man you have described,' said Leabharcam, loosening her hold on Deirdre for she had no wish to frighten the girl beyond recovery, though she was well frightened herself now. But she was full of compassion too, for she herself had loved and been loved in her time. So she sighed in her turn. 'Listen to me,' she said. 'I don't know how or why, but the man you have described is Naisi, one of the sons of Usna of the Red Branch, and you must put him out of your mind or, or . . .' words failed her. But Deirdre was looking out of the window again to where the raven still stood by the bloodstained snow. And through her mind ran the name: 'Naisi, Naisi . . .'

Naisi and his brothers Ainle and Ardán were among the foremost heroes of the Red Branch Knights of Ulster. They were gentle and gallant in peace, but fierce and woeful in war. Naisi was the natural leader of the three brothers, and one of the most renowned of the Knights of Ulster. And he was a musician of great accomplishment who, like many another thus afflicted, was inclined to wander abroad by himself playing his small harp, which he kept in a doeskin case slung from his shoulder, and sit somewhere romantic, or with a view to it, and make music of his own to which he would often put a song about what he saw, or about what he thought or what he felt or remembered, or that sort of thing, as many young men do – only Naisi was (mostly) better at it.

This day he went out with his harp and was sitting under an ash tree that crowned a hillock making a song. And the song he made was a good one that floated elegantly on the mid-day airs. The winter was gone and it was springtime, so the bright leaves were on the trees and the time for Deirdre's marriage with Conor approached. But the closer the day came the more uneasy and restless Deirdre became. She found the restriction of being confined to the garden the worst thing and she wanted to go outside. So with guile and with tears she managed to persuade Leabharcam to allow her to go out for walks now and then – not too often and not too far – but where she felt a freedom that was to her like the freshness of springtime itself. Naturally Leabharcam had refused at first, but then when Deirdre's distress increased she worried lest she become really ill and that the king would blame her for it, so she relented. So it was that Deirdre wandered to the border of the wood, where it met the rolling plain on which the cattle grazed and the hunt coursed and the long grass under the fringy trees was dappled and patterned where the sunlight came down through the leafy branches. And there she heard music and the singing voice of a man.

It was said that when Naisi made good music the cattle that heard it increased their milk yield twofold (and that could be true as every farmer knows who milks), and that men and women who heard him forgot their cares and troubles and were filled with joy. And so it was with Deirdre: she heard Naisi's music, and joy filled her heart. Though, to be honest about it, in Deirdre's case the joy she felt was probably due as much to the fact that she had never heard any man singing before, and making music to go along with it, as to anything else. In any case the music reached deep into her being and greatly affected her.

She went towards it and soon saw Naisi sitting under the ash tree, and as soon as she saw him she knew him, though she had never set eyes on him before. She knew that she should go back then before he saw her, but she couldn't . . . or she wouldn't. Anyway she didn't and, full of shyness but also compelled, she went to pass him quietly with her eyes down thinking, maybe, she might pass without his noticing – but hoping something else, surely. Seeing the girl and struck by her beauty, Naisi stopped his singing and, still plucking the melodious strings of his harp, found his eyes tracking her. He had never seen her before, he knew, at Emhain Macha or anywhere else. And he knew well that a girl as beautiful as this one was would not stay long from the city unless there was a good reason for it.

'Well, by the hokey-fly,' he cried, a bit mischievously maybe, 'if that's not a fine heifer going by.' I needn't tell you that piqued Deirdre, but she was intrigued too. But neither anger nor interest could restrain her sharp wit and, although she didn't look up at him, quick as a flash she came back with: ''Tis easy for heifers to be fine and fair where there are no bulls.'

Now Naisi was no fool. Before she'd finished her answer he'd fixed her from the stories he'd heard and, accordingly, he was, so to speak, circumspect in his reply. 'You have your bull,' he said. 'The bull of the province of Ulster itself, King Conor.'

Deirdre, who had stopped walking, but hadn't looked up at him directly yet, said: 'Then if I have, I don't love him, for he's old and he's ugly; and if I had the choice of the two of you, wouldn't I choose a fine young bull the like of yourself?' And with that she looked right into his eyes – grey-green into hazel – and it was a long look.

Now this couldn't be said to be brazenness on Deirdre's part, for brazenness is a quality acquired by young girls, often at a very early age, who mix with the shyer species of the opposite sex to torment and tantalise them, and Deirdre had never been exposed to that kind of carry-on. So she spoke with her heart and with truth.

But Naisi was still cautious. 'There's Catha's prophecy,' he said.

'Is it that you're trying to avoid me?' asked Deirdre.

'No,' answered Naisi, ''tis the prophecy of the druid.'

'Are you rejecting me so?' she asked.

'Indeed 'n I am,' he said.

Deirdre had never heard of Catha's prophecy and was put out by this. In her confusion she plucked a briar of wild roses with no concern at all for the thorns that pierced her hands and flung it at his head crying: 'Well, you're a disgrace if you reject me now.'

Naisi laughed and ducked and was confused, all at the same time. He had never seen anyone so beautiful (and, let me tell you, because of his accomplishments he was no novice in the matter of beautiful women), and he could see that she was as pure and as truthful as she was beautiful and intelligent, and he wouldn't have been a man at all if he wasn't moved by that combination. Raising his hands to protect himself as she fired more briars at him with the roses dangling from them, he cried, knowing well who she was: 'Deirdre, Deirdre, 'tisn't that I don't love you, but . . .'

With that admission she ran up to him, half laughing and half crying, but a bit angry too. She took hold of his two ears in her hands and shook his head a little bit. 'I'll tell you what you'll have if you leave me,' she said with a grin, 'two ears of mockery and shame.'

Naisi looked at her, seemingly grim. But she saw through him and laughed, and he laughed too. He raised his hands to cover her own and said: 'Let me go, wife!' And with that they put their arms around each other, but only to lean back from the shoulders and smile in each other's faces.

After a moment Naisi disengaged himself and took his harp and began to play. Now it was music of a different sort, joyous and gay, light and majestic all at once, and all from the profoundest depths of his heart. 'Twas the sweetest, the most moving, song he ever made, and it was for Deirdre alone. She sat with him, part, too, of his music-making, until his brothers came looking for him.

When Ainle and Ardán learned who Deirdre was they were horrified. And when Naisi told them that he was going to take her with him, whether they came or not, they thought he had lost his senses altogether – and maybe he had in a way. However, persuade as they might, they could not change his mind. Naisi was in love. He had given his heart and he was adamant. At length, when they saw that there was no moving him, Ainle and Ardán said no more, but accepted Naisi's decision knowing full well what it involved. When she saw that they had accepted her, Deirdre kissed them all, a kiss each for Ardán and Ainle, and three for Naisi who lifted her to his broad shoulder and together the four of them turned west from the wood.

That night, they spent in their father's castle, Dun Usna. Then, knowing that word of what had happened could not long be kept quiet, with all their following – a hundred and fifty men, the same of women and a like number of hounds and servants – they left their father's castle and went from place to place, from north to south; east to west; serving this king or that with Conor tracking them day by day. For when Conor learned what had happened he sank into a mighty rage that gnawed at him within for vengeance the way a rodent must gnaw or die. This went on for months and all the time they were pursued by Conor and the men of Ulster, seeking revenge and to kill them by ambush and by war, by trickery and by onslaught, by fair means and by foul, but always they escaped.

For any king, I needn't tell you, the offence would have been mighty, but for Conor, uneasy as he was on his throne and insecure too in his person, the slight was unforgivable. The fact was that he had watched over her, harboured her and nourished her; cultivated her like some precious fruit or flower, only to find that just as she was ripe to be picked and displayed and cherished by him before the world as his product and his property, she was plucked from under his hand. Thus, in spite of the fact that he was surrounded in his court with the choice of the women of Ulster, and they only too anxious for his company and to attend to his wants whatever they might be, Conor had developed a desire, both of the body and, like the Greek Pygmalion, of creation, for Deirdre, who was in fact lovelier than anything he could have dreamed of. He had nursed this passion jealously and nurtured it for his old age. He was to have married Deirdre only a matter of weeks after she had eloped with Naisi. Hence, the consuming rage that never left him was visceral and unending.

Conor plotted his revenge and planned the destruction of the sons of Usna with a consuming bitterness that dominated every day of his life from the moment he learned of their 'treachery'. Night and day he harassed them. His armies and his scouts scoured the land, tracking in pursuit of Deirdre and the three brothers and their people. From sanctuary to sanctuary, from refuge to refuge, they were hunted and hounded, losing here a man, there a follower, always flying with their spears turned backwards and fear at their heels like hounds or a nemesis from the eastern world.

At last the time came when there was nowhere left in Ulster for them to hide. The kings and chiefs with whom they had sought safety were too afraid of the wrath of Conor, and they would not go to the treachery of Maeve of Connacht, and Munster was too far and Leinster too weak. So Naisi decided to go and hide in Alba (Scotland). They built boats and crossed the tossed and bosomy sea to the powerful shores of Alba and there drove out the wild inhabitants who had come there from the far north. Naisi and his brothers carved for themselves from this wilderness a kingdom which had its seat in Glen Etive, the winged glen. Here he and Deirdre ruled and meted out justice throughout their little kingdom; and as each day became a week, and the weeks months, and as the years went by, their love for each other grew deeper and stronger.

Now and then they were forced to go to war with the neighbouring savage Picts, but, in time, they were accepted and they established peaceful relations with their neighbours. All but one; and we will return to that story in a moment for it has a bearing on all that was to pass between Deirdre and the sons of Usna and King Conor beyond in Ulster.

Conor's rage for revenge had not dimmed, but he concealed it. For, old though he was, and he with sons in middle age, he burned inside for Deirdre, and he would not have it known. He realised, all along, that it was necessary for him to keep the people happy and attend to affairs of state in their interests and, in spite of his torments, he did so – but only just. The death and humiliation of Deirdre and her love were an obsession with him and the idea of how to achieve vengeance tormented his sleepless nights and harried his mind away from the daylight tasks it should have been engaged on. He dared not send assassins to do away with them, for Naisi's camp in Glen Etive, as he knew from his spies, was strong and formidable. And anyway there were too many friends and sympathisers of Naisi's in Emhain Macha for him to be sure of success even in selecting the right people. He might mount a full-scale invasion, but there were the same problems, only magnified. His people would not stand for such a great undertaking for so little a reason – and that personal. And he knew, from his own experience with Fergus, that if he insisted they were quite capable of deposing him and appointing another. He dared not jeopardise things more.

As often happens (for who is the man who can tell a coincidence from the finger of fate?), the answer came as if by accident one night at a banquet of the assembled Knights of the Red Branch in his castle. Conor sat in his place at the centre of the great western table facing the door, with Fergus, now old but still vigorous, on his right. On the other side was another great warrior, Conal Cearnach, and beyond him the youthful and brooding Cuchulain, of fate-filled aspect.

While they were feasting and being entertained by tumblers and gleemen who performed in the centre of the hall between the tables and, I might add, without raising much in the way of a laugh or a clap from the top table (and the others were fairly muted for that reason except at the far end), two spies came in who had been in Alba for Conor gathering information about Deirdre and the sons of Usna. Conor beckoned them and they came right up to him. He asked them what news they had.

'Well,' said the first, 'we have news of the sons of Usna and of Deirdre, and some of it is good and some of it is not so good.'

'Tell us,' said Conor.

'Well,' went on the spies, taking up the story and passing it from one to another, like musicians with a tune, as they told it – and very polite they were about it too, let me tell you, knowing the man they were dealing with – 'as you know, they were settled in Alba and they made peace with the Picts. But, saving your presence, they were somewhat concerned in case the Picts might see Deirdre and take a fancy to her, so she remained mostly in the inner court of their abode. But early one morning, didn't the steward of the King of the Picts go out spying on them and he saw Deirdre and Naisi (if you'll pardon the expression) lying asleep together.'

Conor snorted into his drinking horn and shifted in his chair, but nodded at the man to go on. But 'twas the other man who took up the story. 'The steward ran off to the King of the Picts and told him, "At last," says he, "we've found a woman suitable for you. The only trouble is she belongs to Naisi and he keeps her hidden. The best thing you can do is to kill him and take her for yourself."

'But "no",' says the king, who is a man, Conor, if you'll excuse me, who fancies himself more than is justified . . .' said the first.

And the second added: 'And he had a good deal of respect for Naisi's troops as well, if I might say so.' And they both nodded.

Then the first fellow resumed. 'So the king said to his steward: "Let you go and see her and tell her 'tis I myself am interested in her and woo her for me that way."'

The second spy took up the story: 'Well, Conor, the steward did that, but it had no effect on Deirdre and she told Naisi everything. And when that didn't work the Picts went to war with the sons of Usna. But before the battle the king sent a message to Deirdre by the steward warning her lest she might be killed the next day. And she told Naisi that too, warning them to fly. So lock, stock and barrel they packed up and went off to Glen Etive, where they are now.'

When he heard this, Conor remained unmoved. He allowed no sign of interest to show, but to make sure he let his eyes rove slowly round the mighty hall, the furthest depths of which were hidden from where he sat. There, he knew, were knights and retainers watching, listening. His eyes returned again past the three empty seats with bare pillars behind them that were those of the distant sons of Usna, and which would remain thus until they returned or were dead. Nor did any remark on this, for Conor had made it clear that no one was to speak of the sons of Usna in his presence. But he could not help it this night and his eyes lingered on these empty places. But even so, even as they did, an idea came to him that had in it the seed of how his vengeance might be achieved.

Excitement kindled in him and it was hard for him to conceal the gleam of it in his eye. But he managed it. Something that his knights had not seen for months occurred. The king began to smile. Gradually his scowl disappeared and was replaced by a lightness of countenance. He joked with those near him and pressed more food and wine on the knights and their guests, and when the banquet was at its height, Conor stood and shook the tree of silver bells for attention. Then he raised his kingly voice and cried: 'Friends, lords and knights of Ulster, I have a question for you . . .' He paused so that they all focused their attention on him, a small smile on his lips (and that in itself was such a rare thing those days 'twas enough for them to do so if he never said a word). Then he went on: 'This is my question. In all your travels have you ever seen or been present at, in any of the fine countries of the world, a more royal court or banquet the equal of this?'

In reply there came a great roar of mixed agreement and dissent, depending on which way the question was interpreted, but it all meant they had never seen or been anywhere to equal where they were; and whether that was true or otherwise is a small matter. When the roar died down Conor waited a while again with that little smile still there and then: 'And there's no want here?' he shouted.

'None!' they shouted back, and half of them believed it too.

'Ah!' said Conor. And this time they had to strain to hear him as he shook his head. 'Ah,' he said, 'but there is.'

The silence was short, and then it was broken by 'Whats?' and denials and questions and the like of that until Conor rattled the *crann tamhail* again. 'There is something missing,' he said gravely. 'And I'll tell you what it is: the Three Lights of Valour of the Gael, as we call them – the three sons of Usna.'

The silence that brought was remarkable: full of energy, but still. Then, knowing full well the effect he'd created, Conor went on: ''Tis a pity,' he said, 'that for the sake of only a woman they can't be with us tonight.'

Well, if the silence a moment before had power 'twas nothing to the tumult that broke out then. Cheering and yelling and men leaping to their feet and pounding the tables with their knives and what all else besides, it took minutes to quieten down. Then a few voices were heard: 'They'd have been here long ago if we'd dared say it,' said one; 'Bring them back and Ulster will be Ulster again,' said another; 'Yes,' said more and not much else for they all wanted to say the same thing, namely, 'Let the sons of Usna come home, Conor.' Conor looked at them guilelessly and spread his hands. 'Sure I didn't know that that's what you wanted. But if it is, so be it. Let our messenger go to Glen Etive straight off and bring them back,' he said.

But that simple statement brought on another, and a different, kind of silence: shuffling of the feet and a looking at one another as the warriors and knights sat down and squinted at the table or at each other. For the truth of the matter was that there was hardly one amongst them who didn't know that the sons of Usna would doubt his word after the way they had been hounded the length and breadth of Ireland. 'Who'll go?' asked a knight from beyond Lough Neagh. 'Whose word would they believe?'

Conor smiled into his beard where it didn't show. 'I take your point,' he said, 'and 'tis a good one. The way it is they could hardly be blamed for doubting the word of any man here.' He looked around. 'And yet,' he went on, 'the anxiety to have them back is clear enough. I wonder what we can do?'

A muttering of questions travelled round the hall, into its corners and crannies, and across its tables; round its pillars and supports until it became a hum and then a buzz. But no one said a word to Conor, who was still standing. Then, for the third time, he shook the *crann tamhail* and there was a hush.

'I have heard,' said Conor, 'I have heard that there are but three men whose word the sons of Usna will believe in any circumstances – apart from my own, of course. But I can't go, can I?' he asked with a laugh. And a sort of explosion of nervous laughter came back at him. 'No,' he continued. 'The king can't go. But if Fergus Mac Ri or Conall Cearnach or Cuchulain went, they would be accepted.' He stopped for he would have been drowned out anyway in the roar that greeted this. 'Then let them go,' cried the Red Branch knights. 'Let one of them go, let all three of them go, and let the sons of Usna come back to us again.'

Now all of this was as Conor had planned; indeed it was working out even better than he had hoped. And later that night when the assembly was relaxed before the fires and listening to the story-telling and the music, and the jars and skins of wine and of mead and beer were emptying, he touched Conall Cearnach on the arm and jerked his head towards his own private quarters. Conall looked squarely at him a moment and then nodded and followed.

Conor had already decided what he intended to say, and how he would say it. He brought Conall into his ante-room and motioned him to sit beside him on a cushioned couch. He put one elbow on his knee and leaned towards Conall, watching the yellow light of the single great candle, thick as a man, dance on his big, strong face. Then he said, 'Conall, you were there tonight. You saw what happened, I suppose?'

Conall Cearnach thought it wise to keep quiet and simply nodded. Seemingly satisfied Conor leaned back again. 'Well,' he said, 'you can imagine my surprise when I heard that! And there was I thinking that the last thing the men of Ulster wanted was to have the sons of Usna home again, which I would have liked. Sure I've wanted that for ages. Nothing I'd like better. Only I was nervous of raising the matter when I thought they wouldn't have it. Are you with me?'

Knowing that Conor was up to something Conall said, 'I am,' and nodded his head again.

Again Conor seemed satisfied. 'Well, now, you know the way things are as well as myself. They're wanted here. And home they must come, especially now after what's been happening over there in that wild place. But you know too,' and he leaned forward again giving Conall a sharp glint out of his eye, 'that Fergus or Cuchulain or yourself must be the ones to bring them back.'

Conall returned his look steadily. He could feel that Conor was getting closer to the point. And he was right.

Once again Conor leaned back. 'Now,' he said, steepling his fingers in front of him, 'a thought crossed my mind; supposing, just supposing,' he pursed his lips a moment as if contemplating the suppose he was about to make, 'they came back under your protection and safeguard,' and he shot a glance at Conall who nodded to show that he understood, 'and supposing,' went on Conor, 'that a misfortune was to befall them – that they might be killed, for example, through some class of mischance . . .' He waved an airy and generous hand. 'Then what would happen?'

Looking back at the king, Conall said: 'If such a "mischance" – and he stressed the word slightly – 'occurred while they were under my protection, I'll tell you what would happen: whoever caused that class of a "mischance", and his family, and every man in Ulster who had done them any harm whatever would feel my vengeance.' And he glared at the king.

Conor frowned. Then he sighed and pretended he hadn't. This wasn't going as well as he'd intended. 'I'd hoped you wouldn't say that,' he replied. 'It makes it very difficult for me. I appreciate your loyalty,' he said. 'Loyalty is a rare and precious thing but it must be guided, not misguided.' Quickly he held up a hand, palm outwards. 'Now, I'm not saying that your loyalty is misguided. But it's a question of what other people might think, do you follow me? I had a good reason for putting that question to you, Conall, and I'll tell you what it is. I need to know – in these circumstances – if your loyalty was to me, or to someone else.' He threw a sharp glance at Conall as he said that and held his eye with his own.

Conall Cearnach glared at the king. He realised full well the trap he'd been lured into, but he wasn't going to allow himself either to be trapped or to lose his temper, either of which would be fatal. But of course the anger boiled inside. He stood up, bowed slightly to Conor, and strode out hanging on to his anger.

Conor snapped his fingers and his steward, a captured Briton who'd had his tongue cut out and had become almost civilised, came in and Conor told him to bring Cuchulain to him. But when he looked at the beardless face of the brooding youth before him, even Conor's purpose faltered and he asked his question without lifting his eyes to Cuchulain's.

While the king was speaking, the youth remained standing, and when Conor was finished it was almost as if he had not heard. Conor was about to repeat his question when, very quietly, Cuchulain said: 'If any harm came to the sons of Usna through you and they under my protection, Conor, not all the wealth of Ireland or the boundless empire of the Romans would keep your head on your shoulders, Conor, instead of theirs.' So saying he turned and walked out.

Conor was white with rage and very shaken, but he was not yet finished. He knew, as he had known from the first, he thought, that he had to rely on Fergus if his scheme was to be successful. Who did he know so well? Who could he manipulate more readily? So he summoned his steward again and told him to fetch Fergus.

He turned over in his mind what he would say to the former king and when Fergus arrived Conor stood and put his arm around his huge shoulders, welcoming him and drawing him to sit beside him so that Fergus felt flattered and important. When they were sitting again Conor turned to the older man and looked at him with candour. 'Fergus,' he said, 'I'll be honest with you. There's a problem about bringing the sons of Usna home, and it's one that troubles me.'

'Problem?' asked Fergus. 'What problem?'

'Well,' said Conor, 'suppose – just suppose, for the sake of argument, that some harm befell them while they were here. What then?'

'How do you mean?' asked Fergus. 'What sort of harm?'

'Well,' said Conor, 'you know the way things stand. If something happened, whatever it might be, who'd be held responsible? Me! Now, what I'd like to know is what would you do in those circumstances? That's the point, Fergus. For instance, what would you do if they came back under your protection and some harm did come to them? It's not impossible. As I said, you know, the way things are . . . they have plenty of enemies. But sure,' he went on quickly, 'that is probably nothing now. You heard what happened tonight. 'Tis yourself or Conall Cearnach or Cuchulain must go for them, and of the three aren't you the most distinguished and reliable? Who else could go? If one of the others went it would look as if 'twas I sent them and not the knights of Ulster. They mightn't come. But if you go they'll know you come of your own accord as a king in your own right.' He smiled expansively at Fergus.

Fergus wasn't sure what to say. He was flattered, of course, but he was wise enough in the ways of men and of kings not to be taken in entirely by the sweet words. But then Conor's question was so veiled in 'ifs' and 'buts' and 'maybes' that it was essentially hypothetical and, as a king himself, he was well able to deal with that. If there was anything sinister behind it he didn't dwell on it. More likely he didn't see it. In his declining years he had been given honour and position by Conor, which suited him well. His anger and desire for revenge over the way he had been tricked out of the kingship was long dead. To be the man responsible for bringing home the distinguished exiles and see them welcomed and fêted, that would raise his prestige to a suitable level for his station among the nobles and people of the province. And Conor wouldn't last forever and there was his own family to consider. Therefore, after he had considered what had been said for a suitable time, he faced the watching Conor and answered; 'This is how it seems to me, Conor; if a man of Ulster harmed them while they were here, I'd avenge the hurt and disgrace. But I am satisfied that such a thing would be impossible seeing that they would come under the protection of your own sovereign word.'

The answer pleased Conor, and he let it show. But it wasn't enough for him. 'I agree,' he said. 'What could happen? But just supposing,' he said, 'supposing that something did happen. What then?'

'Then,' said Fergus, his brow darkening, 'I'd have revenge.'

'On whom?' asked Conor with sly eyes.

'On whoever was responsible, of course,' growled Fergus.

'Ah!' said Conor, leaning back. 'And in those circumstances, Fergus, how would you see my position?'

'You? How would I see you?'

Conor nodded. 'Would you have revenge on me too?'

'On you?' asked Fergus. 'Why should I? Don't I know you wouldn't have anything to do with such a thing? If you were that vengeful would I be here now? What harm could come to them under the seal of your word?'

'Right!' said Conor. 'I knew you were the right man; a true king. Tomorrow, go with my message to the sons of Usna beyond in Alba. Tell them that I – that the people of Ulster – want them back as soon as possible. Let them hurry to their home and let there be no delay. Tell them,' he said, and paused. 'Tell them to eat no meat from the time they leave home until they reach Emhain Macha and can eat the feast I'll have here prepared for them. And that is only the beginning of the extent of welcoming they'll have.'

Hearing this delighted Fergus and he lost no time himself. Early next morning he was where the king's ships were anchored above near Dun Borrach, and put to sea in the face of the rising sun before it cleared the eastern waves, bound for Glen Etive. He took with him his two sons, Illan Fionn (the Fair) and Buinne Roe (the Red), together with his own shield-bearer, Caillan. (It was one of these two sons that he hoped would be elected by the nobles of Ulster to the kingship when the time came.)

Conor had come, with every appearance of anxiety and goodwill, to speed them on their journey, and stood watching the ship until it was out of sight on a long tack north. But no sooner were they vanished than he began to put his plan into effect. He rode quickly towards Borrach's castle which dominated the harbour. Borrach was the local chief and, by Conor's order, had not been told until the king arrived that he was on his way.

'I believe,' said Conor without preliminary when he met the flustered Borrach in the bawn of his castle, 'that you are preparing a feast for me.'

'Indeed, I am, Conor,' said Borrach. 'And a great feast it will be too . . .'

But Conor cut him short. 'Well, now,' he snapped. 'Aren't you very kind?' Then softer, 'And 'tis a great hardship to me that I must disappoint you this time. But you can be sure that I'll make it up to you some other way. I know that a thing of this kind isn't undertaken lightly, and I understand you've put a lot into it, but there are important matters in Emhain that only I can deal with and my hands are tied. There's no gainsaying it. I must postpone my visit to you to some other occasion. But I'll tell you what I'll do,' he said brightly as if the idea had just occurred to him. 'Isn't Fergus Mac Ri a king himself? And I'm after giving him his rightful place beside myself in Ulster, so here's what I'd like you to do. Accept him in my place at your feast and 'twill be the same as if I was there myself. As you know, he's just gone off to Scotland for a few days on a bit of an errand for myself; and when he comes back let you be there below at the pier to invite him instead of me and I'll hold the honour paid to him as good as if it had been paid to me.'

Borrach was very flattered by this speech and, since he was not a nobleman but a *brúdenach*, he was not aware of the reason for Fergus's going to Scotland. So, with satisfaction oozing out of every pore of his face, he raised his two hands before him with palms towards Conor. 'Put your mind at rest, Conor, he'll feast with me for three days,' he emphasised. 'And I can tell you what I'll put before him will be such as is seldom seen even in your own palace at Emhain Macha. I'll honour him for the three days as if 'twas yourself was in it. And what's more,' he went on, 'I know he won't refuse for isn't it well known he's under *geasa* not to refuse any hospitality that's offered to him?'

'Is that a fact?' asked Conor. 'You surprise me.'

'Indeed it is,' said Borrach, pleased to be able to tell the king something he didn't know, 'and won't he be delighted?'

'Delighted!' agreed Conor. 'And why wouldn't he? Three days at a king's feast in the best *brúden* in all Ireland!'

Like all the other knights of the Red Branch, Fergus had made certain vows, called *geasai*, when he was elected to the Knights. To violate one of these vows, which had been taken in the presence of the king and nobles and the assembled knights, was to be utterly dishonourable. So, when he said that, Conor smiled to himself. His snare was now tightening nicely.

Wittingly or not, Conor had now ensnared Fergus in a classic trap. When he returned and Borrach declared his invitation, Fergus would find that he was committed simultaneously to two *geasas*, with no option but to break one of them.[3] Conor banked on Fergus, in his dilemma, choosing to protect himself from the greater disgrace of breaking his knightly vow, particularly if he might make an acceptable accommodation in respect of the imposed one, namely his protection of the sons of Usna and Deirdre. This he might have achieved by keeping them with him until his knightly obligation was discharged. But, anticipating this, at the same time that Borrach invited Fergus to his feast, Conor extended a specific command by special herald to the sons of Usna that they come to Emhain Macha without delay, and this was an obligation on them that they could not refuse except by breach of their own honour. Therefore Fergus would have no choice but to delegate the responsibility for protecting the sons of Usna to his own sons, Illan Fionn the Fair and Buinne the Red. And it was in that way that Conor intended to separate the sons of Usna from their protector and get them into his power.

Fergus's ship made its way north and east through the rough channel between Ireland and the wild coast of Alba. He went onwards past the Irish colony of the Dal Riada,[4] and then turned eastwards towards Loch Etive, which led deep into the glen of the same name at that time beyond the extremities of Dal Riada territory. His ship left the rough seas and nosed its way into the long narrow channel between heather-covered slopes on either side of the loch. The bow of the boat clove the rippling water, turning it white and brown near the ship, a contrast to the blue and silver of the dancing surface where it caught the sunlight and the sky. Fergus stood in the bow, a mighty figure, his royal blue cloak moving slightly as the ship thrust forward, and then he threw back his head and raised a great hunting cry.

It was a late spring day full of warm sunshine and wild flowers and alive with the hum of insects. Away above the loch and the glen a pair of eagles swung gently through the sky on motionless wings, their long pinions spread like fingers. As Fergus's ship glided silently up the narrow loch, Deirdre and Naisi sat in the *grianaan*, the sun garden, of their castle, a chess board between them. Beyond this sun-kissed bower the lazy noises of the community that had grown up about the castle was all that disturbed the peacefulness. But Naisi, though it was his move, was far away. His face was sad and his mind in Ulster and Deirdre knew it and wished with all her heart that it wasn't so and that there was something she could do to ease the heartache she knew he felt. As she was about to speak to him, if only to see the sadness in his face relieved, they heard, distantly carried over the water, the shout of Fergus from far down the loch.

Naisi's head jerked suddenly alert and his eyes widened. 'The cry of an Ulsterman!' he exclaimed, head cocked, ears straining.

Deirdre too had recognised the cry, and with the recognition came a cold grip of fear. 'How could that be?' she asked, her brittle laugh belying the innocence of her question. ''Tis only some hunter. Your move, Naisi . . .'

Naisi picked up a piece and tried to concentrate. But again Fergus opened his throat to the hunting cry he knew so well; and again; and each time it was closer until Naisi at last threw down the piece he had been holding all the time and leaped to his feet. This time he recognised the voice. 'It is an Ulsterman, Deirdre. And what's more, 'tis Fergus Mac Rí himself. I'd know that cry anywhere. I have heard it often enough.'

He started to turn to run for the loch shore, but Deirdre quickly stood up too and laid her hand on his arm. 'I know,' she said, 'I know. But Naisi . . .'

He paused, impatient to be gone, and looked down at her anxious face. 'What is it, *a chróidhe* (my heart)?' he asked.

'Last night—' she began, and faltered. Then she gathered herself, and went on, dreading what she was about to say, dreading what Naisi's reaction might be, and dreading too the outcome. 'Last night I dreamed a dream and it frightened me.'

Naisi frowned. 'What? A dream? You bother me with a dream at a time like this?'

'Naisi, my love, listen to me. I dreamed that three birds flew here from Emhain, an old eagle and two hawks, a red and a white, each carrying a drop of honey in its beak. They gave these three drops of honey to us; but when they left they took with them instead three drops of blood. It was our blood, Naisi.'

Naisi smiled. He could see she was disturbed. 'And what does that mean, my little druidess?' he teased, taking her hand and smiling. His depression forgotten.

But this made Deirdre more upset than ever. She clutched his hand and held his arm. 'What it means, Naisi, is this: that Fergus is coming with messages of peace, sweet as honey. But he will take back with him three drops of blood – bitter death – you and Ainle and Ardán.'

Naisi threw back his head and laughed so that his throat moved. 'And what about the hawks?' he asked; and with that there was another halloo from the loch and there were one, two, three voices in it.

Deirdre's heart turned over in her breast with love and terror.

'Three black birds and three drops of honey and three drops of blood,' laughed Naisi. 'You have the magic numbers right, *a gradh*, three threes make nine. But listen, you know Fergus. If we can trust anyone, we can trust him. Away off with you Ardán and bring him here and we'll follow on and meet him on the way.'

Ardán, with Ainle beside him, was already running to the shore. When they reached it, the sight of Fergus stepping off his curved ship, with his two sons and the taste of Ireland about the whole thing, was like the taste of summer rain on parched earth to him, and he threw his arms around Fergus's neck with a yell, and Ainle along with him, and the five of them had a very happy reunion there on the beach. Then they turned and walked up to meet Naisi and Deirdre coming along behind. When their greetings were over, Naisi and Deirdre asked what was the news from home.

'What news!' exclaimed Fergus. 'Great news! The best of news!' He looked round and beamed at them. 'The King, Conor, has sent me to bring you home to Ulster. Your places in the Knights of the Red Branch are held and all that was yours will be restored to you. I am your pledge of safety in his name.'

'What need have they to go?' asked Deirdre. 'Aren't they as powerful themselves here as Conor is in Ulster? Why would they want to leave that?'

'True enough,' said Fergus – which, of course, it wasn't, for how could they be as powerful as Conor? But logic wasn't in Deirdre's mind, any more than it would be in the mind of any other woman in such a situation – 'But 'tis hard for a man to be abroad when he could be in his own place. Wouldn't it be better to be at home in Ulster than in this wild place, powerful and all as you are, with no one here but your own few people and the stags belling on the hills for company? Wouldn't you be better off at home with your friends and your relations?'

'That's right,' said Naisi, 'what use are land and power to me here when I'd rather be at home in Ireland? Deirdre, chicken, I know how you feel. I understand your fears. But sure you have no reason for them. Hasn't Fergus told us we're under his protection? And if we can't accept that we can't accept much. It's good enough for me. We'll go tomorrow.'

Still Deirdre could not get the memory of her dreams out of her head. Fear of what might happen continued to trouble her in spite of the reassurances she heard and she continued to argue against returning to Ireland from Alba where they were happy.

'Don't worry, *alanna* (my child),' said Fergus. 'I myself am the pledge of your safety.'

Still Deirdre wasn't satisfied. 'Please don't go,' she begged. 'We will be tricked. In my heart I know it.' She cried and became so distressed that the three brothers didn't know how to comfort her.

Then Naisi said: 'Deirdre, *a chróidhe*, we all understand the way you feel. Why wouldn't you be distressed after all that happened, and that dream you had? But that is all it was – a dream. Fergus has given us his word and pledged his honour for us. What more could anyone ask? We'll go tomorrow, and that's an end of it now.'

So all that night was spent in talk and remembering and exchanging news, but it was the four men who talked. Deirdre was silent and full of foreboding. While the night was still young, she excused herself from the company and went to her room and sat a while before going to her bed. She lay, in sadness and heartache, staring through the window at the glen she loved so much and where she had been so happy, now bathed in the pale, cold light of the moon that matched her melancholy.

Next morning, Fergus's ship slipped back down the loch bound for Ulster. On board were the returning exiles, leaving their following behind in Glen Etive. While the men relaxed and let the day and the ship take their course, Deirdre sat in the stern and looked at the loch and on either hand at the wooded slopes and rounded hills of her beloved Glen Etive, and she made this song:

Dear land of Alba, I would not go
From your green slopes beside the sea;
My heart is heavy, dull and slow,
To be abandoning your peace with Naisi.

Dear Glens I know and love so well
Where he and I made love together;
Knowing the cuckoo's summer spell
And the hush of the snow-clad winter heather.

Dear to me your crystal water;
Dear to me your sunlit sea;
I'd never leave your welcoming laughter
Only to be with my love, Naisi.

The morning after that they nosed into the harbour below Dun Borrach, and Borrach himself, having been warned of the ship's approach, was at the quayside to meet them. Having welcomed them he turned to Fergus and said: 'Fergus, my lord, there is a message from the king.' Fergus nodded, well satisfied with himself. But that didn't last but a minute. 'He says you are to represent him at my banquet for the next three days,' continued Borrach, 'for 'tis long arranged, and the sons of Usna must go on to Emhain that he may welcome them with a banquet of his own.'

Fergus's face had been reddening with rage while Borrach spoke. Now he was like a furious cock. 'You have done wrong, Borrach,' he roared, 'to invite me to a banquet I cannot refuse, knowing I am pledged to bring the sons of Usna safe to Emhain Macha without delay.'

Borrach was put out by this and quailed a bit before Fergus's anger. But he was far more nervous of Conor and what he might do if he failed him. They were standing a little apart from the others, and he whispered to Fergus. 'Listen,' he said, ''tis all right. It was the king himself who told me. You are to represent him here with me,' he added hurriedly as Fergus glared at him, and went on rapidly, 'You know well he has problems of his own in the city. If your only worry is the sons of Usna beyond, sure what harm can befall them between here and Emhain Macha and your own two strong sons going along with them to protect them as well as if you were going yourself?'

Fergus was torn between two obligations. His sworn commitment never to refuse a feast confronted his commitment to protect the sons of Usna and he was confused and troubled. If any doubt whispered in his mind about the motives of Conor he closed his inner ear to it. He could appeal to the sons of Usna concerning his obligation to them, but there was no appeal to the *geasa* he had undertaken when he became a Red Branch Knight. He explained his dilemma to Naisi and said: 'There you have it. What am I to do?' He looked from one to the other of the three sons of Usna, but it was Deirdre who answered for them.

She looked at him coldly and maybe it was contempt that glittered in her eyes with the tears. 'The choice is your own, Fergus,' she said. 'You must choose between a feast and the lives of the sons of Usna. It seems to me that they are a high price to pay for a dinner.'

Fergus went white. 'I won't forsake them,' he said. 'Nor will I break my vow. I will stay and fulfil my obligation here and my two sons, Illan Fionn and Buinne Roe, will go with you and protect them and my honour.'

The look Naisi gave Fergus would have withered any other man. As it was it made Fergus's eyes do a little bit of a shifty dance. Naisi said to him – and he was put out enough not to try to hide the way he felt: 'We don't need your sons' protection, Fergus, or any other protection. We'll look after ourselves.' With that Naisi turned on his heel and walked away from Fergus, the anger in him almost visible. He was followed by his brothers and Deirdre and Fergus's two sons, leaving Fergus alone and desolate where he stood.

Deirdre, who had almost to run to catch up with Naisi, called after him 'Stop!' Above all things she wanted to persuade him to stay where they were and leave going to Emhain Macha until Fergus could accompany them. 'We could go to Cuchulain at Dun Dealgan,' she urged, 'and stay with him until Fergus can come with us.'

Naisi shook his head as did his brothers. 'No,' he said, 'that would look as if we didn't trust the king and would be an insult to him and would be seen as cowardice on our part.'

'In any case,' said Buinne Roe, 'Illan Fionn and myself will be with you and give you the same protection as if Fergus was with us.'

So they went on and with each stretch of the road they covered Deirdre's anguish increased. Between that and the strain of the journey she was pale and exhausted when they reached Slieve Fuad. After they'd eaten a little and rested awhile they made to resume their march. But then Naisi noticed that Deirdre had fallen asleep. He put his hand on her shoulder gently so as not to startle her; but when she opened her eyes and saw him a wave of terror seemed to cross her face and she shrank back so that he gathered her into his arms where she clung shivering.

'What is it, *a cróidhe?*' he asked her. 'What is the matter?'

Her voice was muffled as she answered for it was riddled with tears and her head was buried in his breast. 'I dreamed a dream,' she said, 'and I am afraid.'

'You and your dreams,' said Naisi gently. 'You have too many dreams, my love.' As best he could he comforted her, his arms around her all the time.

But even in her despair, Deirdre's strength of mind asserted itself and she looked up at him and said: 'While I slept, I dreamed; and I dreamed that I saw the bodies of the three of you and that of Illan Fionn too, naked and bloody and headless. But there was Buinne Roe also standing over without a mark on his body.'

'Hush!' said Naisi, glancing at Buinne. 'Whisht! It was only a dream.'

'Oh!' she cried, 'Naisi, I'm frightened! We should not go to Emhain Macha. I have this feeling. Something bad is going to happen . . .'

Now Naisi was no fool and whatever about Deirdre's dreams it was pretty obvious that something was going on. Moreover he was concerned because Deirdre was upset. On the other hand his honour and that of his brothers, and his father's name, were at stake. He had been invited by the king under the protection of Fergus and to refuse the invitation without sufficient cause would disgrace him forever. So, in spite of Deirdre's distress, they pressed on to Emhain Macha, hoping that what they feared was, like Deirdre's dreams, behind them, but, fearing the worst. At the same time, he tried to comfort Deirdre the best way he could, and I'm afraid it wasn't up to much. As they approached over the low round hills towards the city with the sun sinking before them they could see a great cloud hanging over it in the evening sky. The belly and flanks of that cloud were painted blood red. Small flecks of it were whipped off at the edges by little winds like drops of blood from a carcase, and Deirdre cried as they approached: 'Look! Blood hangs even over the city. Isn't that enough for you?'

But now that they were so close Naisi could not let himself be persuaded. Her anxiety only gave him concern for her out of his great love for her. Deirdre understood that so she went on quickly. 'Naisi, we have come this far and you have ignored all the omens that I have pointed out to you. It may be that you are right and that I am wrong. But there is one infallible means by which we will know if Conor is to be trusted or not. He will not harm a guest in his own house. So if he welcomes us into his palace we have nothing to fear. But, Naisi, listen to me now: if he directs us elsewhere then you may be sure he means treachery.'

So they went on and when they reached the great gate of the city there was a messenger there from Conor to welcome them in his name and light them through the narrow streets of the dark city with the torch that he carried. This messenger said: 'The king welcomes you and has asked me to guide you to the House of the Red Branch where there is a banquet in your honour.' And he turned and began to walk towards the great palace which was the House of the Red Branch.

Then Deirdre cried; 'Naisi, what did I say? He's planning something. We should go. Now!'

But Naisi laughed at her fears and asked: 'Where is it more proper for three champions of the Red Branch to be welcomed back than the House of the Red Branch itself?' But the truth of the matter is that Naisi said this more to comfort Deirdre than because he believed it. Now a serpent of suspicion laid its eggs of doubt in his mind in a way he could not avoid. The fact that Conor had not come to greet them was one thing; but that he did not bring them to his own palace was another.

Illan Fionn said: 'Don't be afraid, Deirdre. Naisi is right. And anyway we are here with you.' And he looked at her, smiling. But she saw his stomach contract.

And so they were guided to the House of the Red Branch where they were welcomed by the steward, but left alone with the banquet that was spread out. It was then that all Deirdre's predictions fell into place and each one of them knew in their hearts that something was wrong. Although they were none of them interested in the food that lay before them, Naisi picked up the quarter of a young roasted pig and began to eat it, advising the others to do the same, for now he guessed they might need sustenance before the night was out.

The servants and serving people moved round them, shadows in the shadows, saying never a word in that great hall. And this somehow contributed to their growing anxiety. Deirdre looked at the men and nodded at each one. They all understood that they should be prepared.

Now, in order to ease Deirdre's mind and take it off what portended, Naisi called for a chess board and said to her: 'When we last played in Alba and my mind was on other things you beat me. Well, now that we are at home again, I'll beat you.' He smiled at her, but Deirdre did not smile back. The weight in her heart was unappeasable with the fear of what she felt was about to happen.

While this was going on Conor sat in his own palace, impatience and brooding solitude alternating in him like the moods of a wild March day. The thought that Deirdre was so near and still unobtainable ate at him to the marrow of his bones. In his agitation to get some information about her he summoned Leabharcam the old nurse and said: 'You must do something for me. You must go and see Deirdre and look at her carefully and report back to me. You must tell me if Deirdre is still the same as when she was being reared by you.' He looked at her from under his lowered eyebrows. 'And if you report that she is I tell you there is not on the ridge of the world to this day a woman so beautiful.'

Now, Leabharcam and Deirdre still loved each other as they had when Deirdre was a small girl. And so when Leabharcam reached the House of the Red Branch they fell crying upon each other's necks. With kisses and tears and laughter – and also with lamentation – Leabharcam welcomed them and loved them and through it all warned them about Conor. She held Deirdre close by the hand and by the arm and she looked at her and she said, 'Be careful, child.' And then she looked at Naisi strongly and said: 'And you, Naisi, and your brothers – and the two of you, the sons of Fergus – you be careful too.' Then she paused for a moment to control her voice because the tears were near the surface. 'I know,' she said, 'that here in Emhain it is planned tonight that the three Torches of the Valours of the Gael, yourselves, are to be attacked and killed. So guard well and defend yourselves so that you can last until Fergus comes to help you.'

After that they talked a while longer and then, so that she might not be accused of staying too long, Leabharcam returned to the king. And Conor looked at her sharply, and asked her what she had seen.

'Well, Conor,' she said, 'the way of it is I have good news and I have bad news. And I'll give you the good news first, and that is that the sons of Usna that you sent for have returned and will stand beside you in the future.'

Conor scowled. 'And the bad news?' he growled.

'Ah – ah, wisha –' said Leabharcam woefully, 'the bad news is that care and worry and time and suffering have changed Deirdre so much that she has little left of the beauty that made her so remarkable and she growing up.'

Conor sat back and looked at Leabharcam. And, strange to say, instead of anger and frustration his jealousy left him like a cloud lifted by the wind from a mountain-top, and a kind of satisfaction settled in its place.

However, later that same night he began to think again, when the wine and the mead that he had been drinking to boost his satisfaction took hold of some twisted cords in his mind. The vision of Deirdre as she had been returned to him. With it came the old desire and he began to wonder if what Leabharcam had told him was the truth. So then he called a man named Trendorn, a hired soldier from the land of the Picts, and he said to him: 'Tell me, Trendorn, do you remember who killed your father?'

'Why should I forget?' glowered Trendorn. 'It was Naisi, the son of Usna, who killed my father.'

'Right!' said Conor. 'Now I want you to do something for me. Go to the House of the Red Branch where Naisi and his brothers and Deirdre are this very minute and look at what you will see. Then come back here and tell me what Deirdre looks like.'

So, in the dark of night, Trendorn made his way to the House of the Red Branch where the doors and windows were barred and bolted and nothing but spears and arrows of light came forth into the darkness through the cracks and chinks of the shuttering. Naturally enough Trendorn was nervous. He thought that the sons of Usna might be in ambush for someone like himself. He knew they would have no mercy on him if they caught him and he had no wish to follow in his father's footsteps before his due time. So he climbed, by means of a ledge here and a ridge there, to a little window high above the door and looked in.

What he saw astonished him; and, most of all, he wondered at the beauty of Deirdre as she sat playing chess with Naisi, opposite from where he was looking. But he was fascinated by her beauty too long and Deirdre looked up to see his face at the window, at which she let out a gasp. With that Naisi turned with the speed of a hawk and, following her eye, saw Trendorn. Before he could duck out of sight, and in one motion with the turn, Naisi flung the chess-man he was holding so that it struck Trendorn full in the eye so hard that it blew the eyeball from its socket and knocked him to the ground.

When Trendorn returned to Conor and told him what had happened, instead of being angry, Conor was pleased. He knew that he had the truth. Nonetheless he assumed an anger and stormed into the great hall of the palace where some of the nobles were assembled. Raising his voice, Conor cried out: 'There is a man in this city who has wounded my servant and would himself be king.'

Now he let his jealousy have full rein again. Knowing from Trendorn that Deirdre was as beautiful as she ever was, he severed all restraint on his anger and roused his soldiers with the alarm that, out of spite and malice, the sons of Usna had tried to kill Trendorn.

Conor strode from the palace and summoned a battalion of foreign soldiers he had standing-to in the courtyard precisely for this purpose, only waiting for an excuse to attack the Red Branch House forthwith and to bring the sons of Usna to him. The mercenary troops attacked and tried to set the House of the Red Branch afire, but without success. The huge doors of oak held them back, and, from inside, the besieged men picked off one here and another there with javelin and tathlum until they had to retire out of range. At that point, Buinne Roe, who was the elder of Fergus's sons, said: 'It is up to me to make a circuit and kill who I can of our attackers, for 'twas on me that my father laid the charge of protecting you.' So they opened the wicket and with his own few followers Buinne Roe rushed out to face the mercenaries and quench the fires that threatened the Red Branch House. In the fighting they killed and slaughtered and wounded more than a hundred of the attackers.

'Who is that destroying my attack?' asked Conor.

'Buinne Roe Mac Fergus,' said someone.

Conor stood thinking for a minute. 'We bought his father,' he said. 'Now we must buy the son.'

So saying he stepped forward with his arm raised, and kept going until the fighting stopped. That fearful noise that is like no other became still the way thunder becomes still across a hill, and the fighting men stood back and eyed each other, wary and breathless. For quite a few moments, Conor looked long at Buinne Roe. He looked at his heavy face, the great clenched hand over the sword hilt, and the heaving chest. Then, with a kingly wave of his hand, he summoned him.

Still full of his battle-fury, Buinne stalked across the bloody sod, his dripping sword before him even as he approached the king. Their eyes quickly locked. And then, without preliminary, Conor said: 'Buinne. You don't know what you're about fighting me. I have given your father enough land for a thousand cattle, and the cattle to go with it. You will get the same if you cross to me to fight against these traitors.'

For long seconds Buinne did not take his eyes from Conor's. He made only one movement, and that was to turn to go back. But between him and the Red Branch House he saw rank upon rank of armed warriors, dark and fearsome, their spearheads half the height of a man again above their heads, flickering in the light of fires, their rigid swords, yet unbloodied, waiting for him. Then he knew that he must die. He knew too that the sons of Usna would die, and it occurred to him that they would die whether he died or not. Slowly he turned back to Conor and looked at him full in the face. But when he spoke his eyes shifted.

From the shuttered windows of the Red Branch House they saw him walk slowly around Conor's shoulder, his back to them, and they knew. Deirdre's cry burst from her heart. 'Buinne has deserted you, Naisi!' she wailed. 'Like father, like son.'

A great shout had come from the throng outside when they saw Buinne joining them, and the echoing thunder resumed again on the door of the great hall. Then Illan Fionn said: 'Now it is my turn. My sword is in my hand and as long as it is I will not be a traitor to my obligations like my father and my brother.' With that the wicket was opened and Illan Fionn and his men charged out spreading like a river to meet the sea, swinging in a circle around the House of the Red Branch, and back, and again; three times they circled the house, killing more than three hundred of the king's men in their circuit, before rushing in again to safety.

Deirdre and Naisi still sat before the chess board, for it is the thing that a great champion and his woman should never show a sign of fear or of alarm no matter what the circumstances. But it was clear where their minds were for the pieces were as they had been for nearly an hour. Sitting together like that with the appearance of calm seemed also to calm their own hearts.

Now Conor's forces rushed in in spite of the arrows and stones and javelins from the defenders to try with fire to burn them out. And again Illan Fionn and his men sallied forth in a great rush destroying them and their work, together in one red rout.

When Conor saw the great damage that Illan Fionn had done to his own soldiers, he was furious and asked who this warrior was. 'Illan Fionn,' he was told, 'the second son of Fergus.'

'Ah-ah!' said Conor. 'I see.' Then he turned to look behind him.

And seeing his own son, Fiachra, he called him. 'Fiachra,' he said, 'you and Fergus's son, Illan Fionn, were born the same night. Now, take my shield, Ocean, Flight my spear, and Victory, my sword, and challenge him to single combat. You carry my honour with you. Vanquish him before he does us more harm.'

Whatever about his honour, which was fairly stained at that stage as anyone might guess, Conor had the form right. And it was a measure of the fear in him that he selected his own son and gave him his own weapons to tackle so great a warrior. But he had little choice. And so Fiachra went and challenged Illan Fionn; and there between the hostile silent hosts and the House of the Red Branch these two fought a fair and warlike, a red and bloody, manly, bitter, savage, hot and vehement, terrible battle by the flickering torchlight and the light of the fires that burned about the smoky edges of the brazen battleground. It was a contest such as few men had ever witnessed, with neither one nor the other gaining a decisive advantage and both men raining blows that would have split any other opponent into two mortified halves.

Then, with a sudden twist and a stroke he had learned in the east, Illan Fionn hurled Fiachra to the ground and the king's son was forced to seek refuge beneath his father's shield, the Ocean. It was a wonderful round shield in the Greek pattern; and it was magical and mystical too – and it was called the Moaner on that account. The reason was that in battle it would cry out whenever the warrior who carried it was in danger. And, if it was mortal danger, the moan of the shield would be heard across the great face of Ireland and would be answered by the three great moaning waves of Erin – the Wave of Thuatha at the Bann, the Wave of Ruari in the Bay of Dundrum, and the Wave of Cliona in Glandore.

And now it moaned. It moaned across the land and the three waves answered. And on the far side of the city, Conall Cearnach heard the moan; and, remembering what Conor had said earlier that there was man in the city who would be king, he thought it was that Conor himself was in danger. He rushed through the throng and saw the shield on the ground with a figure beneath it, and another above it, waiting for the death blow. Without stopping or pausing, Conall struck the standing warrior.

Illan Fionn staggered and fell, with Conall Cearnach's spear between his shoulders. 'Ah! Ah!' he cried. 'Who hit me from behind when he might have had a fair combat?'

'And who are you,' snarled Conall, for he still didn't know Illan, 'to attack the king?' He still thought that it was Conor under the shield.

'I am Illan Fionn, Fergus's son, and you are Conall Cearnach. You have done wrong to kill me when I was defending the sons of Usna who are in the Red Branch House under my father's protection.'

Conall Cearnach was appalled at what he had done. 'By the gods,' he cried, 'you will not go unavenged.' And with that, he raised his sword arm and with one blow took the head from Fiachra who had stirred to rise from beneath the shield. Then, in grief and rage, he turned and walked, fierce and silent, from the battlefield.

Before he died, surrounded by his enemies, Illan Fionn called with his last breath to Naisi to defend himself as well as he could. And, staggering in his death agony, he moved to the Red Branch House and flung his weapons through the wicket open to receive him, so that his enemies would not have them. But the shadow of death fell on him before he reached the wicket itself, and he too fell and died before the great gate of the Red Branch House.

With that another battalion of mercenaries swarmed to the attack trying to fire the house again. But Ainle and his men rushed out like Buinne and Illan before them and held them back for a while. When they began to flag Ardán and his men came and, finally, Naisi and his own men came and fought. And one by one throughout the night their followers were killed or sorely wounded so that in the end the three brothers stood alone fighting their enemies. So terrible was the slaughter they wrought on the hosts of Conor that he feared his army would be destroyed. For, as the poet said, 'Until the seashore sands and all the forest leaves; the gleaming dewdrops on the morning grass and the fiery stars of night are calculated, it would not be possible to tabulate the heads and the hands, the severed legs and sundered limbs that there lay red and bloody at the hands of Naisi and his brothers.'

Finally, the three brothers and their few followers made a Greek phalanx with Deirdre in its centre and hurled themselves towards their enemies. When Conor saw this, he shouted at his druid, Catha, and said: 'Catha! In the name of the gods it would be better for us if these three fought for us than against us. With their few followers they have near destroyed my army. I will willingly have them back into my service. Now, go to them and bring them to me under my pledge that no harm will befall them.'

Now Catha, who was also the grandfather of the brothers for it was his own daughter who was their mother, was no fool and knew his king, but he still trusted him, for Conor's face was earnest and in his eyes lay the sombreness of truth. So the druid went and before the phalanx of the sons of Usna, raised up in the minds of those within it a fairy wood through which he reckoned no man could pass, so black and tangled were its limbs. Yet, without a pause, without a halt to see the way, the sons of Usna and their phalanx came on and through it. And then Catha stood before them, tall and straight against the pale light of dawn behind him, and raised his arms. Sweat rolled from his brow; his eyes rolled back so that only the whites showed and his face was lined and gaunt. Then it seemed as if a stormy sea, roaring and boiling, rose up before them on the plain to prevent their progress. But on through the waves they went without a backward glance, Deirdre protected by the three brothers.

Conor was furious, for he saw his army being decimated and his enemies escaping. 'Catha,' he snarled, 'your spells are hopeless. Try again.'

With that Catha willed with a strength he had not suspected he possessed. And so powerful was the force he exerted that all those around, even the king, could feel the power of it. The druid directed the accumulated strength and knowledge of his mind at the sons of Usna. Then it seemed to them and their followers that a frightful bog spread before and around and under them and clung to their feet dragging them down and clogging their limbs the way that they couldn't move, so that they were floundering in it like fish spilled from a net on the soft sandy slopes of a shelving beach.

They seemed held fast in the green and brown and deathly grip of this morass. Then, quickly, the king's men ran to where they stood – for the bog was in their minds only – and cruelly bound them with chains.

So Catha raised the spell and reminded the king of his promise. But Conor laughed in his face, the truth gone from his eyes. He clapped Catha on the shoulder, his good humour returned, and said: 'You're getting old, Catha. You have forgotten what it is to be a diplomat.'

Catha looked at him and recoiled from what he saw, which was more than the corruption of a man, even if he was a king. Catha saw the beginning of the end of his prophecy. But even he could not foresee more than it had been given to him to see. 'I have forgotten nothing,' he said. There was death and destruction all round them. He turned his back on the king and walked through it into the pale morning.

Conor ignored him. He was elated. In front of him were the three sons of Usna in chains and, beside them, Deirdre. One of his men tried to restrain her, but she shook him off. Then Leabharcam ran beside her, sobbing, and asking her forgiveness.

All of this Conor ignored, for he saw only one thing. The sons of Usna – dead. So he called aloud for one of his men to kill them. But no one stirred. Conor looked round. He called again. And still no one answered. A third time he called, and now he was angry, knowing why they would not come and knowing too that it was a criticism of himself. In his anger, he looked at the brothers and cursed them intemperately, but there was no answer from the sons of Usna, or from Deirdre, except to look with contempt and silence.

Now in Conor's palace there was a hostage who was the son of the King of Lochlann, which today we call Norway, and his name was Mainne Rough-

Hand. He was half savage and half wild and would do anything the king ordered him to, which is why Conor kept him in the palace rather than in the fort of the hostages. Conor would make him do the most outrageous things when he was entertaining for the amusement of his guests, like biting the heads off chickens and tearing a live cat to pieces with his rough hands.

Conor sent for Mainne because he had remembered that in the victorious battle after which this son of Norway's king came as hostage, the sons of Usna had killed his brother. So when Conor looked down into those empty little eyes under their ridged brows and told Mainne what he wanted, he was not surprised when a grin of pleasure spread across the other's savage face. Mainne was small and his hair was matted, but he was as broad as he was tall, like an ape from the shores of Africa, and with something of the same smell, only worse. He stooped swiftly and picked up Naisi's own sword, a gift from Manannan Mac Lír, and swung it so that it sang above his head. Then, quicker than you might follow it with your eye, he turned a complete circle and with one blow, all in the one spiral movement, struck the three heads of the sons of Usna from their shoulders. If there was any exultation it can only have been in the heart of Mainne. For Conor, to his astonishment, there was nothing but a sadness. And from the assembled men of Ulster came three great cries of sorrow and lamentation. Deirdre fell beside the three bodies wailing and weeping in an extremity of grief.

The men of Ulster made a grave for the sons of Usna where they were placed standing shoulder to shoulder and with their heads replaced where they should have been. And, as the stones of their cairn were built, Deirdre made this lament for them.

> The lions of the hill are gone
> And I am left to weep alone.
> Without my love I can't abide –
> So dig their grave both deep and wide.
>
> That I would live with Naisi dead –
> Let not such shame of me be said.
> Without my love the day is long
> For life is nothing now he's gone.
> The mountain hawks from me have flown
> And I am left to weep alone.
> My grief the turning world will cover
> Until I lie with my true lover.

So you who shape that yawning tomb,
Fashion it with care. Leave room
For me to come and lie beside
My love, in there, where we may hide.

I am Deirdre, full of sorrow,
Without a vision of tomorrow;
Without them my life is past –
And, for me, it will not last.

Afterwards, Conor brought Deirdre to his palace. She lived there for a year. But if he expected her to thaw in that time or hoped that she would show him any favour, he was mistaken. For during the entire year that she was there, she neither smiled nor laughed nor showed any other sign of enjoyment in her life.

At last Conor realised two things. And these were that the deaths of the sons of Usna that had obsessed him for so many years meant nothing when accomplished; and the other was that the love he had felt, or thought he had felt, for Deirdre, failed, if it had ever existed, before her disdain. He realised that he did not in fact love her at all. So now to try to get some satisfaction he began to taunt and provoke her with his cruelty.

He approached her one day as she sat on the battlements looking across the green plains towards the blue mountains in the distance. And he tried to upset her by saying: 'Deirdre, above all else on earth, what is it that you hate most?'

Without looking at him or moving her head she replied: 'You, yourself, and Eoghan of Durracht,' which was the name and title Conor had given to Mainne for his job as executioner.

Though he knew what her answer would be, nevertheless it stung Conor. But he smiled and said: 'Well, in that case, since you have spent a year with me, it seems to me to be only right that you should spend another year with him.' If he thought that this would provoke a reaction in Deirdre, and make her plead with him not to do so or make her turn to him that he might prevent this fate, he was mistaken, for she showed no sign even that she had heard.

So, his anger now kindled again, he ordered his chariot to be harnessed to the swiftest horses he had. And calling Mainne – or 'Eoghan', as he now preferred to be called – he told him what he had decided. Conor smiled at him and Mainne smiled back; and it was not the sort of smile that any woman would want to see. But Deirdre might as well have been at the other end of Ireland for all the notice that she took of it.

So when the horses were harnessed to the chariot, the three of them, with the charioteer, mounted the royal four-wheeled vehicle, and drove towards Durracht.

Deirdre sat between Conor and the still smiling Mainne, who looked at her sideways from time to time, anticipation lingering on his damp lips. They galloped the horses and the great chariot across the hills and plains of Emhain, the black clods thrown up by the stampeding feet of the horses like a following flock of birds behind them. The chariot creaked and swayed and rattled with a great noise to show that it was the king, or some mighty lord, who was passing, so that they had to hold to the straps in their passage.

At one time Conor looked at Deirdre, and then to Mainne, and then in front, when they were coming up to the pillar-stone of the grave of the sons of Usna. And from malice he said: 'Deirdre, the look you give to Eoghan and the look you give to myself is like the hot look of a ewe between two rams.' With that, Deirdre stood – for the first time in a year showing emotion – and with a cry she leaped and sprang from the chariot as they passed the great pillar-stone, and smashed her head against it so that she died there upon the grave of the Three Lights of Valour of the Gael: Naisi, Ainle and Ardán.

And so, as she had asked, they buried her in the same grave as the three brothers. And when they placed her in the tomb her arm fell about the neck of Naisi and her mouth rested on his mouth and so they were together again. And all the men of Ulster who stood by cried and grieved aloud. And it is a fact that then, from their grave, there grew two straight and slender trees of yew, the branches and leaves of which entwined and made an arch spanning the pillar-stone.

That, then, ends the story of Deirdre and the sons of Usna – but not the prophecy that Catha foretold on the night she was born. For it must be said that Fergus, when he had completed his duty at Borrach's banquet, and learned of the death of the sons of Ulster, and of his own sons, and of his disgrace, stormed from Conor's court in a mighty rage and with all his people went to Connacht. And it is the truth that there, mindful of his word and in a fire of immense rage, he gathered the hosts of Maeve and made war on Ulster. And Catha cursed Conor so that none of his breed or seed would ever again rule in Emhain Macha. And so it came to be. For it is known that when the great Cuchulain died, tied by himself to a pillar of rock and standing alone to face the hosts of Connacht, something died in Emhain Macha too, so that it failed and rotted and became overgrown with great and waving tufts of grass. And there were those, casting their minds and memories back to the night of Felim's feast and what they had been told about the storm and the strange cry from the womb and Catha's prophecy on the night Deirdre was born, who wondered.

FOOTNOTES

1 The extended family relationship from great-grandparent to great-grandchild from which the nominees for kingship of a group/territory were selected, one of whom was elected by the communal peer vote system.

2 The great universal fear of the Celtic peoples was that the end of the world would come when the sky fell onto the earth.

3 This conflict of mutually exclusive commitments and the drama that ensues are central to many stories in Irish mythology. See *Of Gods and Men*, Donal O'Neill (Macdonald/Futura, London, 1987)

4 In those days, the Irish were called Scots, a name that was theirs for many hundreds of years afterwards. About 300 BC, they established a colony (which became Argyll) in what is now Scotland, and gradually extended their sway over the whole country. It remained an Irish colony until the sixth century AD, when it acquired home rule at the Council of Drum Ceat. From then on, the two countries were known as Scotia Major (Ireland) and Scotia Minor (Scotland) until the name 'Eireann' was adopted by Ireland.

The Sons of Tuireann

First Period: Mythological Cycle

There are those who say that the Tuatha de Danaan never existed at all; that they are the spirits of the dead. Others say that they are a fairy people, the people of the *sidhe*, who live underground in great forts or raths in the Otherworld. But they are both wrong. The truth of the matter is that the Tuatha de Danaan – the People of the Goddess Dana – were the first of the Celtic peoples to become lords of Ireland. They came from Spain, having reached there by traversing the Mediterranean from east to west, and bringing with them the magic and mysteries of Egypt and of Persia and the rich worship of the goddess Dana – or, as some call her, Danu – from whom they took their name. They became masters of Ireland after two battles fought near a place called Magh Tuire (Moytura), the Plain of the Pillars, in what is now County Roscommon. This plain got its name from the great number of pillars that were stuck in the ground before the battles and to which mercenary troops were tied in order to prevent them from running away.

The first of these battles was against the Firbolg, themselves a people of the Celtic race (more or less anyway). It is held that they were a mean, low-spirited lot, originally servants, if not slaves – or bagmen – which is how they got their name, since *firbolg* means 'bagman' (though others say they got it from their huge stomachs since *firbolg* also means 'belly-man'. There's not much in it). The gist of the story is that they were slaves or *fudirs*, that is to say non-persons before the law, who escaped from Phrygia to Ionia (nowadays called Turkey), where the city Miletus was, at the time of the exodus of the Tuatha de Danaan along the Mediterranean to Tartessia in the south of Spain. But the Firbolg, true to their nature, took advantage of the disturbances that caused the exodus (a Persian king by the name of Kurus, or Cyrus) and revolted against their de Danaan masters. As if that wasn't enough, they went off then and, having taken the overland route to Brittany in Gaul, ended up in Ireland too. Well, I needn't tell you it didn't please the de Danaan too much when they arrived and found their former slaves planked before them like cocks on a dungheap, and no sign of them moving.

What happened was that the Firbolg refused to give legroom to the Tuatha de Danaan when they arrived from Spain and so both sides felt a war coming on. And it did at Moytura where the de Danaan routed and killed multitudes of Firbolgs in four bloody days and drove the most of the remainder west into Connacht, which was a merciful and considerate thing to do, after they had blinded the chief men, keeping only about half as slaves and hostages. (Connacht, I may as well tell you, is so called because there was once a king there called Con and he was also a magician. He was showing off one day and in a fit of swank didn't he cover the whole province with snow so that from then on it was called *Con-sneachta*, 'Con-acht' or 'Con's snow'.)

Well, as they had suffered a few hardships and tribulations in the battle themselves the de Danaan were happy enough with the arrangement that confined the Firbolg to Connacht, which wasn't a very prosperous place in those days (tourists being few and far between at the time), and so was considered suitable for ex-servants and slaves and that class of people. The Crimson City of the Firbolgs, Cathair Cro-Fionn in the middle of the country, was taken by the Tuatha de Danaan who changed its name to Tara.

Not the least of the Tuatha de Danaan losses in the battle was the fact that their king, Nuada, who had led them from Spain, had had his right arm cut off between the shoulder and elbow by a hairy Firbolg champion by the name of Sreng. To make bad worse the de Danaan had a law that no man with a blemish or an impediment could be king and, according to that law, 'twas a poor look-out for Nuada, and a not much better one for the Tuatha de Danaan who had placed great reliance on his judgement as a king (a point of view Nuada didn't discourage too actively, I can tell you). Of course he was tormented with pain with the arm. The truth of the matter is he came close to dying altogether after Sreng separated him from it.

But didn't the de Danaan have a great physician by the name of Diancecht? Dam' good doctor though he was, like some others in his profession, he was an unpleasant class of a man, inclined to be short with other people he didn't think as clever as himself and to treat them like some kind of inferior species – which didn't go down too well with everyone, especially those who were a bit short in the temper themselves. Maybe 'tis a consequence of seeing patients helpless before them when they're being treated, or it could be from the fact that they're even sometimes cured. 'Tis hard to say. Anyway Diancecht did what he could with the stump of Nuada's arm and then made a silver one for him which he set in place of the old, so that forever afterwards the king was known as Nuada of the Silver Hand. Still and all Diancecht didn't make such a great job of the stump for Nuada was forever sick and ailing and troubled with pain from the arm and so, between that and the law, he was rendered unfit to be the King of Ireland. That was the law and dam' the bit anyone could do about it. But Nuada wasn't giving up without a struggle. If he couldn't be king he could have a *tanaiste* – or regent – of his own choosing. So what did he do? Didn't he make Bres, of all people, regent? And this Bres was a dam' bad choice, let me tell you. What everybody knew but Nuada, wasn't the same Bres putting horns on him and cuckolding him and making a right eejit of him behind his back with his own wife – a strap by the name of Maeve who had the looks, but little loyalty.

The Tuatha de Danaan's second battle at Moytura was against a much more formidable enemy altogether than the Firbolgs, called the Fomorians. They were not Celts, but a people of woeful aspect with the unnatural habit of standing on one leg, turning against the sun and perpetrating unpleasant nastinesses on those they disliked, which was everybody except themselves. They came from the north – what later came to be called Lochlann – and were uncouth and wild in their ways and manners. They were also very powerful as our story illuminates.

Well, to make a short journey of a long road, wasn't Bres only half de Danaan (and that on his mother's side). His father was a frightful beast of a man, by name Balor, who was also the war-chief of the Fomorians, no less. And that, by the kind of coincidence that makes the drama of history come alive in the living-room, made Balor the uncle of one of our principal characters, Lugh Lamh Fada himself, the Il-Dana, who happened to be Balor's grandson (and therefore Bres's nephew), but it is very complicated because there is the mystery and magic of incest concerning Lugh's birth, too. Anyway, you can see that while it might have been a good notion to give the regency to Bres, if Bres was an honourable man, but Bres was not an honourable man. The first thing he did when he became regent was to lay the people of Dana under a tribute to his own father's people, the Fomorians, that he exacted himself with the utmost severity, saying that if it wasn't paid the Fomorians would do terrible things.

This was going on for about four years and, during all that time while the tribute was being paid, Nuada was in great pain and suffering from his arm and unable to help his own people. Then one day, about that time, Nuada's steward was above on the ramparts of royal Tara sunning himself and looking out across the gold and green plain stretched around it with his one eye (having lost the other in the same battle that Nuada lost his arm), when what did he see coming towards himself and the city but an easy-going chariot driven by two young men who didn't seem to be in any kind of a hurry? When they came up to the wall where the steward was looking at them they called a greeting up to him and the steward – a man by the name of Ronan – called back down to them.

'Welcome,' he said, 'and who are ye? And where might ye be from?'

'We're the two sons of Diancecht,' they said, 'Miach and Omiach, and we're pretty good physicians ourselves.'

'Is that so?' asked the steward.

'Indeed it is,' said Miach.

'And what's more,' said Omiach, 'I'd go further and say we were the best in Ireland.'

'Aha!' said the steward, who didn't believe them. 'If ye're that good maybe ye could put an eye back where my own used to be?'

Now Ronan had an oul' cat that he kept about the place for killing the mice that used to be a nuisance especially at harvest time and this cat would follow him like a dog, although it wasn't that Ronan was particularly attached to cats. It was more that the cat was attached to him. Anyway, this day wasn't the cat thrown down on a piece of sunny stone beside Ronan with nothing moving only the tip of its tail that was beating in slow time to some cat-tune of its own in its head, I suppose.

Miach looked at the cat and he looked at Ronan and he said: 'I could put the eye of that cat there lying down in the sun where your own eye used to be.'

'You could?' asked Ronan disbelievingly.

'I could,' said Miach. And with that he jumped up on the wall from the roof of the chariot and did whatever he had to do and the thing was done.

(But although Ronan was delighted for a week it soon turned out to be a mixed blessing. As sure as he put his head down after a hard day's work to go to sleep, the same eye would leap and stay open as bright as the noonday sun watching for the screech of a mouse or the flight of a bird or a rustling in the reeds. And that was bad enough; but when he wanted to enjoy himself at a banquet, or a meeting or some other jollification, that was just when the eye chose to go to sleep, and close itself. But that was in the future.)

When he got it, and as soon as he could see with the second eye, off he ran as fast as he could to Nuada to show him his good eye and tell him about the two great physicians who had just arrived at Tara. 'Bring them in,' said Nuada.

So the two brothers, Miach and Omiach, were brought in through the great gates and along the streets until they reached the palace. And as they were brought into it what did they hear but a great and woeful sigh.

'There's no doubt,' said Miach, 'but that is the sigh of a warrior.'

'I agree with you,' said Omiach. 'And what's more it could be a warrior with a *daol* blackening his side,' he said thoughtfully as another deep sigh echoed up from the depths of the palace.

Now a *daol* ('day'ull') or a *darbh-daol* ('dorruv'), as 'tis sometimes known, is a thing to be avoided, although that is no easy matter if it takes a fancy to you. It is a thing something like a beetle or a cockroach or maybe even a sort of a tick and it will fasten on a man – or a woman for that matter. But whereas a tick will suck the blood of a person, a *daol* will suck their spirit and take the life and goodness out of him – or her. And that was what Omiach thought was wrong with the person who gave that sigh. And it was Nuada.

Well, they were brought in to Nuada and they saw him lying there with the silver arm their father had made for him gleaming (for it was polished every day) even though the room was dark with the drapes drawn. They pulled them back to let in the light so they could examine the king. They undid the straps and the buckles that held his arm to the stump and drew it away. Sure enough out of it bounded a *daol* and away with it through the palace with the whole household following it (and they cornered it too and killed it eventually).

So they doctored the stump. But there was Nuada now with only the stump and the silver arm lying before him. And the advice of the two doctors was, 'If we were to replace that it would only encourage another *daol* to come and take up residence inside it.'

Now you and I and many other people might think that it was the like of gangrene was troubling Nuada. But I have yet to hear of a gangrene that leaped out of a silver arm and ran through a house until it was killed by the household. And in any case what Nuada wanted was for the two young doctors to replace his arm the way they had replaced Ronan's eye. So they searched high and low for an arm of equal length and thickness to the king's. But an arm isn't always an easy article to locate when you want one, particularly if it's unattached. And nowhere amongst the Tuatha de Danaan could an arm be found of the right size – except that of Muadhan, the swineherd. So, anyway, they were about to cut that off Muadhan when the king heard what they were up to. He pointed out that that was no use at all because even if it fitted and worked it was still the arm of only a swineherd, not a king, and there was a law against that class of a person – or even a part of him – becoming the king.

So the whole royal household went into a hugger-mugger and thought for a long time. And finally one of the nobles asked: 'What about the bones of the king's own arm? Would they suit?'

'Nothing would suit us better,' said Miach. 'Why didn't you think of it before?' And with that the king and a whole gang of the nobles and lords of Tara went off to the battlefield of Moytura to look for the arm. And I needn't tell you, that after three or four years, or whatever the time was, the arm was in no great condition when they found it. However, they extracted it from the little hole that it had been put into (for a sort of small dolmen had been built over it) and gave it a rub to remove the loose bits, and brought it back to Tara.

When the two brothers had a look at it they hummed and hawed for a while, measuring it and feeling the bones to see if they were still strong and poking at it and muttering the way doctors do. After a while Miach said to Omiach: 'Do you want to set the arm or go for the herbs that will put the flesh back on it?'

And Omiach said: 'I'd like to set the arm.'

So off with Miach for the herbs; and he spent a good while getting them until he brought them back. And they cooked them and did what they had to do and wrapped them around the bones, and that's how the arm was set and clothed with new flesh by them – and if a doctor could do that today wouldn't he make his fortune? But the art is lost. Now, although 'tisn't properly part of this story at all, 'tis no harm to know what the result of all this was.

(Miach was the older of the two brothers. And, because he had substituted a real arm, flesh and bone set joint to joint and sinew to sinew and clothed with flesh all in three moments in place of the silver arm made by his father, it was acknowledged that he was a better doctor. This enraged Diancecht, his father, who was a proud and envious, and worse, an arrogant, man, so that when Miach's superiority was clearly demonstrated by the attitude of the people towards them both, his fury overcame him and he took his sword and killed Miach. It wasn't shame or remorse that overcame him afterwards for in his bitterness he secretly buried the body where he thought it would never be found. But from the grave there grew, up through the soil, three hundred and sixty-five healing herbs, one for every known sinew and joint of the human frame, and each herb capable of curing the disease that afflicted the part from which it grew. Miach's sister, Airmead, who loved her brothers, plucked and gathered them in their proper order into her cloak so that the knowledge that he had possessed before her was passed on to her by Miach in that way. But Diancecht's bitterness and envy and jealousy were so great that when he heard of what had happened he came and mixed the herbs in such a way that their separate and grave virtues were confused and so were lost forever.)

The new arm had made a new man of Nuada – but still not one to oppose the Fomorians. And, one day, after these events had taken place, he and his people were standing together on the hill of Uisneach at Tara awaiting the annual visit of the Fomorian tax-gatherers. It was a bitter wait and the taxes that Bres had imposed were these: a tax upon each trough in which corn was kneaded; a tax on the kern or grindstone that ground it; a tax on the baking flags; and, in addition, an ounce of gold for all the people of the Tuatha de Danaan who could be stood together on the hill of Uisneach. It was a tax that was equally hard on a man's pocket and his stomach. But what was worse was that if it was not paid, the man or the woman who failed to do so would have his – or her – nose cut off by the Fomorian tyrants.

As Nuada and his lords and knights stood waiting silently and glumly for the hated tax-gatherers to arrive, they saw coming across the plain from the east – which was the direction they expected the Fomorians to come from – a group of armed men who were led by a young man the like of whom they had never seen before. He was taller and broader than any man there and about him there was a radiance and an air of command like the sunset and the golden sun itself. This was the Clan Mananaan – Lugh Lamh Fada and his foster-brothers – the sons of Mananaan Mac Lír.

Mananaan's real name was Oirbsen, the Navigator, whose Palace of the Apple

Trees, Amhain Abhlach, was north and east, on the island that is now called Arran in the Firth of Clyde. And he was Lugh's foster-father; for Lugh himself, known also as the Il-Dana or the Man of Sciences, was the son of Cian and a grandson of Balor, warlord of the Fomorians. Because of his upbringing and background, he had no love for his grandfather's people.

He rode proudly at the head of his group of foster-brothers on Mananaan's horse, Aonvarr, which could race as swiftly as the winds of spring or autumn, equally on land or sea. Moreover it was said that no rider could be killed from her back. On his own back he wore Mananaan's armour which protected whoever wore it so well that he could neither be wounded under it nor through it or over it. On his breast he wore the torc of Mananaan which defied the weapons of the world to pierce whoever wore it.

Lugh also wore a jewelled helmet to protect his head and when he rode up and took it off the eager face of this warrior of science and knowledge was as bright and as wholesome as the sharp curve of the watered coast on a sun-filled summer's day. At his side hung Mananaan's sword, Freagra, the Answerer, whose bite was death and which, when drawn, so afflicted the strength of an enemy that it became no more than that of a woman.

And it was in that fashion that Lugh Lamh Fada came to join Nuada and his people standing on the hill of Uisneach waiting for the Fomorians. When they saw them first, of course, Nuada and his knights thought that the people coming in the distance were the Fomorians, but they quickly saw that that was not the case for they could see when the newcomers came closer that they were not in the least like the Fomorian barbarians. And so, in spite of their general sadness and uneasiness they greeted them.

But hardly had Lugh and his companions been welcomed when, in the distance, they saw the dust and shimmering movement under the sun that indicated the approach of more men. But these were a very different group of armed men in every way. There were eighty-one of them and each was more surly and evil-looking than the one who was counted before him. Led by Eine, Coron, Eidfath and Cokpar, these were the Fomorian tax-gatherers and these four had the reputation of being the most cruel and fierce of all of them.

Now, when they got close to the hill, Nuada and his lords, who had been sitting in chairs and on bales of grass brought specially for the purpose, stood up out of respect – or what passed for it – to the astonishment of Lugh, who asked: 'How is it that you stand for the likes of these savages and do them that honour when you won't stand for me?'

'To tell the truth,' said Nuada, 'the way it is we daren't do anything else. If there was one of us, even a child a month old, who stayed sitting in their presence, they'd use that as excuse enough to murder us all.'

Lugh said nothing for a moment when he heard this terrible statement. 'By the gods,' he said then, ''tis they themselves that should be killed.' For a long moment he stayed deep in thought, staring down at the toe of his boot while the king and all his people stood silently before the Fomorians who were coming up the hill, growling and laughing amongst themselves. Then: 'By the gods,' he said again, 'I think I'll kill them myself.'

'Don't,' said Nuada, 'for if you do you may be sure the Fomorians will come with their whole army and destroy us completely. You'll only do more harm than good doing that.'

'That's not how I see it,' cried Lugh. 'These are evil men and if we don't put a stop to this oppression only the gods'll know how long more it'll last. Is that what you want?'

Without waiting for an answer he turned and started down the hill towards the Fomorians in his fury. And with that, Mananaan's incomparable sword, the Answerer, leaped from its scabbard into his hand and what did he do but raise an attack on the Fomorians that scattered and slaughtered them in all directions until only nine out of the eighty-one that came were left alive. And those nine survived only because they threw themselves under Nuada's protection and ran around behind him against the vengeance of Lugh. There they were, cowering behind Nuada, when Lugh stormed up from the red battlefield below, where the dogs were already sniffing the sundered corpses. Some of his rage had passed off him, but when he saw the fearful faces behind Nuada he growled: 'The only reason I'm sparing you is so that you may go back and bring the news to your king as a warning. Go on now, quick, out of here!'

Then to the halloos and shouts of the Tuatha de Danaan the nine survivors were chased down the hill and back to their ships across the plain – and if they received a few bangs and slashes on the way what can I tell you about that except that the people who had been tormented by the Fomorians for so long were giving vent to their own anger? Anyway they set out, across the black and the bottomless sea, back to where they'd come from to tell Balor all that had happened.

And when he heard what they had to say – before he killed them, and you may believe it for 'tis the nature of things and of Balor in particular – Balor turned to his own chiefs and asked them this question: 'Who is that man?' But he got no satisfaction for they didn't know him either. Then Caitlin, Balor's queen and also his sister, if you please, said: 'There is only the one person it can be and that is the Il-Dana, our own grandson, the son of our own daughter; and how I know this is that, as you'll remember, 'tis prophesied that when he comes to Eire our power there will end.'

Now Balor didn't enjoy listening to this one bit – or much else that Caitlin ever said at that time – but he didn't believe her either, because while he had also heard this prophecy, he had good reason to know that it would never materialise, for he had taken certain steps to prevent it. These are what they were, and the reason for them was this: that there had been another prophecy too which Caitlín didn't know about; which was that it had also been prophesied that he himself, Balor, would be killed by this grandson. And so, when his daughter – she was called Eithlenn and was married to a de Danaan prince by the name of Cian – became large with her first child, didn't Balor make his plans. If it was a girl he'd do nothing and leave the child grow up as his granddaughter. But, sure, of course I don't have to tell you; you know already. 'Twas not a girl child; it was a boy. And in the night when all was quiet, Balor had the infant taken from its nurse (he had her strangled to make it look good), and given to one of his retainers. That man lived a good way off by the sea, and the instructions he got from Balor were to take the child as far as he could out into the cold depths and abandon it there.

But, of course, Balor, being a king, didn't tell this man why; and this man, being his retainer, didn't ask. And as you know as well as myself, there's no plan that hasn't got a hole in it somewhere that you can't see. And this plan of Balor's had a dam' big hole in it. The fact of the matter is that because one didn't tell and the other didn't ask, the infant survived.

This man who was to drown Balor's grandson was a married man, and his wife had been pregnant with their first child. But, coincidences being what they are – and what they are is frequent and a mystery on which the world often changes its course – hadn't she given birth to a stillborn child only a few days before Balor gave out his instructions. Now that raised an interesting situation, if you like, for, like a cow that's lost its calf, she had become distressed and violent too, if the truth be known, and unsettled so that the retainer was 'sna trithíbh dúbhtha (in the black fits) between concern and pity for her, and at her screeching and temper. So, after Balor's men were gone, leaving the child behind to be got rid of, he saw no harm at all in substituting the living child for the dead one, and that's what he did.

To give matters the proper appearance, he disposed of the body of his own son in the sea the way he was supposed to do with Balor's grandson. And when the little body was washed up a few days later and Balor received the news, didn't he create a great hullabaloo. Oh, the crying and moaning and weeping of him, and the gods below in their black forts knows what all else besides, and commiserating with his daughter and telling her he wouldn't rest until he found and gave justice to the abductors of her baby, his own grandson? (And he did too, for he had three men that he didn't very much like – and there were a fair share of them around, so he had no trouble at all making a selection – he had them asked a few questions by his champion and a few of his companions with hot knives and buckets of water and a few other things, before he cut off a few pieces belonging to them and then hanged them; and so he told his daughter that justice had been done.) And all that time that he was moaning and ollagoning, he was delighted with himself inside behind all the tears and the rest of it for he felt safe now from the prophecy.

Anyway, Lugh survived and eventually came under the patronage of the great Mananaan Mac Lír himself, who recognised him for who he was when he saw him, and that, of course I needn't tell you, was because Lugh lived by the sea and you'd want to be a right eejit altogether not to know that Mananaan was the lord of the sea, as well as of a few other things.

None of this was known to Balor. And so when his wife, Caitlin, told him what she did, he didn't believe her, even though she was a sorceress, since he knew that this man – whoever or whatever else he was – could not be Lugh, the Il-Dana. Therefore Balor and his chiefs, with Caitlin and all the druids and philosophers of the Fomorians and their twelve sons, sat in council to decide what they were going to do.

And Bres was there. And after they had discussed the position and come to no conclusion, it was Bres who made a proposal; and they listened to it because it was his policy that had been flouted, and he who had been insulted by Lugh and the people in Ireland. 'I'll take with me an army of the seven great brigades of horsemen of Fomorians and kill this man and destroy him and bring his head to you, Balor, here at the palace of Berva.'

So their plans and preparations were made and Bres, who was in charge of it all, watched over it with a careful and critical eye. He had ships hauled ashore, careened and newly caulked; planks were replaced where that was needed, and another army of men and women who knew the working and making of ships and weapons, stores and provisions, armour and tackle, assembled and worked by day and by night by the light of gigantic fires along the beaches. When all was ready the ships were refloated and loaded with the new provisions and weapons. Meantime Luath the Long and Lugh the Story-teller had gone purposefully throughout the length and breadth of Lochlann to summon the cavalry soldiers Bres needed. When all were assembled and their weapons checked this great army set sail for Ireland.

As he looked at the great fleet assembled in the harbour, a powerful feeling filled Balor. Who was this upstart who had challenged his authority in Ireland? Whoever he was he'd soon know that he'd done a wrong and foolish thing. As he looked at Bres before the latter went on board ship to lead the fleet abroad on the wide ocean, he told him: 'You are to find this man, destroy him, and cut off his head. When you have that done, tie cables to the island of Ireland itself that gives us nothing but trouble, and never has, and then tow it away, far to the north, beyond Lochlann, and let the mighty ocean fill its place. Leave it there in the cold north where no more of the Tuatha de Danaan will ever follow, and those on it will wither. Do that and nothing less and let us be rid of this troublesome place and its troublesome people forever.'

Then with rounded and blazing sails filling the endless sky above and with one common stroke the new-rigged fleet went out from the harbour on the moving sea, over the mighty sea and the awful and cold abyss, mounting the ridges of the waves and the treacherous mountains of the bottomless ocean until they made a harbour at Eas-Dara, Ballysodare as it is now called, in Sligo. They fell upon the country and let their fury loose upon the kingdom of Connacht, which they devastated and destroyed. And they got help from the Firbolgs, who were related to them, in this destruction.

The king of that part of Ireland was the Bodhbh Dearg. He was a son of the Dagda Mor, Eochaidh Ollamh, the great king and oracle of the Tuatha de Danaan, whose palace was beyond at the Boyne near Tara – and I can tell you you can still see it today, or a good bit of it, if you happen to pass that way. And so the Bodbh Dearg sent to Tara for help.

And, as it happened, Lugh was still there – probably because he guessed (and why wouldn't he?) – that Balor would come back with an army in a rage. But he also had another reason, which was that he had a little bit of trouble with another bunch of Fomorians who'd been left behind in part of the rich midlands while their kinsmen were planning this attack. You can be sure they knew all about it; but they said nothing, not even to Lugh when he rounded them up. When news of the attack in Connacht reached Lugh – and it was dawn when it reached him, with the eastern spear-point of day piercing the lingering night to the west – he immediately prepared to go to the help of the people of Connacht. But first he thought he'd better ask Nuada to see what help he'd provide. 'Look,' said Lugh, 'ye know what the situation is. I'll go off and I'll meet them as fast as I can, and I'll hold them as long as I can, but I'll need more men to go with me, which is why I'm here. What can you give?'

Now as he knew from past experience, battle with large numbers of enemies wasn't exactly Nuada's favourite pastime. He didn't like to think about it. Caution was his watch-word.

He looked down where the stump went into his silver arm, and 'twas itching badly, and he said: 'I dunno.'

'You dunno what?' asked Lugh.

'I dunno,' said Nuada. 'Could I give my men to seek out revenge on something that wasn't done against myself?' (Which only goes to show the kind he was. A good leader in some things, no doubt, but always ready to tip the cap at anyone he thought was stronger or better than himself. And there are a few like him left still. And in powerful places too!)

Well, when Lugh heard this, he was vexed in himself I can tell you, the anger mounting up in him like bile in the throat of a man with a hangover. And, the way he felt, he didn't want to say anything in case he'd say too much. So, turning on his heel, he strode out of the palace, leaped on the back of his horse, and rode off west from Tara.

He wasn't long on the road when in the distance he saw three armed men riding towards him. And when they came closer he recognised them as his own father, Cian, and his uncles, Cu and Cethenn. 'What has you up so early and abroad on the road to the west?' asked his father, Cian, 'and you looking troubled?'

'Trouble enough,' said Lugh. 'The Fomorians have landed beyond in Connacht and are destroying the Bodhbh Dearg's kingdom and I'm on my way now to see what I can do to help him. And while I'm at it I'm wondering what in the way of help I may expect from you?'

His father and his two uncles exchanged looks and then looked back at Lugh. 'To be sure,' said Cian, 'we're with you and there's not one of us but will keep a hundred Fomorians from you, or maybe two for they're not all that good when they're faced with it in the heat of battle.'

'Fair enough,' said Lugh. 'But I have another job for you first. I'd like you to ride through the country and summon out the warriors of the Sídhe to come and fight alongside us from wherever they might be. If we have them with us we'll be sure of victory no matter how many Fomorians there are.'

'Very well,' said his father; and with that they separated.

Lugh continued his journey to the west; his two uncles went south and east; and Cian, his father, made his way north through the plain of Muirthemne in the centre of Ireland. And you might think that the rest of this story is all about the battle that followed with the Fomorians, but you'd be wrong. For, although this is a story about the sons of Tuireann, we have said very little if anything at all about them up to now. But now is when their story properly begins.

Cian hadn't gone very far across the rich and verdant plain of Muirthemne when he, in his turn, saw three armed warriors in the distance cutting across his path. At first he thought, 'Good,' to himself. 'Here are my first recruits.' But when he got a bit closer – for he was blessed with the eyesight of an eagle or a hawk – didn't he recognise them as three de Danaan princes, the sons of a man called Tuireann, between whose family and his own there had been a long-standing feud, and that one of great bitterness, for many years. These three were named Brian, Uar and Uraca; and so deep was the feud between the two families that it was a well-known fact that should any of them chance to meet outside of a lawful place, it was as certain as it is that the sky mightn't fall – at least not without the greatest calamity that would bring all men to their graves – that no one would survive the encounter but whoever was the stronger. Accordingly, as soon as he recognised the three sons of Tuireann, Cian thought to himself: ''Twould be a fair and a great fight if my two brothers, Cu and Cethenn, were here with me, no doubt. But since they're not, and I am only the one against three, the best thing I can do is to fly or hide myself, or get out of this the best way I can, whatever that may be.'

Now there was a herd of wild pigs snorting and rooting in the rich and abundant soil of the plain, and Cian, who happened to be a bit of a druid as well as everything else, gave himself a little tap with his own druidical wand and changed himself into the appearance of one of them so that within a minute he was in the herd rooting and snorting away like the best of them – the pigs, that is. But no sooner had he done so than Brian, who was the eldest of the sons of Tuireann and had a good pair of eyes himself (though not an eagle's), said to his two brothers: 'Tell me, did you see ere a sign of a warrior crossing the plain a few moments ago?'

'We did,' they said, they having fair sight too.

'Well, then, where is he?'

'That's a good question,' they said, looking round.

'Well,' said Brian, 'aren't ye the right pair? Out here in wartime, in open country; ye see an armed man and when he disappears ye give it no more thought than a pig in a heap of –! Well, I wouldn't want to be depending on the likes of ye and that's a fact. And I'll tell ye something else,' he went on, ''tis plain that whatever else he is he's no friend of ours. If he was why would he want to go and hide himself?'

'There's sense in that,' said Uar.

'There is,' said Uraca.

'You may be sure of it,' said Brian. 'And I'll tell you something else. I know where he is.'

'You do?' exclaimed Uar.

'Where?' asked Uraca.

'I'll tell you,' said Brian, 'whoever he is he has changed himself, with some kind of druid's wand or the like of that, I suppose, into a pig. He's rooting around now with that group over there. There were only five a minute ago and now there are six.'

'Well,' said Uar, 'you can't hide much from you.'

'You have a good eye,' said Uraca, 'and what you tell us is bad. But what's worse is this: don't you know as well as the two of us that if we hurt one of those pigs the man who owns the herd will have the three of us bound in duty to pay a fine, or even worse, he might ask our lives for it.'

'He might ask,' growled Brian, who knew a bit more about the law than Uraca did.

'Well, anyway,' said Uar, 'how are we going to find out this enemy if we don't kill them all?' He looked at Uraca, who nodded agreement.

'If ye're not the bright specimens,' jeered Brian. 'Two princes of Ireland, no less, schooled in all the arts of a warrior, and with all ye're schooling ye don't know how to tell a magic pig from a real one. Well, may the Greek demons blast me, if that's not a good one.'

'Whisht!' cried Uraca, looking round. 'You never know with them fellas. They might be listening!'

'Let them listen away,' snapped Brian. 'They're out of their territory here; and even if they weren't, I wouldn't be afraid of the likes of what the Greeks might think. If ye'd listened to what ye were being taught instead of having ye're minds on other things ye'd know how to do it. I know,' he said. And with that he gave each of his brothers a whack of his own druidical wand – for he belonged to the same class of men as Cian himself – and turned them into two sleek, eager, fast and slender hounds that straightaway put their keen noses to the scent and raced for the herd, the froth flying from their fangs like spindthrift over the waves.

Streaking low over the plain, they came coursing down upon the herd. Only that they couldn't keep their mouths shut like decent people, but had to go growling and yowling like hunting hounds, they might have got him there and then; but, sure, Cian, still in the shape of a pig, heard the noise and recognised the danger he was in and made a break for the nearby wood seeking shelter. But Brian cut across his path and put his spear through his chest.

The pig was hurled arse-over-tip and ended up bent on his back with the lance sticking out of him like a reed out of a river. 'Ah!' he cried in the voice of a man, 'why did you do this to me knowing what I am?'

Brian looked down at him with no trace of pity in his face. 'Your voice,' he said, 'is the voice of a human, but your shape is the shape of a pig. And to be honest with you I don't know you either from your shape as a pig, or by your voice as a man.'

'Well, you should,' cried the pig. 'I am Cian, son of Cainnte and father of Lugh, and I ask quarter from you.'

Uar and Uraca, who had been given back their human forms by Brian after the chase, had come up by this time. And when they heard the words of the pig, they said, 'To be sure, we'll grant it,' for they were a generous enough pair, but led by Brian, 'and we're sorry it happened the way it did.'

But Brian wasn't as easy a man. He remembered the age-old feud between their families and the wrongs done his own by that of Cian (though, to tell the truth, Cian himself had never done them any harm), and he remembered all he had been told by his father and his uncles about the clan of Cainnte, and he said: 'If you had seven lives, and seven times seven lives, indeed and indeed I swear by all the gods of the vast sky that I'd take every one of them.' And he looked down at the pig with no sign of emotion, good or bad, on his face at all.

'Well,' said Cian, 'if that's the way of it there's not much I can do. But give me a last request before sending me on my way.'

'What is it?' asked Brian.

'Let me back into my human form before you kill me,' said Cian, 'for I'd rather die as a man than as a pig.'

'I will,' said Brian; and then he added, 'and you might as well know that in some cases I think less of killing a man than a pig.'

With that Cian, with a great effort – for he had little enough strength left with the blood spilling out of him where the lance entered in – did whatever magic was necessary to return himself to human form so that it was the man that now lay on the sward of the plain with Brian's lance protruding from his chest, and not a pig.

'And will you grant me quarter now?' he gasped.

'I will not,' said Brian. And the other two nodded.

Cian looked back with haughtiness and contempt at the three men looking down at him. 'Indeed,' he said, 'there is no doubt that you are truly the sons of Tuireann and you nurse your vengeance for old wrongs very deep and are about to kill me . . .' And then he paused and let his eyes move from one to the other of them. 'But vengeful and all as you are, and desperate as my plight is, I've circumvented the three of ye in the end.'

'How is that?' asked Brian.

'Because if you had killed me as a pig the *éric* fine on me would have been only that of a pig. But now that I am a man again, and head of my clan, it is the *éric* of such a man that you'll have to pay; for I tell you now, and I swear by it' – and he took hold of the shaft of the lance that stood out from his chest – 'that the very weapons that kill me will cry out the nature of the deed for my son to hear.'

'In that case,' said Brian grabbing the shaft of his lance and putting his foot on Cian, 'it's not with weapons we'll kill you but with the stones and rocks of the Plain of Muirthemne itself.' And with that he yanked the lance from the stricken Cian and, bending, picked up a boulder the size of a man's chest and hurled it down on him. Uar and Uraca, though they were taken aback by the ferocity of Brian, nevertheless followed suit after a moment, laying down their weapons and lifting the great stones of the plain to hurl at the defenceless and wretched Cian so that before long he was no more then a bloody and a battered corpse.

Then they dug a deep grave and buried him standing and facing north, the direction they'd come from. But the earth herself was angry at the deed, for the truth of the matter is that the sons of Tuireann and the sons of Cainnte were kin, and refused the body from them, throwing it up from the depths again to the surface. Six times the sons of Tuireann buried the battered body of Cian, and six times the earth rejected it and sent it back again to the surface, bleeding and covered in dirt. But they buried it a seventh time, and this time the earth did not refuse it and Cian remained where they placed him, standing and facing north from where his enemies had come.

When that was done they picked up their weapons again – with relief so far as Uar and Uraca were concerned – and set out again on their way west, for when they met Cian they had, in fact, been on their way to join the forces being summoned to face the Fomorians, having heard the news already. But even as they turned to take the first steps from the place, from under their feet, faint and muffled, they believed they heard a voice that cried: 'There is blood on your hands, sons of Tuireann, and there it will remain until we meet again.'

Uar and Uraca were very frightened by this unusual turn of events, and wanted to unbury the body again and bring it to Tara and face whatever was to be faced. But Brian brushed their fears aside, saying: 'Whatever else he is and wherever that voice came from, Cian is dead and can do us no harm.' And so they went on west to the battle.

Meanwhile Lugh had gone on ahead of them through the settlement at Ath Luian, or Athlone, and across the mighty Shannon by the ford there, on through Roscommon, Moylurg, and the Curlew Mountains. Then he reached the plain where the Fomorians had their camp that was now filled with the treasure and plunder of Connacht and boastful fighting men of the Fomorians. It was after dark then and the plain was speckled with the darting fires of the Fomorians, so Lugh circled their camp to see what he could. And those in the camp were disturbed by his presence, which was radiant and terrible.

'That,' said Bres, 'is a strange and remarkable thing, to see the sun, that rises every day in the east, now rising in the west.'

'Remarkable it may be,' said his druids, 'but 'twould be a lot better for us, maybe, if it rose where it's supposed to. For we don't think that that rising sun's of the heavens at all.'

'Why so?' asked Bres. 'What else could such a light be but the light of the sun rising?'

'We'll tell you,' said the druids. 'It is another kind of sun altogether, and what you see now is the light from the flashing of the weapons of the Il-Dana, whose head you seek, together with his own remarkable radiance. It is he who killed our tax-gatherers. For he is here and around us.'

Soon after that Lugh himself arrived at the camp and greeted them.

'What do you want?' cried Bres, unsettled by this strange behaviour. 'You are our enemy and should not be here.'

'I have every right to be here,' said Lugh, who was as cunning and clever as he was mighty and brave. 'Every right in the world.'

'How is that?' asked Bres.

'I'm surprised at you, Bres, not to know the answer,' said Lugh. 'Only one half of me is de Danaan, but the other half is Fomorian. Am I not?' he demanded. And, of course, there was an excuse for Bres all right, for this was the first he had heard of it. 'Am I not the son of the daughter of Balor himself? And because of that I'm here in peace and all I ask is for you to give back the milch cows you stole from the people of Connacht, and a bit of compensation along with them, and that'll be the end of it.'

With that, a bad-tempered Fomorian chief – and he must have been pretty bad, because they were a bad-tempered lot – shouted out: 'May the light of day abandon you, whoever you are, before you get a single one of them!' That started a general roar from the Fomorians, all in the same vein.

But Lugh was equal to them. He wasn't the Il-Dana, the Man of Science, for nothing; and what did he do but cast a spell over the assembled herds of cattle so that every fruitful and milking cow was returned, like the snap of your fingers, to its owner, and nothing but the dry and barren cattle were left to encumber the Fomorians (for Lugh loosened them too and sent in a bunch of gadflies to torment them so that they ran this way and that amongst the Fomorians, scattering them before their stampeding hooves. And that is how it was for three nights until the Tuatha de Danaan army came up to deal with the distracted Fomorians. Soon after that the Bodhbh Dearg arrived too with an army of his own of three thousand.

Well! That was the battle, I needn't tell you! The Fomorians composed themselves before it began while Lugh dressed and armed himself and had a consultation with the Bodhbh Dearg about the best way to handle matters. He put on all the gear he wore when he was first seen by Nuada. Besides that he put on his back by its strap his great dark blue shield and took two bronze-socketed, yew-handled, deadly spears that were said to have been tempered in the venom of poisonous snakes from abroad. Then the combined Tuatha de Danaan army, led by its kings, and its heroes and with all the warriors, made a battle phalanx with a breastwork of shields and a glittering rampart of spear-points out through it. They advanced on the Fomorians.

The Fomorians had formed up too and, when the Tuatha de Danaan phalanx was within range, they hurled many flights of venomous darts and javelins at them so that the air was full of their hissing and thick and dark with their flight, like flocks of deadly birds that left men after them screaming and wounded on the saturated ground. Nevertheless the phalanx of the Tuatha de Danaan kept advancing towards the Fomorians until it was the mighty, broad-bladed spears that engaged between them, and clashed and made a din that was awful, and thrust and hacked at warriors on either side. When the spears were dropped or broken they drew their wide-grooved, gold-crossed swords and met foot-to-foot and shield-to-shield while over and above them rose the terrible din and wrath of battle.

Lugh, at the head of the Tuatha de Danaan forces and in the midst of the dreadful carnage, looked this way and that in search of the battle-pen of Bres from where he would direct his own army. Off across the bloody battlefield strewn with naked dead and lamenting wounded and bits of both, he saw it in the distance and rushed through the upheaval and burst through the battle-pen to where Bres stood surrounded by his fallen bodyguard.

Lugh raised the Answerer to make two halves of him, but even as he did so Bres cried: 'Lugh, would you kill me and I your uncle? There's enough of war. Let there be peace between us now and I will undertake, by the sun and the moon, by the sea and the land, and by all the elements, to bring my Fomorians to your assistance at Moytura, where you must surely face my father, Balor, when he knows that you are alive and who you really are, his own grandson, bound to kill him.'

So that was done, and all the Fomorians dropped their weapons when their druids too appealed to Lugh. After that the Fomorians acknowledged Lugh and, half broken and half relieved that they were still alive to feel that way, went back to Lochlann with their druids and men of learning who gave them good advice – but not soon enough.

Well, that was the end of that battle, or skirmish if you like, for the real second Battle of Moytura didn't take place for a while after. But, whether or which there was a lot of blood spilled in it. Anyway, when the danger was over and the last Fomorian had left the field, what did Lugh see but two of his own people sitting down with their backs against a rock resting after their exertions, and a row of heads around them to show that their efforts hadn't been wasted.

'Did you see ere a sign of my father, Cian?' he asked.

'Not a sign,' they said.

'Maybe he was killed by the Fomorians,' said Lugh.

'Divil a kill,' they replied, 'where there was divil a sign of him in the battle at all.'

'In that case,' said Lugh, 'he's dead surely, for if he was alive nothing would have prevented him from coming.' He paused and thought for a minute. He looked out over the battlefield into the distance where the sun was beginning to go down, staining the sky red and yellow and green, and he made the following rather pompous statement, which was a common enough kind of thing to do in those days, the troubled times that were in it: 'Until I know how he died and who it was that killed him neither food nor drink will pass my lips.'

Accompanied by a small band of his own people, Lugh retraced his steps back to the place where he had met his father a few days before. From there he tracked him north to the plain of Muirthemne where Cian had turned himself into the shape of a pig. Then a strange thing happened.

Lugh was riding ahead of his small band, but when he came to that place the horse stopped. And Lugh himself wanted to stop too so he made no effort to urge his horse forward. Instead he dismounted and, without knowing in the world why he did so, he walked this way and that across that small bit of plain. And as he walked a voice came – in a way that would echo down the centuries to another time and another prince in another country – from the very stones beneath his feet, and it whispered in a tone that could be heard if he was as deaf as the Old Man of the Woods (which he wasn't), but could not be heard by the others at all: 'Here, Lugh, lies the body of your father, Cian, forced to assume the shape of a pig when he saw the sons of Tuireann, Brian and Uar and Uraca, making for him, who found and killed him, but returned to his own form. They killed him with the very rocks you see round you. The blood on their hands, Lugh, will remain there until they meet Cian again.'

It seems that stones have a habit of speaking, when they speak at all, in that queer fashion. Lugh listened to their words carefully until they were finished. Then he called his people to him and they went directly to the spot where Cian was buried, and what did they do but disinter the body in order to see how Cian had been killed. And when they saw the way the poor body had been battered and beaten by the stones and the dreadful condition it was in Lugh was a silent man for a long time.

Then he paid his dutiful respects to his father's body and, by all the elements, swore revenge on the murderers, the sons of Tuireann, who had killed their relative – and he added a terrible prophecy in these words: 'I swear that because of this fratricide the curse of brother against brother will be the curse of Ireland for countless generations.'

When he had made that prophecy – and it still lingers – Lugh stood still and made the following lament beside the new grave of his father and the mound they erected over it.

> Bleak and fearful that noon was Cian's fate.
> This mangling of the warrior claws my hate.
> By her roadways to the east; by her soil to the west;
> Ireland will have nothing good, only badness.
>
> By the death of Cian, victor in affrays,
> My senses are weakened to darkness, always;
> My biased reason remains a slave,
> 'Til the fountainhead of Clan Tuireann fills the grave.
>
> 'Twas the sons of Tuireann by whom this was done.
> Now, let me tell you, for it is no illusion;
> I say it again, it is no frivolity of fun,
> It will be held against their grandsons and their grandsons' grandsons.

Then, when Cian's name had been engraved on the monument that was erected over him, Lugh stood back and turned to the people who were with him and said: 'From now on, forever, this place will be called "Cian". So, let us now go to Tara, where Nuada is waiting to hear what has happened. But,' he warned them, 'say nothing whatever about this matter here until I do so first.'

Then they went to Tara; and when they got there Lugh was received with all the honour that you would expect. Nuada brought him in to sit at his right hand at a great banquet, for news of the success over the Fomorians had already reached Tara, and they were celebrating the victory when Lugh arrived. Lugh smiled quietly but said nothing. All the time he seemed calm and under control, but his eyes were watchful and roaming and searched the great hall until they found the sons of Tuireann. And that wasn't difficult because they stood out even amongst the assembly of champions and heroes that was there. They were known to be foremost and outstanding in all feats of arms and sports, in addition to which they were tall and handsome beyond any other man there. Indeed, it was only Lugh himself who exceeded their heroic deeds in the battle. And because of this Nuada had honoured them also so that they too were beside Nuada, but on his other side.

Then Lugh raised his hand and asked that the silver bells of silence be rung. This was somewhat surprising as it is customarily the king who is first to ask for it, but it was done and, as the notes rang out, the hum and the clatter of conversation died away and everyone looked up expectantly towards Lugh. Then Lugh said: 'Heroes of the Tuatha de Danaan, I have only one question to ask and it is this: "On those who knowingly killed your father, what vengeance would you seek?"'

For a moment there was an extraordinary silence. Then Nuada asked: 'What do you mean, Lugh? Surely it isn't your own father, Cian . . .' and he looked round the hall as if seeking Cian, 'who has been killed?'

'It is indeed,' said Lugh, 'my father who has been killed. And what is more I see in this hall with us those who killed him. And they know better than I how they did so.'

The sons of Tuireann didn't move, but Nuada jumped to his feet and cried: 'The man who killed my father would take not one day, or two days, but as many days as it would take him if I lopped off a member from his body each day until he cried for death from the torment under my hands. And then I would delay it.'

When he said this there was a mighty shout of approval from the assembly. And Lugh noted that the sons of Tuireann joined in like the rest. So, when the clamour died down, he said: 'Now I can tell you that the murderers of Cian have passed judgement on themselves, for they joined with the rest of you in your agreement. This assembly can bear witness that I claim the right to put an *éric* fine on them for Cian, my father. Should they refuse my *éric*, I won't violate the sanctuary of the king's palace; but I tell you, by the gods, they will not leave here without settling accounts with me at the doorway.'

Then Nuada said: 'Indeed, Lugh, you are giving them a generous opportunity. If it was I had killed your father I would be satisfied, and more than satisfied, if you accepted an *éric* fine from me.'

Hearing this the sons of Tuireann leaned towards one another and whispered amongst themselves under Lugh's watchful eye.

'He knows,' said Uar.

'It's obvious,' said Uraca.

'It's to us he's talking,' they both said, 'and however he knows, he knows, and it seems better that we should confess rather than try to hide it further and have him condemn us.'

But Brian shook his head. 'I don't know,' he said. 'How could he possibly know what happened? I think he's only trying to get a confession out of us because he's not sure. And if we confess he wouldn't accept an *éric* when he knows for certain.'

But Uar and Uraca persisted, saying: 'Since you are the eldest, it is you who also have the right to confess. But if you don't, we'll do it ourselves.'

After they said this Brian sat in his place for a moment, thinking. And then stood up and cried: 'I believe that what you are saying is meant for us, Lugh. The enmity between your father and his brothers and our family is well known. So that if any one of them is dead on either side the most likely ones to have killed him are thought to be from the other side. And in this case the most likely ones are ourselves. But Cian was not killed by any weapon of the sons of Tuireann,' he said, thinking this might put Lugh off. But then Brian looked over at Lugh's implacable face. Then he looked at his brothers beside him, and he went on: 'In any case, in view of what I have said we will, nevertheless, give you the *éric* as if we were responsible.'

There was a gasp in the hall from the guests, for few believed the sons of Tuireann were guilty. But Lugh looked gravely across the king and held Brian's eye. Then he nodded and said shortly: 'Very well. I will accept an *éric* from you even though you doubt my word. What is more I will tell you here and now what that *éric* is. And if it is a thing that you think any part of it is too much, then I will remit that part.'

Brian looked at his brothers and they nodded; and then he said: 'That seems fair enough to us. Now tell us, here in front of this assembly, what your *éric* is.'

So Lugh stood up and put his hands behind his back and, without addressing the sons of Tuireann, spoke to the whole assembly. 'This is my *éric*. First, three apples; second, the skin of a pig; third, a spear; fourth, two horses and a chariot; fifth, seven pigs; sixth, a hound pup; seventh, a cooking spit, and eighth, three shouts on a hill,' he ended.

During this speech those in the hall had been looking at him with increasing astonishment. They looked from Lugh to the sons of Tuireann and saw the look of relief mixed with perplexity no less than their own on their faces. For there were many there who did not believe the popular and heroic sons of Tuireann were guilty, but had accepted the *éric* for the honourable reasons stated by Brian. Uar and Uraca even smiled slightly in their relief when Lugh finished. But Brian frowned.

'Now,' said Lugh, 'that is my *éric* and that is what I want from you. If you think it is too much, or any part of it is too much, I will redeem that part of it now. If you do not think it is too much, then you must see about fulfilling it.'

'So far,' said Brian, without standing up, 'we do not consider it too much. In fact,' he went on, 'it seems so trivial that I suspect treachery. It is so light and so inconsiderate that if you were to multiply it a hundred times . . .'

But Lugh interrupted him, raising his hand so the silver bells of silence were rung again, and Brian stopped immediately. 'I do not think my *éric* is too small,' said Lugh. 'I will be satisfied if you fulfil it. Moreover,' he went on, 'I guarantee here and now as a de Danaan before the assembled de Danaans here to ask no more from you and to seek no further vengeance of any kind once it is fulfilled and paid if you accept it. All I ask is that since I have guaranteed this here in front of the de Danaans in court, that you give me a similar guarantee that you will faithfully complete the *éric*.'

This made Brian suddenly angry: 'Are not our word and we ourselves sufficient guarantee?' he cried.

Lugh looked back at him and said quietly, 'No. You are not.'

So, grudgingly and in anger, but also in guilt, the three sons of Tuireann agreed to be bound in a solemn oath that they would complete their fine, provided Lugh did not increase his claim later. And as security and guarantors, they asked Nuada, the king, and the Bodhbh Dearg, King of Connacht, to stand for them. And they made this pact there and then in front of that assembly of the Tuatha de Danaan chiefs and princes in the hall of Moycuarta in Tara.

That didn't take long and Lugh remained standing throughout. And then he said: 'Now that that is agreed and there is no going back on it let me tell you in detail what the *éric* involves.'

The sons of Tuireann nodded, but said nothing.

'The three apples I require,' said Lugh, 'must come from the garden of the Hesperides and from nowhere else. There are no apples in all the world like them, for they are the colour of gold and have immense power and virtue. They are as big as the head of a month-old child and never grow less no matter how much is eaten from one of them. They have the taste of honey and if a wounded man or one in deadly sickness takes a bite from one he is cured immediately. Moreover,' he went on, 'if a warrior has one of these apples he can perform with it whatever feat he will by casting it from him and after it will return by itself to his hand. And, brave though you are, Brian and Uar and Uraca, I do not think you have the ability – something about which I have no regrets – to take these apples from those who guard them; for it has been prophesied that three young knights from the west would come to take them and the king who owns them has set guards, and more guards, around about the gardens.'

Lugh paused for a moment and looked around. The faces of everyone in the hall were now very grim, but Lugh went on as if he didn't notice. 'The skin of the pig I want is that of Tuis, King of Greece, and I'll tell you that when this pig lived every stream through which it walked turned to wine for nine days thereafter. And if, for some reason, the pig touched a wound or a sickness, it was instantly cured. The druids of Greece understood that it was not the pig, but the skin that held the virtue, and so they flayed it and preserved the skin. And that is the second part of my fine. Nor do I think that you will have any success in getting that even if you succeed in getting the first, for it is guarded by the king as his greatest treasure and he has sworn to kill anyone who attempts to take it.'

Quickly Lugh continued: 'The spear I want is the venomed spear of Pisear, King of Persia, called the Slaughterer. In times of peace it must be kept in a cauldron of water to prevent it destroying the palace. Whoever carries it in war can do what he will with it. And that is the spear I want, and I doubt if you will get it.' He looked stonily at the sons of Tuireann, who looked back, silent and white-faced.

'The steeds and the chariot I want,' went on Lugh, 'are those of Dobar, King of Sicily. That chariot excels any in the world. And no matter how often those horses are killed, they will come to life again if their bones are brought together in the same place. You will not get them easily. The seven pigs I require,' he continued, 'are the pigs of Asal, King of the Golden Pillars, which, though killed every day, will be found alive the following day again. The hound pup, Failinis, that you must get, belongs to the King of Iora. So great is her power that the wild beasts of the forest fall helpless before her. The cooking spit is to come from the Island of Fincara guarded by the warlike women of that island, any one of whom is capable of handling three champions such as yourselves without tossing a curl of her hair. The hill on which you must give three shouts is the hill of Mokeen in Lochlann, which Mokeen and his sons are solemnly bound not to permit. Moreover, it was with them that my father was fostered, and even if I were to forgive you his death you may be sure that they will not. Even if you succeeded in all the rest of this *éric*, which you won't, then they will make sure to avenge my father's death. And this, sons of Tuireann, is the *éric* I place on you and the *éric* I want from you.'

When he was finished and they had heard this the children of Tuireann were mighty shaken I can tell you. But, shaken or not, they stood up and without saying a word to a sinner, walked straight out of the great hall of Moycuarta and off to their father's house and told him what had happened.

Naturally the old man wasn't too happy when he heard what they had to say and he shook his head and looked severe and then he gave the following advice to his sons. 'I don't like the look of this at all,' he started off. 'I don't want to be disheartening, but at the same time it seems to me ye signed yere death warrant when ye dropped them stones on Cian, a thing ye had no right to do. If ye were going to kill him at all, ye might have done it decent, if I might say so. Now, as far as this fine is concerned, I can tell ye that no man can get it without the help of either Lugh or of Mananaan himself – and they won't, either of them, be inclined to give it. You can be sure of that. So the best thing ye can do now is go to Lugh and ask him if he would lend you Aonvarr of the Flowing Mane. And I can tell you also he won't thank you for asking and he won't give it to you.'

'Why would we ask him so?'

'Will you listen to me?' said his father. 'If you had done more of it in the past ye mightn't be in this fix now. He won't give it to you because it doesn't belong to him, but to Mananaan, and what he'll say to you is that he wouldn't give the loan of a loan to any man. But that's only an excuse. When he has that said, ask him for the loan of Mananaan's boat, the Wavesweeper – which will be more use to you anyway – and he won't refuse you that, for 'tis *geasa* on him not to refuse a second request.'

So the sons of Tuireann went to Lugh and did what their father advised and, sure enough, as Tuireann had said didn't Lugh refuse them Mananaan's fine horse, for the very reason they had been told.

'All right so,' said Brian, 'if you won't lend us the horse will you give us the loan of the Wavesweeper of Mananaan?'

When Lugh realised how he had been tricked he was angry, but there was little he could do about it. 'Very good,' he acknowledged. 'The Wavesweeper is in the harbour of the river Boyne, and you have permission to take it.'

When they returned to Castle Tuireann and told their father he was uneasy. 'It is better than nothing,' he said, 'and I hope it will be of great help to you, but I have my doubts. Obviously Lugh wants to get as much of the *éric* as he can before the battle of Moytura, which is bound to come soon. I think that must be what was in his mind or he would have found some way of preventing your second request as well. But for the things that are of no use to him and of danger to you he will give you no help at all and be all the more satisfied if you are killed while attempting them.'

But his three sons were so elated at having tricked Lugh, that they didn't pay enough attention to what he was saying. They set off to find the boat at the Boyne harbour and were accompanied on their journey by their sister Eithne who went with them to say farewell. But when they saw the boat Brian was horrified. Instead of the large sea-going ship he had expected, what they found was a small open canoe or currach. In his anger Brian kicked it and cried: 'What use is this to us? It is only a coracle. And in any case it won't fit more than two of us.'

His words alarmed Eithne who reminded him that the currach was magic and that one of its attributes was to extend itself to accommodate whatever was necessary to be carried. Moreover, she pointed out, it was forbidden to criticise it in any way. Then she said: 'That was a fearful thing ye did all right, no doubt, and I'm ashamed of ye for it. But blood is thicker than water and I love the three of ye whatever ye did, and what ye did is now done. But I'm afraid the consequences will be cruel.'

Then she made the following poem and her brothers answered her:

Eithne
Oh come all ye young maidens and listen to me,
And the black deeds committed by my brothers three.
They killed noble Cian the father of Lugh
And brought down on our heads this punishment due.

The sons
Oh dear sister Eithne your chiding's too strong
We are warriors still and regret we've done wrong;
Believe when we say it we'd rather death's blow
Than to live here in cowardice, and that's why we'll go.

Eithne
Rise up then, dear brothers, and brave the wild ocean,
Seek out this bold *éric* with ardent devotion.
Your punishing exile – 'twill pierce you to bear it –
It saddens my heart, if I could I would share it.

Then Uar and Uraca and Brian got into the currach which, as their sister had said, expanded when they did, so that it took themselves and all their gear with ease. Then, waving to grief-stricken Eithne, they turned it eastwards and out into the open sea.

'Now,' said Uar, 'which way should we go?'

'Aye,' said Uraca – who understood that that was the proper thing to say in a boat – 'shall we turn north or south?'

'We'll follow the pattern of the *éric*,' said Brian, 'and since the first things that Lugh demanded were the apples from the Garden of the Hesperides, that is what we will go for.' And, with that, he spoke to the currach saying: 'We command you, Wavesweeper of Mananaan, take us forthwith to the Garden of the Hesperides.'

As it always did the currach responded immediately to the voice of whoever commanded it. And no sooner was Brian finished speaking than it raised its noble upturned prow and bounded forward across the green and white-crested bosom of the endless waves faster than a wolf-hound in flight or the whistling winds of March. By the quickest and shortest route it flew and never stopped nor veered nor altered its course until it swept in below to a harbour not too far from the Garden of the Hesperides.

Then Brian asked the others: 'Well, so much for that. Now we know the Wavesweeper will do what we ask. The thing is what do we do next?'

'Go and get the apples, to be sure,' said Uar.

'Aye,' said Uraca, 'isn't that what we're here for?'

'We must have a plan,' went on Brian as if they hadn't spoken. 'The garden is bound to be well guarded, perhaps with the king himself at the head of the guards. So we must think of a way.'

'Well,' said Uar, 'it seems likely we're going to be killed anyway, so maybe we should just go bravely and meet whatever we must meet and let that be an end of it.'

'Therefore,' said Uraca in agreement, 'maybe the best way is to go and attack them; and if we succeed well and good and if not we'll be just as well off to die here.'

'Indeed?' observed Brian. 'Maybe that would suit the two of ye, but it won't suit me. Soldiers should be intelligent as well as brave. So let's consider this and think of a plan so that people can say of us afterwards, if we don't survive, that at least we were prudent and skilful besides being brave, and that they may respect us for our cunning and not despise us for our foolishness.'

The other two looked at him, downcast, and he went on. 'I've given this a good deal of thought. And it seems to me that the most practical thing for us to do is to give ourselves the appearance of hawks, go up towards the sun, and then dive suddenly into the garden. The guards won't be able to use their heavy weapons against us and we should be able to avoid their light ones if we're prepared for them. So we can dive in and swoop up and, when they've fired all they have at us, sweep down again and carry off an apple each. I'll try to take two if I can.'

The other two thought this was a very good plan, so that is what they did. Brian gave each of them a whack with his druid's wand and before he had the second one done, the other had the appearance of a hawk of incomparable beauty and speed. And when the two hawks were there on the ground beside him turning their heads quickly from side to side and peering at the world with their sharp eyes, he gave himself a tap too and said whatever words were necessary. With that the three noble birds spread their wings and took off, soaring high into the blue sky. When they reached a great height they could see the garden down below them and they circled and hovered high for a moment and then, as one bird, folded back their wings and came flashing down through the vasty dome of the limitless sky with the wind whistling through their tapered pinions. But didn't the guards spot them anyway and begin to fire showers of arrows and other missiles at them. The three brothers dodged and twisted and turned until all the guards' ammunition was gone, and then they swooped up high again, peeled off at the top of their climb, and suddenly they were diving down on the glittering trees. The two younger brothers carried off an apple each and Brian took one in his talons and one impaled upon his beak, and almost without pause and without having been wounded or touched, they soared again into the noble sky and veered west for the harbour where they had left the Wavesweeper of Mananaan.

In spite of their speed and their cunning, the news reached the king, and he had three daughters who were noted sorceresses throughout the length and breadth of the lands of the east. Quick as a wink they transformed themselves into three griffins and pursued the hawks out to sea, throwing great tongues of fire after them and around them from their open horrible and screeching mouths. Flames overtook and burnt and blinded the hawks so that they could bear the heat no longer.

'Begor,' said Uar, 'that's a warm welcome.'

'Warm is right,' said Uraca. 'My tail feathers have nothing but a spine left on them, and I'm afraid this heat is beginning to cook the apple I carry.'

Brian, who wasn't finding the going too pleasant either, looked back and said: 'I'll see what I can do.' He tapped his two brothers and himself with the druid's wand, which was all the time tucked into a fold in one of his wings, and turned them into three white swans, a bit scorched around the back-end, maybe, and they flew below to the sea.

Now, although the three sorceresses had power, they hadn't much in the way of brains – it might have come from turning themselves into griffins so often, for griffins are notable for stupidity. Anyway, when the griffins saw that the hawks were gone, what did they do? Only give up the chase and go home to their father, puffing out a lot of smoke because they'd burned up most of the stuff that makes the flames. So the sons of Tuireann, in the shape of the swans, made their way back to the Wavesweeper.

They rested a while before taking off again; and then they decided that, since it wasn't too far away, they might as well go to Greece and have a look for the skin of Tuis's pig and see if they could get that. So they got into the currach again and Brian ordered it to take them to a harbour near where Tuis had his palace. And again, when they got there, Brian asked the other two: 'What way do you think we ought to approach this since we must go to the court?'

'What other way would we go,' asked the other two back, 'but as ourselves?'

'I don't agree. This king is bound to be a bit suspicious of three warriors coming in like ourselves and mightn't take too kindly to that, and if I was in his position I'd be strongly tempted to separate their heads from the rest of them.'

'Well what, so?' asked the other two.

'It seems to me,' said Brian, 'that surprise is always our best bet. The best thing we can do is disguise ourselves as poets and learned men from Ireland, for I know that poets and scholars are held in very high repute by the noble Greeks.'

'Fair enough,' said Uar and Uraca, 'but what'll we do if they ask us to demonstrate our art? We haven't a hexameter or a spondee between us, or a decent poem, let alone the ability to make one up, and not much chance to learn between now and then.'

'Isn't it the great pity,' asked Brian, 'that you didn't take the opportunity when you had it, like myself? For, as you know,' he went on modestly, 'I'm as renowned as a poet as I am at anything else.'

Anyway, in spite of their reservations, he persuaded them. So they put the poet's knots in their hair and walked up to the palace gates. There the guards asked them what they wanted. 'It's not what we want,' said Brian barefacedly, 'but what we can give. We're three poets from Ireland and we have a poem for the king.' So the guards sent a message into King Tuis and he said: 'Bring them in, so, for if they've come so far in search of a patron, maybe they've found the man they want.'

The truth of the matter was that his own poets had given up trying to please him because he was a small ugly man who was also lazy and not much with either the sword or the spear (though his three wives had little cause for complaint). All the same he took a few precautions and he commanded that the court should all assemble and be made to glitter and be more splendid than it already was for these three foreign poets, so that when they left – if they ever did – they could tell the world that it was greater than anything they knew for grandeur and pomp and circumstance. So there was great brushing and polishing for a while before the three sons of Tuireann were brought in in their disguise as poets. They came in to where the king sat surrounded by his nobles in the great banqueting hall. They bowed low and greeted the king who welcomed them and invited them to join in the feast that was being laid out before them. And they were impressed, and there's no doubt about that, for they had seldom seen a household so full of merriment or a banquet so splendid or a palace more magnificent. And when they were full of food and wine the king's own poets stood up and threw a few poems at the king and the guests. And in spite of everything they were very good poems.

Speaking low Brian whispered a bit uneasily to the others: 'They're not bad.'

The other two nodded unhappily. 'They're not,' they said.

'It's our turn next,' said Brian. 'Have you ere a rhyme or a riddle at all?'

'Not an alliteration or a recitation,' whispered Uar.

'Not a verse,' said Uraca. 'How can we recite for the king? If you ask us to fight we will, or to die if we must, but a poem is beyond us.'

Brian gave them a look of absolute disgust and said: 'A fine pair of warriors that can't even make a poem!'

Then he stood up himself and asked for attention while he made his own poem, which was this:

> There once was a fine king of Greece
> Like an oak tree in war and in peace.
> Now we'd like for that verse
> A pigskin, of course
> Without meanness this skin, please, release.

When he had that said it struck him, maybe from the want of reaction by the king, that it wasn't clear; so he went on:

> There once was a fellow who said,
> 'In war quite a few fall down dead.
> But a generous gift
> Can prevent such a rift
> And the donor can hold up his head.'

That didn't do much better, only that Tuis shifted in his seat as if there were ants or some other invaders under his clothes, so Brian ploughed on:

> Another man said, 'Don't you see
> An attack by my host, you'll agree,
> Is one, I suppose,
> That I'd have to oppose,
> So please give us the pigskin for free.'

'That is a very good poem, I daresay,' said the king, 'but I don't understand one word of it.'

'I'll interpret it for you,' said Brian. 'It means that just as the oak excels the other trees of the forest, you excel all other kings in nobleness, generosity and greatness.'

Tuis nodded in agreement . . . and why wouldn't he?

'The next bit means simply what it says, that you have the skin of a pig that I want to get from you as a reward for my poem. And, of course, the next bit then is fairly clear too. It means that if you give me the gift I'm looking for you can hold up your head with honour, but if you don't I'm afraid the two of us will have a bit of a war between us. And that is what my poem means,' concluded Brian.

The king looked at Brian in amazement. And he looked at his two brothers. Then he looked at the dumbfounded host of his nobles, friends and soldiers. And then he laughed. And then he said: 'If it wasn't for the fact that you had mentioned my pigskin I might, out of kindness, have praised that poem of yours even though it wasn't very good. And it seems to me, oh poet, that you are a very foolish man indeed to ask for that skin. Let me tell you that if all the poets and scholars of Ireland and all the chiefs and nobles of the whirling world demanded it from me, I'd refuse them, unless they took it from me by force. However, there's no doubt that you're men of courage and audacity and I won't let you go unrewarded. I'll give you three times that skin full of red gold in payment for your poem.'

Brian looked back at him in appreciation. 'That's very generous of you,' says he, 'Tuis, and good luck and good health to you for it. I knew well I'd get something worth while from you if I asked for what I wanted boldly. But, you know,' he said, 'I am a very suspicious man by nature. And grateful as I am for your offer, I'm afraid that I couldn't accept it for fear your servants might cheat me in the measuring unless I see them measure it myself out of the skin with my own two eyes.'

King Tuis laughed and said that that was audacious, but prudent. And so his servants and soldiers took the three sons of Tuireann to the treasure house to measure the gold. One of them brought out the skin from its special place to be filled.

'Now,' said Brian, 'measure the two skinfuls for my brothers first, and you can do my measure last because it was I who made the poem.'

With that the servants turned to do what Brian had told them, but even as they did so, Brian whipped out his sword, grabbed the skin with his left hand, and with his right hand knocked the man nearest him clean off his feet unconscious with a blow from the flat of his sword. Wrapping the skin about himself and turning with his brothers they rushed back through the palace attacking everyone they met on their way until they reached the banqueting hall again, only being careful to wound and not to kill. The entire assembly there, when they saw the way things were, attacked and harassed the sons of Tuireann. But, even with their battle fury reined in, and their rage under control but in mighty desperation, they hewed and cut and thrust and fought their way through the great hall so that not a champion nor a noble nor a warrior wasn't damaged or wounded before them as they went. Finally Brian and the king came face to face and Tuis attacked him with courage and strength for all his smallness and being a bad hand at the sword. But brave as he proved to be, and strongly though he fought, he was little match for Brian and soon fell with a lump on his head as big as an egg.

While that was going on, Uar and Uraca were cutting and waylaying all round them until there was no more to be done, and only the women and children and servants were left whole amongst the wounded. After this great battle, the three sons of Tuireann went round with the pigskin giving each of the wounded a rub of it and, wonder of wonders, isn't it a fact that as soon as it touched a wounded man, he was made whole again – but a bit weak, which is just as well or the battle might have started all over again. Then they took a bit of a rest in the palace with the women before returning to the Wavesweeper to continue their quest. It was while they were resting like that that King Tuis came to and, when he saw what they were at, wanted to attack them again even though he was by himself, but the women (and there was a fair number of them by that time) for some reason of their own wouldn't let him, and so the sons went off safely with the skin.

They sat on the beach beside the boat and considered where they would head for next. The upshot of their cogitations was that they decided to go to Pisear's kingdom of Persia for the blazing spear. So, they turned their backs on the blue and white of Greece and commanded the currach to take them eastwards towards the Persian empire. And it occurred to Brian as the currach sped over the rearing waves, since they already had the apples from the Garden of the Hesperides, together with the pigskin from Tuis, that these might be of help in getting the spear. Moreover, he advised his brothers, although his brothers hadn't been too happy about it, that the disguise of poets had served them well. So he proposed that they remain in that disguise at Pisear's court too. And when they arrived there they were welcomed as they had been welcomed at the palace of Tuis, and were brought into the great hall where Pisear was celebrating a banquet with his nobles and chief people. They were received with kindness and invited to join the banquet.

'Begor,' whispered Uar out of the side of his mouth, 'I could get used to this.'

'It has its points,' said Uraca.

'Whisht!' snapped Brian.

Well, it wasn't long before Pisear's poets began to sing and play their instruments and make poems for the assembly. When they were finished Brian said to his brothers a bit sarcastically, 'Let the two of you get up now and make a poem for the king.' But Uar and Uraca refused, saying that they couldn't; but they'd fight if he asked them to do that.

'That'd be a strange way to make a poem,' said Brian. 'But never mind. I have my own poem for the king. And I'll sing it for him now.' And this is the poem that he made.

> Today Pisear has small need of spears.
> His enemies battle lines are smashed.
> Nor has Pisear cause for tears.
> It is not he who shall be gashed.

The yew is the king of all the trees.
The noblest one of all, they say.
May the great spear shafts create a breeze,
Through the bodies of those they slay.

There was a silence when he finished; and then the king said: 'That's not a bad poem . . . if I could understand it. What does the reference to a spear mean?'

'It means,' said Brian, 'that I want the get your spear as a reward for my poem.'

'That is a very foolish request to make,' said Pisear. 'For no man who ever asked me for my spear escaped punishment for the asking. The greatest gift I could give you, or the greatest favour these nobles here could get for you now, is to spare your life.'

With that Brian remembered the qualities of the apple of the Hesperides that he had in his hand, so he threw it at Pisear. So powerful was the throw that it knocked the king's brains backward through his head. Then Brian and his brothers drew their swords and began to lay around them until those who remained standing fled in terror and there was nobody left in the banqueting hall except the sons of Tuireann. After that they searched the palace, high up and low down, until eventually, deep below in the furthest dungeon, they found a great and mighty cauldron of hissing and bubbling water where the blazing spear was kept with its head down and its shaft sticking up like a ladle out of the pot, for fear of the damage it might do unbeknownst. They picked it up, cauldron and all, and left the palace in a hurry and back to Mananaan's currach. Not surprisingly they felt a bit tired after their great exertions, so what did they do only take a bit of a rest for a few days to recover their strength. And while they were doing that they decided that their next stop would be Sicily to take the horses and the chariot of Dobar the king there.

They were now in very good spirits after the success of their first three quests; so, with greater confidence than they ever had before, they commanded the Wavesweeper to take them west to Sicily. When they landed there Brian brought with him the great spear of Pisear and suggested to his brothers that they should pretend to be mercenary soldiers from Ireland willing to serve the king for money. 'In that way,' he said, 'we will learn how and where the horses and chariot are kept and guarded.'

So they agreed to this and the three of them set out for the palace. It so happened that King Dobar was attending a great fair on the plain in front of the palace with all his people and as the three warriors from Ireland came towards them the crowd drew back and made a path for them so that they were able to walk straight up to the king. He asked them who they were and where they came from for, of course, even though they were a bit sunburned by this time, they still looked like foreigners.

'We are three soldiers from Ireland,' replied Brian, 'looking for service and pay from the kings of the world.'

'I see,' said Dobar. 'And will you serve me for a while?'

'Why not,' said Brian, 'isn't that what we're here for?'

And so they made a pact with the king that they would serve him faithfully and then ask their own reward and that he would give them a place of honour in his kingdom. They did that and remained with him for a month and a fortnight gathering information and familiarising themselves with the island. But in all that time they neither saw nor heard anything of the steeds or the chariot.

So then Brian said to the others: 'We're not making any progress. We know less about the horses and the chariot now than we did when we came here.'

'What'll we do so?' they asked.

'I think,' said Brian, 'the way to deal with this is this: we'll go to the king and pretend that we're on our way because we've heard of these horses and the great chariot and yet, while we have been here and in a place of honour, we have never been shown them, and that this is an insult to us, and unless we see them we will leave his service.'

So that is what they did next. They put on all their travelling gear and took their spears and their helmets and their shields and their swords and presented themselves to the king, who looked at them in astonishment.

'Where are you going,' he asked, 'dressed up for travelling? I gave you no instructions to go anywhere on my behalf.'

'Well now, Dobar,' said Brian, 'the way of it is this: we have served you well and faithfully for a month and a half. And soldiers of Ireland such as ourselves are accustomed to being the most trusted guards and praetorians and champions of any king whom they give their service to. And we guard their most precious possessions as strongly as themselves. Moreover, we are accustomed to being advisers and counsellors and men of insight as well. But that's not the way you've treated us, Dobar. You have kept secrets from us.'

'What secrets?' asked the king in astonishment.

'Well,' said Brian, 'we're after hearing that you have a chariot and horses which are the best in the world, and yet we have never seen them.'

'Oho!' laughed the king. 'If that's all that's bothering you it's an easy matter to fix, and no need whatever for you to leave my service. Indeed if I'd known that troubled you I'd have shown them to you long since. But in any case I'll show them to you now, for I can tell you I never had in my service any soldiers or advisers in whom I had a greater trust.' And, of course, if that wasn't the misplaced trust . . .

Anyway, Dobar sent for the steeds and the chariot and had them yoked and brought, prancing and tossing their heads, before the three sons of Tuireann.

And he told them that these horses were faster than the winds of March and swift equally across both land and water. Then Brian, who was an honourable man in his way and wouldn't deceive the king more than he had to, said: 'Now, Dobar, King of Sicily, please listen to me. We have served you faithfully up to now on the terms you put forward yourself, which is that at the end of our period of service we would claim our own pay. And now I propose to do that.'

'Well,' said Dobar, 'I'll be sorry to lose you, but of course that was our bargain and I am agreed to it, so what is it you want?'

'I'll tell you,' said Brian, 'we want those steeds and the chariot and these are what we mean to have and nothing less.'

With that the king fell into a terrible rage. He leaped to his feet with the anger bursting out of him like waves of heat from an over-boiled pot. 'Reckless and foolish men,' he said, 'instead of a good reward you have chosen your own deaths, which is what you're going to get now for your presumption.'

The king and all his guards turned towards the sons of Tuireann intending to kill them. But Brian had been watching his opportunity. He sprang for the chariot and grabbed the reins in his left hand and with his right threw the charioteer to the ground. Then, lifting the blazing spear of Pisear in his right hand, he and his brothers slaughtered the hosts of Dobar so that the king and his men fell under this onslaught and those who were not killed fled for their lives. Then, with this prize to add to the apples from the Garden of Hesperides and the spear of Pisear and the pig's hide of Tuis, they drove quickly back to where they'd left the magic boat of Mananaan. Naturally they hadn't come through such a battle unscathed, so they rested a while until their strength returned after touching their wounds with the pigskin, and then they had a little conference and the result of that was that they decided to go in search of the seven pigs which were the property of Asal, the King of the Golden Pillars.

So they put the chariot and the horses into Mananaan's boat and instructed it to sail as quickly as possible over the boundless sea to that destination. But, as they came towards the shore, they saw that it was lined deep with armed men and that every cove and harbour was strongly fortified, for their fame had gone before them throughout the countries of the world and the story of their being banished from Ireland to seek and carry off the gifted jewels and prizes of their keepers was known throughout civilisation, and even in places like Sassana that were only half civilised here and there. Paying little heed to the hundreds of mightily armed men ringing the shores and the cliffs, Brian directed the Wavesweeper to sail straight into the main harbour. When they were only a short distance from the pier, King Asal himself came forward to meet them and put up his hand and asked them to stop where they were. So Brian gave the instruction to the Wavesweeper, which stopped instantly in the still water of the harbour, riding the translucent, gentle swell with an easy motion.

King Asal looked at them for a moment or two without saying anything until Brian and his brothers almost began to get restless. And then the king said: 'Tell me, warriors from Ireland, is it true that it was by your hand that so many kings have been overcome wherever you have been?'

And Brian nodded and said, 'Yes,' and that he regretted it, but that it was the truth.

'And what is your reason,' asked Asal, 'for what seems a strange and bloody pilgrimage against those who have done you no harm?'

Then Brian told him that they had no choice in the matter. Standing in the prow of the Wavesweeper he said across the gentle water: 'It is the fault of the Il-Dana, Asal, Lugh Lamh Fada, and of the unjust and terrible *éric* he has put on us which we are bound to pay. If those kings to whom we had gone had given us freely the precious things we sought we would have departed in peace. But since they didn't and tried to kill us, we had no choice but to fight against them unwillingly, and take what we needed, for you know nobody was able to stand against us.'

'And what brings you here?' asked King Asal, knowing full well the answer he would get.

'The seven pigs you have,' said Brian, 'for they are part of our fine.'

'And how do you propose to take them?' asked Asal.

'Well,' said Brian, 'we would prefer to take them as a token of your kindness and friendship, and if that were to happen we would be grateful. But if that is not how we are to get them, then we will fight for them and either bring them with us after the outcome or fall ourselves in the attempt – but that is unlikely, I think.'

King Asal looked at them for another little while. 'You put me in a dilemma,' he said.

''Tis no greater than the one that we're in,' said Brian.

The king grunted and said; 'If our fate was to be that of Greece and Persia and Sicily then it would be a grave misfortune for us to give battle.'

'Indeed,' said Brian, 'I think that is the truth.'

So with that Asal and his council and his chiefs gathered together there in his tent on the shore and considered the position. And the upshot of that was that they decided to give the pigs to the sons of Tuireann of their own free will, since they knew that up to now no king, however powerful, had been able to withstand them, and that the sons were possessed of great and wonderful powers. When Asal came back and told the three champions of this decision, the sons of Tuireann were overcome with wonder and amazement and gratitude at its wisdom. They were sick of slaughter themselves and gave heartfelt thanks to King Asal for a decision which, though it wasn't really made in friendship, was certainly made out of sagacity. They were entertained that night in Asal's palace where they feasted and thanksgiving was given all round for the fact that there was to be neither battle nor bloodshed. And on the following day they were escorted to the king's presence where the pigs were given to them.

With that Brian made a poem in praise of Asal.

> Among lords of the world there is none,
> Oh great king of the pillars of gold,
> Whose wisdom compares with your own,
> Whose story will ever be told.

> For a king who protects his own people
> And hands Fate his good name for a bet.
> Shows discernment and conscience in choosing
> To offer them life and not death.

King Asal was pleased with the poem and then asked the brothers where they intended to go next.

'I think,' said Brian, 'that we'll go to Iora for the hound pup, Failinis, which is another part of the *éric* that we have to fulfil.'

'Is that a fact?' asked Asal. 'Well, in that case we can do each other a favour, maybe.'

'Anything that it's in our power to do,' said Brian, 'we will gladly do for you, seeing as how you've been so good to us.'

'I'll tell you the way it is,' said Asal. 'The favour we can do for one another is this: my daughter is the king's queen and I will do whatever I can to persuade him to give you the pup without a battle and that way save her whatever misfortune might follow otherwise.'

This was good news for the sons of Tuireann and they agreed immediately. But King Asal, being the prudent man he'd already shown himself to be, didn't much care for the look of Mananaan's frail currach for such a journey, in spite of its marvellous qualities and all that was in it, and insisted on going in his own ship. This was prepared and in due course the little currach and the great ship sailed out of the harbour together, past the wonderful golden pillars that gave the land its name and that shone glinting in the morning sun in harmony with the glittering waves. The two ships set their prows for Iora. And, of course, Brian had instructed the Wavesweeper to keep pace with the king's ship, which it did.

No more than at the Land of the Golden Pillars, when they reached Iora their fame and progress had gone before them and the whole shore was lined with fiercely armed men who shouted a warning at them to stay where they were, because of course they knew who it was and what they had come for. Asal shouted across the interval between the two ships advising the brothers to do that and that he would go ashore by himself and try to persuade his son-in-law to show the same wisdom that he had. So he did that and was taken peacefully and respectfully to the palace. The king asked him why he had brought the sons of Tuireann to his country, so Asal explained and finished by saying that they wanted the hound pup that the king had.

'In that case,' said the king, 'it's little sense that you showed in coming here with them, for there aren't three warriors in the entire world to whom the gods have given enough strength or good luck as to take that pup, either by force or goodwill.'

This attitude upset Asal very much because he knew well that if there was war and bloody slaughter his own daughter, if she survived it, would very likely be left a widow. So he pointed out the great destruction that the three sons had already done wherever they had been, and that the same would have happened to himself except that he had given the seven pigs freely.

'The great Kings of Greece and of Persia have been beaten and overpowered by them,' he said, 'for they have arms that no mortal warrior can withstand. My sincere and earnest advice to you is to give them the hound pup in peace.'

But the King of Iora was a different kettle of fish altogether to himself. He was a man of fiery words and anger who believed strongly in his own rights – and, of course, it is hard to blame him in this instance. Nevertheless his attitude troubled Asal who understood what was likely to happen, and he went back and told the sons of Tuireann how matters stood. But he pleaded with them to go easy on his son-in-law. So Brian and his two brothers armed themselves then and declared war on the king and the warriors of Iora and a fierce and bloody battle began on the shore as they leaped onto it from their currach. The army of Iora was great and its warriors were brave, even though nothing could stand against the sons of Tuireann.

As it raged on the battle became so fierce that the three brothers were separated from one another; Uar and Uraca were carried in the fight away from Brian where he wrought desperate death and destruction with the blazing spear of Pisear. With it he drove a path through the din and the smoke of battle towards the battle-pen of the King of Iora, who was surrounded by his guards. As Brian forged through the enemy throng, no man could stand against him, so great was his battle-fury. When he reached the battle-pen he burst in like a thunderbolt and, though the king put up a powerful and venomous defence, Brian, who could easily have killed him, held back in spite of the danger to himself, so that the king would become tired. Suddenly when the opportunity presented itself he leaped at the king and tied and bound him and carried him off to where Asal was at the shore. Then throwing the king down at Asal's feet he said: 'Here is your son-in-law for you; and I can tell you, by my weapons, it would have been far easier to kill him three times over rather than bring him alive to you like this.'

When the army of Iora saw that their king was defeated by Brian and made a prisoner they threw down their arms. There was a pact of peace made between the King of Iora and the sons of Tuireann, though mind you it wasn't done with any grace, and the hound pup was reluctantly given to the three renowned warriors from Ireland. Then they took their leave of Asal with kindness and regret and friendship. They also shook the hand of the King of Iora, who wouldn't look them in the eye, and returned to the Wavesweeper.

In the meantime, Lugh, the Il-Dana, had been following the successes of the sons of Tuireann with mixed feelings. His own spies kept him closely informed of all that was happening and at this stage he knew that they had acquired all those items of the *éric* that would be of use to him in the forthcoming battle with the Fomorians. He also knew that they hadn't yet got the cooking spit or given the three shouts on the hill of Mokeen. So what did he do? Off with him up to the Brugh na Boinne where he got his books – and they weren't the kind that you or I would call books at all, but thin plates of wood about the size and shape of your hand and pointed at one end where they were held together by a spigot the way they could spread out like a fan – and started reading a spell that he sent after them over the sea from Ireland. And do you know what? Didn't that spell fall on them as they were sailing from Iora so that they forgot the rest of what they had to get and were filled with immense homesickness.

Now don't ask me what class of a spell it was that Lugh made, because I don't know. But it wouldn't surprise me at all if they were homesick anyway after all that work and that Lugh might have been cunning enough to send some persuasive messenger out to them telling them 'twas all right to come home. Anyway that's what they did; and it so happened that when the Wavesweeper came up the Boyne again, Lugh was beyond with Nuada at the great fair on the *faitche* before the city of Tara, as they now called it. (It used to be called Cathair Cro-fionn when the Firbolg had it.) He wasn't long learning that the sons of Tuireann had landed below. And what did he do then? He left the fair and, without telling anyone, went into the fort inside the city, the fort of Cathair Cro-fionn, and closed the mighty gates and doors behind him. There he armed himself in the armour of Mananaan and the cloak of the daughter of Fleas and waited.

Not long after, the three sons of Tuireann were seen approaching the fair. When they were recognised, the word went round and the whole multitude flocked out to meet them, gazing in wonder at what they had brought and, naturally, welcoming them home. Nuada himself went out to greet them and asked if they had fulfilled the *éric*.

'Look around you,' said Brian, 'and see for yourself. Now, can you tell us where Lugh is so that we can give it to him?'

'Well,' said Nuada, looking round too, 'he was here a minute ago, so he can't be too far off. I'll send for him.' The whole great fair of Tara was searched for Lugh without finding him.

'I know what it is,' said Brian, 'he's after learning that we've come back with these wonderful weapons that even he couldn't stand against and he's barricaded himself inside one of the castles of Tara for fear we'd attack him, or gone back to his own place maybe.'

Eventually messengers found out where Lugh was and told him that the sons of Tuireann had come back with the *éric* he wanted and were ready to give it to him. But Lugh wouldn't trust them. The answer he sent back was that the fine should be given to Nuada to hold in trust for him. So the sons of Tuireann did that, turning the wonderful treasures they had won over to King Nuada there on the great lawn before the palace of Tara, keeping only for themselves their own arms. And Nuada sent a messenger to Lugh telling what they had done.

And when Lugh was satisfied that all had been done as he wanted he came himself and inspected everything closely. Then he stood back and put his two hands on his hips and said: 'Indeed, yes, this is an *éric* great enough to pay for anyone who was ever killed, and for anyone who ever will be killed until the end of time. But, nevertheless and notwithstanding that it is great and tremendous and many times over great, there is one fine that must be paid in full to the very last . . .' and he looked at the three sons of Tuireann, who looked back at him in puzzlement at this strange speech, wondering what he was getting at. 'That is an *éric* fine,' continued Lugh, 'from which it is not lawful to hold back even the smallest part.'

And he looked from the sons of Tuireann to Nuada and back again. And King Nuada nodded in agreement, and Brian said: 'Well, and is it not the case that you have the full *éric* here before you?'

But Lugh went on as if he hadn't heard a word and he said: 'Moreover, you, King Nuada, and the King Bodhbh Dearg and the people of the Tuatha de Danaan are the guarantee that my full fine will be paid. Therefore while I see here the apples, the skin of the pig, the blazing spear, the chariot and the steeds, the seven pigs, and the hound pup . . .' and then he paused and looked at the three sons of Tuireann and said, 'where, sons of Tuireann, is the cooking spit of Fincara, and I did not hear that you gave three shouts on the hill of Mokeen.'

When they heard this, the sons of Tuireann were put out entirely and were overcome with a weakness, for they had thought – whatever the reason for it – that they had paid the whole fine. And now here was Lugh telling them they hadn't. When they recovered they said nothing to anyone but left the fair and went straight to their father's castle at Howth. When they told all this to their father and Eithne, their sister, and that, though they thought they were finished and safe and had completed the *éric*, they now had to set off again on another voyage, the joy of their parent and their sister at their safe return was turned to sadness and bitterness.

So they spent the night with their father and sister and next day the three brothers prepared to set off in their own ship, for they no longer had the benefit of the Wavesweeper to take them wherever they wished to go. And this was a great handicap. And no longer did they have the magic protection and power of the blazing spear or any of the other great things that they had already recovered. So it was as if they were setting off alone for the first time again.

They sailed out of wide Dublin Bay with the hill of Howth on the one hand and Wicklow Head on the other, and made across the loud, murmuring sea in search of the island of Fincara. Three months they spent wandering the endless ocean, finding landfall here and there on one island and another, but never found the least information about Fincara. Until, at last, in a very distant place, they met an old man; old, old and toothless and almost eyeless, and these were hidden deep in his head with folds of flesh about them like the shell of a walnut. And he told them that when he was young he had indeed heard of this island of Fincara, and added that he wasn't one bit surprised that they hadn't been able to find it for, unlike any other island, it did not lie on the surface of the ocean, but was deep down beneath the seething waters, where it had been sunk in times long past because of a spell put on it by a vengeful magician.

So Brian put on his diving suit and his helmet of clear glass and, telling his brothers to wait until he came back, he leaped over the side of the ship and sank from sight. It is said that he was half a month stalking the salty and mountainous rocky floor of the undulating ocean, seeking the island of Fincara before ever he found it. And when he did he was astonished to find that when he set foot on it he needed his diving suit and helmet no longer and, moreover, to see that it contained many houses and a great palace nobler than any he had ever seen. And it was to this that he immediately hurried. Reaching it he found that it was open and unlocked, and within were a group of very beautiful women engrossed in womanly pursuits of needlework and embroidery around a table in the centre of which, incongruously, was a cooking spit.

Seeing it, Brian walked straight through the group of women, picked up the spit and turned and walked towards the door again. While he was doing so not one of the women spoke or moved, but each of them had her eyes fixed on him from the moment that he entered, admiring his manly bearing and fearlessness. But when he started to walk off with the spit they could contain themselves no longer and burst out laughing. One of them said: 'We know who you are, Brian, and you are a brave man to attempt what you are doing. But even if your two brothers were with you now, the weakest of us – and there are a hundred and fifty of us here – could by herself prevent the three of you from taking the spit. Nevertheless,' she went on, 'because you are so brave and courageous as to make the attempt knowing the danger, and because you are a fine-looking man who has stirred our admiration, we will permit you to take it since we have many more. But there is a condition.'

THE SONS OF TUIREANN

'What's that?'

'You must remain here with us for a little while, for our pleasure, and do all you can to please as many of us as you may.'

So Brian stayed with them for a while, thanking them as best he could, and asking them if they'd like him to summon his brothers so that they could thank them too. But they said 'no', that his thanks were sufficient. So then he made his farewells and returned to the surface of the turbulent sea to find Uar and Uraca. They had stayed in the same place while Brian was away fearing that if they moved they would lose him for good. And after the two weeks and four days that he was gone they were about to draw the anchor and set their sails to leave fearing that he was dead when they saw the shimmering glitter of his glass helmet rising up towards them from the bosom of the waves.

And when he reached the surface and waved at them with a hand that clutched the cooking spit, they were overjoyed. So Brian rested for a while in the boat, for he was considerably tired, and told them everything – well, almost everything – that had happened. And when they had eaten, for the brothers had been catching fish most of the time, they knew that the time had come for them to set out to give the three shouts on the hill of Mokeen, and they also knew that this was most likely to be their most difficult task. They fetched the prow of the ship round until it pointed north and sailed off on a tack with the westerly wind until finally they saw the green hill of Mokeen rising smooth and lofty from the shores of the sea. But also there was Mokeen himself, who saw them before they saw him, and he knew at once who they were and what they were coming for and he waded into the green and black, the broken and frothy sea, and shouted out to them: ''Twas you killed my friend and my foster-brother Cian. Now you've come here to fulfil the *éric* that Lugh has put upon you, to give a shout upon this hill. But I can tell you that when you come you will meet not the opportunity to give shouts, but your deaths. For there's no way you will leave these shores alive.'

When Brian heard these words he was consumed with an almighty rage and leaped from the boat and charged through the tumbling surf towards Mokeen. And the two great warriors attacked each other with great ferocity. Of such magnitude was their onslaught on each other that it can be compared only to the roaring fury of two great bears destroying the forest or the laceration of lions or the awesome conflict of great and barbarous beasts from unknown lands, until at length Mokeen fell dead. And with that the three sons of Mokeen came out to do battle with the three sons of Tuireann.

And then a fight began that surpassed all the fights that ever were or ever were told of. So immense was the noise of this great battle that the very waves retreated from the edge of the mountain, curling back in terror. The mountain itself, across whose face they struggled and battled and spilled each other's blood, split and sundered and poured forth the fire of its heart so that the sky blackened with smoke and the smoke reddened with flame. If a man were in the east as far as the Hesperides, or in the west as far as the world's end, he would stop whatever he was at in wonder and fear and say that the gods were in dispute beyond the margin of the world amongst themselves.

For three days they fought and shook the mountain with their stamping feet, clashing shields, and whistling weapons. And at the end of that time the three sons of Mokeen put their bitter, leaf-shaped spears, held by their heavy iron shafts hissing through the bodies of the three sons of Tuireann. But this brought neither fear nor weakness to the three heroes, for as the three sons of Mokeen thrust with their spears, so did the sons of Tuireann and they in turn put their spears through the tired and battle-weary sons of Mokeen, who then fell dead on the battlefield in front of them. Then there was a great silence.

The battle-fury of the three brothers faded and they stood wearily, surveying the scene of their combat for a moment. And as the silence thickened and fell upon them, they, too, fell to the ground by themselves, lying there on the blood-stained grass. They remained there for three days, neither moving nor speaking, as if they themselves were dead. Darkness veiled their eyes and it was only their great strength and endurance and the hardiness of their bodies that enabled them to survive the wounds they'd received.

Brian was the first to revive and, seeing his brothers lying there, he called to them and asked; 'Are you all right?'

With one voice the other two answered: 'We must be dead, or as near to it as makes little difference.'

Brian struggled to his knees and then to his feet and leaned upon his spears and said: 'Get up the two of you, my poor brothers, and let us make the three shouts on the hill before death claims us all.'

But they were unable to rise. So Brian gathered one under one arm and the other under another, and with all his remaining strength lifted them even as his own life's blood flowed in rivers from him, and standing where they were they raised three feeble shouts on the very hill of Mokeen that Mokeen and his three sons had done all they could to deny them. Then, with Brian still supporting them, they staggered to their ship and on board. Then they turned the prow as best they could south towards Ireland and fell back on the deck.

For days the ship moved listlessly across the ocean, with no guidance but its own. But all the time it drifted south in the direction of Ireland. While they were still far off Brian lifted his head and looked across the sea to the west and cried: 'There, there I see the hill of Howth and the very castle of our father rising beyond, above the sea.'

Uar, who lay still on the deck because he had no strength to lift himself, cried: 'Brian, if only we could see them once it would make little difference after that if we lived or died. So on your honour and of your love for us, lift us so that we may see.' Then Uar and Uraca sang this lament:

> Lift us, Brian, to lie on your breast,
> Son of our father, generous and strong
> Torch of Valour, let us rest
> Against your shoulder, to gaze upon
> The gentle land of Ireland across the sea.
> Let us look, oh soldier, hero,
> On Usna, Tailteann and noble Tara,
> Dublin and that smooth Boyne we knew
> And shared in happy youth with you.
> If only we see Howth beyond
> With Castle Tuireann to the north
> We'd welcome death as a fond
> Release from pain with our last breath.

And that was the first and almost – but not quite – the last poem ever made by Uar and Uraca.

So Brian did his best and he raised them up with a poem of his own:

> How sad, brave sons of my brave father,
> For birds could nest where I draw breath.
> Yet that is not what makes me suffer,
> But that you both are close to death.

And Uar and Uraca whispered:

> We would prefer that death would take us,
> Brian, son of Tuireann, our brother,
> Than to see your wounds make pus
> And you without doctors to cure you.
> Since there are none here to do it
> Miach or Omiach or Diancecht,
> 'Tis tragic, Brian – who suspected no deceit –
> To have parted with the pigskin of Tuis.

Then, as the ship drifted into the harbour of Dublin, with his last remaining strength Brian lifted them so that they could see Howth as they passed under its craggy slopes. Slowly and in great pain the three brothers made their way to the castle of their father. And Brian called out as soon as they were close enough:

'Father, here is the spit. Take it and go to Lugh as quickly as possible and tell him that we have given the three shouts on the hill of Mokeen. Tell him we have now paid the *éric* in full and ask him for the apples from the Garden of the Hesperides, otherwise we will surely die.'

But Tuireann answered with great sadness:

> If the jewels of the world, south and north,
> Were offered to Lugh to ease his wrath
> They'd not suffice, my sons, to save
> You from the sepulchre and the grave.

The three brothers answered with one voice:

> We are one in flesh and blood
> To Lugh, son of Cian, son of Cainnte;
> He'll not deny us now to death,
> Even though we killed his father,
> Oh, don't delay, set out at once,
> Nor be long in your return,
> For if you are you will not find us
> Alive, but for the burial urn.

So Tuireann mounted his chariot and went at a gallop with the sods of the earth rising high behind him from under the racing hooves to the great city of Tara so that when he arrived his horses were covered in lather and sweat that flew about them like foam. There he found Lugh and he gave him the cooking spit and told him what his sons had said. 'They've now paid the fine in full, but are mortally wounded and will die unless you give the magic apples or the pigskin to cure them.' But Lugh turned away and coldly refused him. So Tuireann returned to his three sons greatly saddened and told them what had happened.

Then Brian, in spite of his weakness, said: 'Take me with you to Tara and let me see him and perhaps then he will relent and save us.' So Tuireann laid him in his chariot and drove hastily back to Tara and again they went to Lugh. But even when Brian, on death's doorstep, begged for the skin to save himself and his brothers, Lugh said: 'I would not give it not if you offered me the breadth of the entire world of red gold. I would not give it unless I thought your deaths would follow. You killed my father cruelly and with nothing less than your own deaths will I be satisfied.'

So, then, having done what they could to persuade the Il-Dana to relent, Brian and his father returned to Castle Tuireann where Uar and Uraca lay, the life's blood ebbing from them. And Brian lay down between them and, as soon as he did so, the three of them gave a united sigh and their lives departed from all three at the same time. Then Tuireann and his daughter Eithne stood together above the three heroes and hand in hand sang a lament for their own dead. When they had done so Tuireann and Eithne were so grief-stricken themselves that they fell beside the bodies of the three heroes and died with them, and all five were interred in the one grave. And that is the tragic history of the three sons of Tuireann.

The Children of Lír

First Period: Mythological Cycle

This story begins after the battle of Tailteann and therefore concerns a much older period than that of 'Deirdre', which relates to the Knights of the Red Branch and the people of Ulster about the first century. But its setting is not so old as that of the 'Sons of Tuireann', which is set in the time of the first coming of the Celtic peoples to Ireland, variously estimated, but generally believed to be about the year 800 BC. 'The Children of Lír' is a romantic and tragic story which demonstrates and, I believe, is intended to demonstrate, the decline of the Tuatha de Danaan before the power of the Milesians.

As we have noted, the principal peoples of the early migrations are identified as being the Tuatha de Danaan who were succeeded by the Milesians, from whom descended the Gaelic people. The Milesians took over the country from the Tuatha de Danaan following Tailteann. Because of the subsequent division of spheres of influence – the allocation of spiritual powers to the de Danaan and material rule to the Milesian newcomers – some authorities argue that the de Danaan was simply a name referring to a post-mortem spirit existence. But this seems too neat and too dismissive both of mythological tradition and the comprehensive implications of the name itself, 'People of Dana', to be acceptable without more substantial evidence than conjectural support of a broader theory.

An equally strong case, and one that accommodates tradition, may be made for the existence of the Tuatha de Danaan as real precursors of the Milesians, absorbed by the newcomers who, in turn, adopted the beliefs of their predecessors. The 'battle' of Taileann might as easily have been a victory on the sports field as on the battlefield, thus accounting for traditional attitudes as well as the Tailteann games that survived in one form or another into this century. 'The Children of Lír' is set in the period after the Milesian victory and belongs to the true other-worldly species of mythological tale, which may have contributed to the view mentioned above. It also provides a link with Christianity which is clearly a later suffix and one that demonstrates the third, and most extreme, example of such later reconciliations. The others may be found in 'The Vengeance of Mesgedra' and 'Oisín'. It shares with 'The Wooing of Emer' an additional interest, namely that they both have a character named Aoife (Eve) who brings evil or trouble on the world.

The battle of Tailteann was fought so long ago that no one now could tell you very much about it save its name and location, and about those they might even be doubtful. And, indeed, it is not known whether the battle of Tailteann (at the Fair of Tailteann, a place of meeting every year for the Tuatha de Danaan, where the great games, patterned on those across on the Corinthian isthmus, were held and continued to be held for generations) was of blood and carnage and death and destruction on the jagged battlefield, or of honoured and symbolic victory on the sculptured field of sport. Who knows?

What is known is that at Tailteann the Milesians were victorious over the de Danaan. And it is known too, that there was a great horse-race between a princess of the de Danaan and a princess of the Milesians for the honour and glory of each of their people. Furthermore it is known that it was at this time that Amergin, the great Milesian poet, made this poem that spoke from the heart of the world out of the mouth of a man:

> I am the Wind of the Sea,
> The Wave of the Mighty Ocean;
>
> I am the Roar of the Tide,
> The Bull of Seven Combats;
>
> I am the Hawk on the cliff,
> The sacred Dew on the grass;
>
> I am the loveliest Flower,
> The bold Boar of valour;
>
> I am the speckled salmon,
> The lake in the plain;
>
> I am Poetry and Wisdom,
> The deadly edge of weapons;
>
> I am He who makes Fire for a king.
>
> Who will soften the mountainous crags?
> Who tell the ages of the Moon?
>
> Who knows the resting place of the Sun?
>
> Who the god that makes limitless boundaries?
>
> Mystery in Deaths! Mystery in the Moving Wind.
>
> I!

128

Whatever the means, the Milesians, who fled Miletus in Ionia before the onslaught of Cyrus, brought with them the modern wonders of the eastern world and overcame the Tuatha de Danaan, wresting from them the lordship of Ireland. But even though they were victorious over them, they held the Tuatha de Danaan in high esteem for their knowledge, wisdom and command of mysteries. Meanwhile, they themselves took over the duties of administering the country.

As time passed and the Milesians, their minds turned to the future and its development, became more powerful, exercising their lordship over the world actively and vigorously, the Tuatha de Danaan, themselves once so powerful and mighty, withdrew into a world of mystery and of imagination, of wisdom and accumulated lore, of the half-light and the half-world, where they were their own lords and masters. And it was in that way that each side, Milesians and Tuatha de Danaan, allowed the other to take what was of least importance to itself and gained from the other what was of most importance to itself. It was a very sensible arrangement; and if more of the people of the world when they are facing each other in confrontation had the wit to make concessions with the same spirit and wisdom, the wars and disputes and deaths and mutilations that ravage it might be less. In any case what the de Danaan did was to retire from the seen world of men, which the Milesians now ruled with efficiency, and develop their skills as druids and magicians and people of the spirit, so that in no time at all they ruled on a much higher plane a world that was parallel to but separate from that inhabited by the Milesians. And because they had the wisdom and the ability to do this, and because that impressed the Milesians, the Tuatha de Danaan were given great honour and reverence by the Milesians who acknowledged their superiority in this field.

But long before that, when the Tuatha de Danaan still strode royally on the surface of Ireland, but yet after the defeat, whatever it might have been, at Taillte, their leaders from the five quarters of Ireland assembled to choose a king to rule them. (And you might think it a strange thing to say the five quarters of all Ireland, and in normal circumstances you would be right. But in ancient Ireland there was always another place close to our own – which perhaps explains what the de Danaan were later able to do as mentioned above – and that is the existence between the bark and the tree; between air and water; between cloud and mountain; between man and . . . what? But it is a true fact that the kingdom of Meath in the centre and heart of Ireland was such a place without dimension and became the mystical fifth fifth or the fifth kingdom of Ireland, which had four other kingdoms of substance – Ulster, Munster, Leinster and Connacht.) The reason for this was that they recognised that it would be to their advantage to have a single king like the Milesians, rather than numerous kings who were rivals amongst themselves. So that was decided. And of all their chiefs there were five only from whom the new king would be chosen. They were the greatest and most respected leaders amongst them and were also the wisest and most respected.

There was a time when the de Danaan did have such a king, namely Eochaidh Ollamh (Yoghee Ullav, Eochaidh the Wise, the All-Father), who was also known as the Dágda (Dawgdah, Father of the Gods), who had been their king and ruler and oracle for many years. But Eochaidh had been wounded so severely at the second battle of Moytura that he died shortly afterwards, and that was no surprise because who was it who wounded him but Caitlin, the fearsome sorceress wife of Balor himself. Now Eochaidh's sons were Aengus Óg (Ayngus Ogue, Young Aengus or Mac-Óg, Young son) and the Bodhbh Dearg (Bove Darrug, the Red Healer), the King of Connacht. Aengus lived in his palace at Brugh na Boinne which he had inherited from Eochaidh Ollamh. And the curious thing about Aengus was that he didn't want to be king at all, but just wanted to stay at Brugh na Boinne where he could continue studying the lore and wisdom of people, in which he was the most illustrious of all. The other candidates for the kingship were Ilbreach of Assaroe, Midir the Proud of Brí Leith and King Lír of Sídhe Fionna (Shee Fee-unna). And it is with that man, King Lír, that our story properly begins.

These five candidates were excluded from the conclave of the chiefs of the de Danaan when they considered who would be elected king. And at last they decided that the most suitable would be the Bodhbh Dearg (whose kingdom had been ravaged by the Fomorians on other occasions when Lugh Lamh Fada came to help him), for after all he was the son of the Dágda. When the result was known everyone was happy at this choice – except for one man. And that was King Lír of Sídhe Fionna, a touchy sort of man with a very thin skin, who took the election of someone else as a personal offence. So sure was he that nobody but himself would have been elected that when the result became known he was consumed with anger and frustration. When the announcement was made what did he do but rise up out of his seat at the assembly blazing with white anger and made his way straight out without speaking to anyone, good or bad, or showing any mark of respect to his new king.

Now I needn't tell you, and you won't be surprised, that that kind of behaviour didn't go down too well with the other chiefs, who were angered and wanted to send an army after Lír to Sídhe Fionna (a place in the County Monaghan near Newtownhamilton) to put some manners on him for his bad behaviour. But the Bodhbh Dearg was a generous and wiser man. 'Listen to me,' he said, 'and think before you act. Lír is a powerful and embittered man. If you send an army against him you may be sure he'll defend his territory and many will be killed on both sides. Is that what you want? Let me point out that if that were to happen the end result would not make me any more your king than I am now, or make him any more submissive than he is now.' The wisdom of this impressed the de Danaan lords, and confirmed them in the rightness of their choice of the Bodhbh Dearg as king, and matters were allowed to rest so for a while. And after that the Bodhbh Dearg ruled over the de Danaan from his own palace at Killaloe, while Lír, in isolation and bitterness, lived with his own people at Sídhe Fionna.

'Twas a lonely stand he was after taking and not a sinner of the Tuatha de Danaan other than his own people would see him or associate with him or have anything to do with him at all. And, of course, he grew more and more bitter with every day that passed. And in the middle of all that when things seemed that they could get no blacker, didn't a new misfortune strike him? His wife, to whom he had been devoted all his life and who was his solace and his companion in his isolation, died suddenly after an illness that lasted only three days. She was a young – well, young enough – and beautiful woman, much respected throughout the country and her death was mourned by all the de Danaans when they heard of it.

When the Bodhbh Dearg heard the sad news he was moved to compassion at this new misfortune of Lír's. 'At such a time,' he told his court, 'a man needs what friendship he can get. And as we all know Lír has been isolated at Sídhe Fionna from the rest of us for too long and has been a stranger from the warm hand of friendship. We could help him now if he'd accept it.' Then he expressed the thought that had been forming in his mind since he heard the news about Lír's wife. 'You all know that I am foster-father of the three daughters of Ailill, King of Aran, Niamh, Aoife and Albha (Neeav, Eefa, Olva), the most accomplished and most beautiful women in Ireland. It seems to me that Lír would be a foolish man indeed if he spurned my offer of friendship now in his hour of sadness and loneliness.'

The people of the de Danaan were very impressed by this new evidence of their king's wisdom, no less than by his warmth and generosity. And so heralds were sent to Lír, taking with them the message that if he would submit (as he should long since have done) to the Bodhbh Dearg, the king would offer him one of his three foster-daughters as a new wife, together with his continued friendship.

Now you may be surprised to learn that Lír was very pleased by this message. He'd got over his annoyance at not being elected king himself and had felt isolated for too long. Moreover, an alliance of this kind, both in friendship and by ties of marriage with the king, was not to be lightly rejected. So he set out for Killaloe the day after he received the message with a small retinue of only fifty chariots. It was just as well they took the best of their horses and some spares with them, for they neither stopped other than to change horses and maybe snatch a bite to eat, nor turned aside on their journey from Sídhe Fionna until they reached the palace of the Bodhbh Dearg at Killaloe. They were greeted warmly for everyone was happy to see the breach in the ranks of the de Danaan healed. Lír acknowledged the Bodhbh Dearg as king, and that night the reunion was celebrated with a great banquet.

(Now, before we go any further with this story, which is now about to begin properly, it might be no harm to explain that there are many notions of how the Tuatha de Danaan achieved that name. The reason that nobody is sure about it is that the name is so old that it echoes down the corridors of time and is lost in the swirling mists of the ancient past. There are those who believe that the people brought it with them from the eastern world where they had their origin. And there are others who say that they are named from the three sons of Tuireann, Brian, Uar and Uraca, by the goddess Dana, who were known as 'tuatha', or 'sorcerers', because they were skilled in wisdom and magic. But, of course, 'tuatha' also means 'a people'. And, again, there are those who say they were so called because they were three distinct tribes. But that seems a fanciful notion. Then again there are those who say that they were one people of three parts or three estates – such as we are today. Indeed, man has not changed very much for all the time he's been here to think. And the first estate was that of leaders and nobility, for 'tuath' by itself means 'lord'; and the second estate was that of the 'de', or spiritual leaders, druids and magicians; and the third estate, the 'Dan', were the artificers and craftsmen. And, so 'tis said, it was the representatives of these three estates that were there with the Bodhbh Dearg at Killaloe to greet Lír when he came to submit. On the other hand, of course, there are those who say they got their name from the followers of the goddess Dana, and maybe they have the right of it.)

Whether or which, on the following day Lír presented himself before the Bodhbh Dearg who sat with his queen. Beside them were their foster-daughters, Niamh, Aoife and Albha. And the Bodhbh Dearg said: 'Of my three, beautiful foster-daughters, Lír, you may take your choice. And whichever you choose, she will be your wife.'

Lír looked at them with wonder. They were all beautiful; none was more beautiful than the other. Niamh, the eldest, had the beauty of winter. Her hair was dark as the trees of the forest at that time of the year and her skin was as white as the snow about their feet that stretches, smooth and gentle, above the bones of the earth. Her eyes were dark and sparkling, like the frosted night, and her body was as beautiful and slender and well shaped as a doe in November. Aoife, the second daughter, was like the beauty of autumn. Her hair was russet with the glint of gold in it and her skin was the colour of rich cream. Her two deep eyes were hazel with green flecks, and her form soft and voluptuous with the ripeness of youth. The third sister, Albha, had all the light and airy beauty of spring; young and fresh and fair. (But, although she was all that any man could want in the way of a wife, she has no further part in this story so it is enough to say that she was as beautiful as her sisters in her own way and leave it thus.)

Not only were the three sisters beautiful, they were also charming and witty and intelligent, and Lír found it impossible to choose one before the other. So that being the case he said: 'They are all beautiful. And for me to try to select one above another is impossible . . .' (And in saying this he showed more sense than his Greek cousin, Paris, who, when he found himself in a similar predicament, lacked the common sense not to make a judgement.) 'So,' continued Lír, 'the proper thing for me to do would be to take the eldest who will make a fitting wife for any chief of the de Danaan, and there can be no quarrel with that.'

Of course the Bodhbh Dearg agreed and plans for the marriage were made forthwith. And before Lír left to return to his own place the wedding took place and was celebrated. And that celebration lasted a month. After that Lír and his new wife returned to Sídhe Fionna where there was another celebration and wedding feast to which all the nobles and kings of Ireland were invited. They were a happy couple and calm and tranquillity reigned over the whole of Ireland now that the differences between Lír and the Bodhbh Dearg had been put to rest. In due time they had two children, a boy and a girl, and they were called Finola (Finn-Ohla) and Aedh (Ay). They were fine healthy children who grew fat and pink in the *grianaan* of the castle until they were a year old. Then their mother again gave birth, this time to twins, who were called Fiachra (Feeucra) and Conn. But with the birth of these two sons also came a great unhappiness, for Niamh died in her labour and, for a second time in his life, Lír had neither a wife to love or be loved by. He himself nearly died of grief and anguish and had it not been for his children, whom he loved dearly (even those who lesser men might feel were responsible for the death of his beloved Niamh), he would surely have done himself a mortal injury.

When news of the tragedy came to the Bodhbh Dearg his own grief was hardly less than that of Lír, and for a fortnight the whole of Killaloe was thrown into a turmoil of despair and mourning for his foster-daughter. After that the Bodhbh Dearg said to his people: 'In the midst of the great loss and terrible sorrow with which we have been afflicted I have, nevertheless, had time to think that Lír's affliction is even greater than our own, for Niamh was like his shadow, or his right arm, or his unspoken thought. So, in order to bring him back to full life again, and to strengthen the ties that now exist between us, I propose to give him Niamh's sister, Aoife, for his new wife.'

Again messengers went to Lír to tell him of the king's decision. And Lír received the news they brought with a mixture of affection and sadness. He appreciated deeply the Bodhbh Dearg's nobility of mind, but he was sad because he had loved Niamh so deeply and was so sorely affected by her loss. But he also recognised the merit and virtues of the Bodhbh Dearg's proposal, and after a short while he went to Killaloe where he and Aoife were married with great ceremony before returning to Sídhe Fionna.

Now it might be thought that Aoife would resent Lír's remembered love for her sister, and harbour a grudge against him, or her niece and nephews on that account; but if you did you would be wrong especially when, as the years went by, it became evident that she was not blessed with fecundity and was unable to have children of her own. But it was not a problem that troubled her greatly, if at all, at this time, for she loved not only her husband but also his children and those of her sister, to whom she gave the same love that she would have given her own had she been able to have them. She surrounded them with love and tenderness that seemed to increase with each and every day that the sun returned to the world.

They were glorious children, beautiful and intelligent and lively; gentle and gracious. Because of this they were known by the whole people of the de Danaan, who also loved them and were captivated by them and their gentleness (a quality rare enough in many children nowadays, probably due to the fact that it is even rarer in their elders). The Bodhbh Dearg himself loved them with the deep and interesting love of a grandfather, and went frequently to Sídhe Fionna to visit them and shower them with gifts, so that when he was not thinking of going there the thought that was in his mind was of bringing them to Killaloe where he could enjoy their liveliness and wonder.

As the years passed Lír's love and affection for his children increased and deepened as he himself felt the years advancing on him. And it was a very pleasant thing to see, the love of this kingly father encompassing his children and being returned with joy and brightness. The four children slept in their own sleeping booths not too far from where he slept himself, and he developed the habit of leaving his bed before the dawn of the day at the end of the night, and going to them to be with them and play with them and talk to them before the duties of the day started. But it was his very delight in and love for his children that was to bring sorrow in its train.

Perhaps it was that she felt the years of her youth dwindling, or perhaps she unknowingly experienced the deep womanly ache in her body for children of her own before the time was reached when that would be impossible for her. Whatever it was it is impossible to say, but, as time went by, and Aoife perceived her step-children receiving such attention from Lír and from all the others in his castle, she began to imagine that she herself was being neglected on their account – which, of course, was untrue. But that false notion assumed the weight of truth in her mind. A tiny splinter of unreasoning jealousy entered her heart and from then on she was watchful for things which would feed it and make it grow. Suspicion provides its own reasons and envy provides its own logic and it was no long time before the love that she had felt and lavished on the children turned increasingly to alienation and then to hatred, which gorged on the children's obvious delight at the world and everyone else's happiness to see it. So powerful were these feelings, and so strong her jealousy, that it made her ill. And ill, not just in her mind, which had become warped by the obsession, but in her body too, for she allowed the torment to affect that. For a full year she took to her bed, full of bitterness and brooding, weak of a sickness that neither physician nor druid could account for. Her character, and even her visage, altered and changed and with them her speech. And both her way of talking and her appearance were attributed to this sickness of body for which there appeared to be no remedy . . . since none, other than herself, knew what was gnawing within her. Her personal bodyguard, Conán (Coe-nawn) took up his position outside her door and seldom left it except to eat or for other personal matters, and when he did so three other members of her guard took his place.

Lír, who had already lost two wives, was greatly worried and devoted a great deal of attention to her. But even this did not make Aoife feel better. On the contrary, it fed her desolation because she believed that he was doing it from nothing but pity. At the end of that year during which she lay in her darkened room, brooding and thinking, she came to a fearful decision. She rose from her bed and left her room and let everybody see and think that she was well again. Then she called the children to her – a thing she hadn't done for many months – and told them that, in order to celebrate her recovery, she would take them to visit their foster-grandfather at Killaloe. Of course they were overjoyed, both at her recovery and at the prospect of visiting the Bodhbh Dearg.

The three boys were particularly delighted and cheered. But, when her first excitement passed, Finola went quiet and thoughtful. Subdued, she did not join in for she remembered a dark dream of foreboding she'd had the previous night, in which Aoife assumed a dreadful form and performed a number of unnameable acts against herself and her brothers. Not unnaturally the dream alarmed her and she was afraid that Aoife had an ulterior motive. Even though it was only a dream, she did not want to go with Aoife. But also because it was only a dream she was reluctant to speak of her fears in case of ridicule and in case she might be thought ungrateful. And so she was persuaded to go, but especially because she did not want her brothers to be exposed to anything that might happen without her being there to protect them.

They set out on a bright and sunny, but windy, day in Aoife's carriages and chariots with her personal servants and guards who'd come from her father's stronghold in Aran originally. Rounded white clouds with strange grey shapes at the centre and smooth faces and trailing ends hustled across the sky. After a while Aoife called her most trusted bodyguard, Conán, aside and spoke quietly to him.

'Conán,' she said, 'do you really love me or is it just that you are my bodyguard?'

'You know better than that,' Conán replied angrily. 'I came with you from your father's castle in Aran when you were only an infant and I have watched every hair of your head ever since in case any harm might come to you. Even when you were sick who was it that lay outside your door day and night?'

'Then you really do love me,' she asked, 'and would do anything for me?'

'There isn't a thing in the world I wouldn't do for you,' he said, 'great or small.'

'Good,' said Aoife. 'And if I was in any danger, or deprived, or suffering from a loss, what would you do about it?'

'No matter what,' he answered, 'even if I had to face numerous heroes on the battlefields of the world, I would do it to remove any suffering and restore any loss of yours.'

That answer satisfied her. 'Very good,' she nodded. 'Now listen to me. The love of my husband Lír is being stolen from me.'

Conán was astonished because he had seen them together and had never suspected anything of the kind. 'Glory be to the gods,' he replied. 'Is that so? Who is the woman? Tell me her name and it'll be the end of her.'

Aoife looked at him with hard eyes, measuring his loyalty and trying to see how he might react to what she was going to say. ''Tis no woman is stealing him from me in his own house,' she said slowly. 'It is nobody else but those children you see there before you. They have ruined me and destroyed me and blighted my life, and if you love me as you say you do, you will remove them and kill them out of my sight. I will reward you with whatever your heart may desire.'

But Conán looked at her in horror. And, when she saw that, rage and anger rose up in her for she could not understand that he would not agree with her. Since she knew she could do no wrong she felt that all things she might do were justifiable and so she raged at what she saw as his stupidity, but could do little about it. In his horror and distress Conán backed silently away from her and nothing more was said about it between them.

And so it was with each and every one of those others of her bodyguards and retainers that she approached. Every one of them refused, some with contempt, some with horror and some with a warning that nothing but evil and danger would follow from what she contemplated. Blinded as she was with hate and jealousy, she could not understand these attitudes, for Aoife now believed there was just cause for anything she might do. She warned those she approached not to speak among themselves, and they did not. But thereafter there was an atmosphere about the camp of mistrust, whispering and suspicion. So she sat there in her rage, biting her lip and looking out on the troubled waters, surrounded by her servants and retainers who looked aslant at her and murmured to themselves with worried faces.

She was seized with a sudden eruption of hatred when she saw the children playing and laughing by the lake shore and she snatched a sword herself and rushed out into the sunlight with it in her hand intending to kill them there and then; but something – perhaps her womanly nature, or maybe the fact that her retainers were all around her and some of them knew her intention – came between her and her hatred, and she stopped. She went back to her pavilion and ordered that they make ready to continue their journey. This was quickly and silently done and they continued until they came to the shores of Lough Derravarragh near the centre of Ireland, whose dark waters glinted dully like sun reflecting off iron. There they made another camp and while tents and pavilions were being erected others prepared a meal, still silent; still whispering.

Now the children, of course, knew nothing of what had been going on, for Aoife's bodyguards were all of her own people from Aran and would not betray her. So when Aoife came to them and took Fiachra and Conn by the hand and smiled at Finola and Aedh and suggested that they go to the lake and swim while they were waiting for their meal, they suspected nothing. With joyful cries they threw off their kingly clothes and ran into the water shouting and laughing. But as each one passed her, Aoife tapped them with a golden druidical wand and transformed them into four snow-white and mystified swans, who looked at each other in wonder as they floated at the margin of the lake. Then Aoife said:

> Now make your homes on Derravarragh's waves
> And with its noisy birds lament your fate.
> Your friends can search its crags and dusky caves
> In vain, now I have satisfied my hate.

Bewildered and frightened the swans fluttered this way and that way in the shallows of the lake, frantically trying to shake off their new prison of snow-white feathers, soft as a whispered pillow-word in appearance, but as final as the bars of a prison cell for the four children of Lír. At last they became tired and quietened down with the quietness of exhaustion, huddled together, frightened and pathetic, out on the dull lake water, where, to the dignity of all swans, they added the immeasurable sadness that descended on them as they began to understand the full extent of their plight.

The children felt the power of speech fading fast from them for often it was now intermingled with the harsh cry of the swans they had become, for this was in the days before the silent swan had come to Ireland, and with their failing power of speech Finola turned to their stepmother and spoke for them all.

'Oh, Aoife,' she cried, 'why did you do this terrible thing to us? All the love you showed us has been betrayed, and you have destroyed us without reason.' Here Finola paused because her speech was almost gone. But there was something more that she wanted to say, so in her failing voice she went on: 'Aoife, what you have done will cry out down the years until retribution at last reaches you. And beyond that 'twill be a mark of treachery amongst the people of Ireland. You know that your power is not as great as that of the Tuatha de Danaan. Their punishment, Aoife, will be terrible.'

Having said this, Finola put her wings around her three brothers and with their last remaining vestige of human speech they made this song together:

> You, who loved us in days now fled
> Down the vortex of sweet things, now dead;
> Who summoned up those old and horrid words
> In newborn hate, that wrought us into birds,
> Have cast aside the fostered love you bore
> And hurled us forth, from storm to stormy shore.

When the song was done Finola turned again to Aoife and asked: 'Tell us one more thing so that we may know when our misery will end. How long shall we be in the shape of swans?'

The smile that Aoife returned had nothing of pleasantry in it, but only malice. 'That is a question,' she said, 'you would have been wiser not to ask. But since you have I will tell you, and let it be a solace or a desolation to you as you wish. For three hundred years you will stay here on Lough Derravarragh.'

The four swans shuddered and looked at one another, but Aoife wasn't finished. 'You will spend another three hundred years on the cruel sea of Moyle between Ireland and Scotland,' she hissed. 'And after that three hundred years in Erris and Iris Domnann (Ir-ish Downan) on the western seas. Many years will you four swans fly from crag to ice water, and from stormy sea to bitter sedge until the union of Lairgnean (Lar-ig-nawn), a prince who will come out of the north, with Deichte (Detta), a princess of the south. You will remain swans until the Tailceann (Christian tonsure; a name applied to Saint Patrick) comes to Ireland from over the sea, bringing with him a new belief in the Word of God come to earth, and not by your own power, or by my power, or by the power of your friends, can you ever be free until that time comes.'

Then a very strange thing occurred. No sooner had Aoife spoken these bitter and harsh words than the venom and hatred that had poisoned her heart flew with them from her mouth and she was overcome with distress and – almost, but not quite – repentance and remorse for what she had done. 'Twas as if the very release of the words themselves unlocked also the bonds of the jealous hate that consumed her and dissipated it. Looking at the swans she cried: 'Oh, my dear children, what have I done? Since there is nothing now that I can do to alter your situation, I will do what little I can, and that is to enable you to keep your human speech. Moreover I promise that your voices will be so sweet that they will be more harmonious than any music ever heard in the world before. And it will lull to sleep all those who listen to it. In addition to that you will keep your own intelligence and will no longer be sad because you are swans.' Then she sang this song, and while she did so, Finola and her brothers felt and understood the powers of human speech returning to them.

> Fly from me you drifting swans
> And fill with music and ancient songs
> Derravarragh's wind-swept shore
> And coasts where endless ocean's roar;
> A thousand years will not seem long.

> Fly from me you gentle swans
> And make your home on the restless waves;
> Build your nest on the ocean's breast
> Drape yourself in its snow-white crest,
> Seek shelter in deep-bitten caves.

> Unhappy Lír, in grief and pain
> Your names may call across the world.
> His sundered heart will halt and fail –
> His empty hearth repeat the wail –
> On me his vengeance shall be hurled.

> Beyond the margins of an age
> Your agony no hand may cease
> Until across the narrowing sea
> Will come the Word of Him who'll be
> For all the succour and release.

Having done that Aoife, who now hardly knew what she was doing or where she was going, but felt torn by both remorse and the knowledge that she'd committed herself to an unalterable course, turned from the lakeside and ordered her horses yoked to her chariot. Her regret and anguish at the plight she left the four children in was genuine enough, but it was less than her anxiety to protect herself from the consequences of her action. So she left the four swans together on the lonely and solitary lake, swimming close to the shore, and turned her horses' heads towards Killaloe.

As the realisation of their unalterable plight overcame them their panic settled down and, in the midst of their own sorrow, they were overcome with grief at that which would afflict their father when he discovered what had happened. Thinking of that they made this song:

Bound to hardship and to torment here,
Our grief is doubled when we think of Lír
Scavenging the world with his tormented eyes,
Probing empty shadows; pursuing lies
In search of us, his children, wrenched from home
And now four swans on the tempestuous foam.
We face these darkened waters evermore
From friend and family lost on each cold shore.

Now, although Aoife's bitterness and vengeance had somewhat evaporated when she cast her magic on the four children of Lír, she knew she was still in the height of trouble. And, being the class of a woman that she was, that is no fool, she knew well that what she had done would come home to her one day. On the other hand, like a lot of us, she wasn't always too bright when she was in a fix. But, she wasn't what you might call a complete eejit either. She thought 'twould be a good idea to put the evil day off as long as possible – which is the way of women the world over when there's something unpleasant hanging around.

Anyway, when she got to the palace of the Bodhbh Dearg at Killaloe she was given a great welcome for, while the news of her sickness had gone before her, that of her recovery had not. Therefore her foster-father received her with great joy. But after he welcomed her what did he do only ask her why she hadn't brought the children with her.

Well, I needn't tell you, that question had been in Aoife's mind since she left Derravarragh and she had time to prepare her answer on the journey even though, as I say, she knew 'twould be found out in time. Women are women and most of them have a stubborn streak in them that keeps them pointed down the one road they're on no matter what direction it's going in, and when they have done something wrong their inclination is to brazen it out for as long as possible. And it sometimes works too, depending, I suppose, on how much of a fool the fellow they're trying to brazen it out with happens to be.

The Bodhbh Dearg was no fool. To cut a long story short, Aoife knew that she had no choice but to pile one lie on top of another as long as possible. 'The reason I didn't bring them is this: the old enmity that Lír had for you is still not extinguished. He has harboured resentment and envy of you all these years and now has turned openly against you, as he has turned against me,' she said. Then, as those who are sometimes afflicted as she was do, she continued by attributing her own feelings to Lír. 'He would not allow his children to come in case you might do them some harm.'

Naturally enough the Bodhbh Dearg was very astonished by this, for he knew very well that Lír knew that he loved those children as if they were really his grandchildren and not the children of his foster-child. 'That's very strange,' he mused. 'How could that be?'

As we know the Bodhbh Dearg wasn't easily deceived. He questioned Aoife more and more and the vagueness and discrepancy of her replies increased his uneasiness. From the way she behaved he suspected that there was something amiss, but had little idea of what it might be. So, secretly, he sent messengers to Sídhe Fionna to enquire after the children and ask that they might come to visit him with their stepmother. When these messengers arrived and gave the Bodhbh Dearg's message to Lír, he was naturally upset. 'What's this?' he asked. 'They left here to go to Killaloe with Aoife, and should be there now.' The messengers told him that Aoife had arrived and also what she had told the king. This upset and perplexed Lír extremely.

Of course Lír didn't know what to make of this. Hadn't he seen the children go off with their stepmother and where else would they be except at Killaloe? But here were these messengers from the Bodhbh Dearg telling him that not only were they not there, but that they had never arrived. He was a man quick enough to anger as we know and the first thing he did, of course, was to shout at the messengers that they were fools and liars and eejits, and when that didn't seem enough he proposed to have them taken outside where one of his retainers who was very persuasive and well practiced in the matter would remove their tongues out of their mouths altogether to prevent them from repeating similar offences, and maybe poke little bits of hot iron into their eyes too, that way they wouldn't be able to see what they shouldn't. But the two messengers were experienced men and they had met this kind of situation before.

At last they convinced him of the truth of what they said. But if they did that only made Lír worse for he could not understand why Aoife would say such a thing to the king. He'd given her all the love and affection and trust that he could and so far as he knew she had never lied to him or deceived him before – but then, of course, he didn't know it all. He remembered her inexplicable illness and in sudden shock it occurred to him that perhaps her mind had become deranged and that she might have murdered the children while in that condition. Distracted, he ordered his chariots south and, with whatever men he could, set out immediately to go to Killaloe, quartering the ground they covered on the way.

Eventually they reached Lough Derravarragh. And as they came over the hill that conceals it from the north, the four swans were drifting together and feeding just a short distance from the shore, where they were half hidden by a bank of wind-bent reeds. The cavalcade came over the hill above the lake and looked as if it was going to ride on, when Finola saw it. Instantly she began to sing with all the power of music and song that Aoife had left her:

Over the hilltop and down to the lake
Slowly and sadly the warriors make
A path through the heather and by the wild shore;
Tardy the wheels, now, of chariots that sped,
And heavy the feet of the soldiers who bore
Our parents past here when first they were wed.

Their hearts are dull, dull too their shields;
Dull their eyes that reap shorn fields,
The royal hosts of the de Danaan
Under skies of changing hue
Seeking us from dawn to dawn,
Who've found us here, and lost us too.

The music lapped over the lilting waves and encompassed the reeds and the
bushes, the trees and the hills in a web of magical notes so that Lír and his
followers halted in astonishment at the lakeside. Lír himself walked to his knees
into the water, his heart racing, for he knew that what he saw and heard was of
immense significance to him. Nervously he spoke to the swans, asking them how
it was that they could speak.

'Oh, father,' cried Finola, 'do you not know us?'

Lír staggered and almost fell, and Finola went on: 'It is I, Finola, and these are
Aedh and Conn and Fiachra —'

'In the name of the gods . . .' stammered Lír.

'We have been changed into what you see,' went on Finola, 'and ruined by
the hatred and witchcraft of Aoife, your own wife, our aunt and stepmother.'

Lír fell to his knees, there in the water, and three great circles of grief and
lamentation such as the lake had never heard arose from him. He beat the frothy
water with his hands. Tears flowed from his eyes. He gasped for breath and
looked as if he would lose his reason and become a demented person. But the
four swans drifted towards him and stretched out their elegant necks and after a
while he became calmer and was able to ask them: 'What must I do to restore
you to your proper shapes?'

'There is nothing anyone can do,' answered Finola. 'For three times three
hundred years and longer we must be locked into this form, until Lairgnean
from the north and Deichte from the south are united under a new faith from
the east.'

Then Lír and all his people again raised shouts of lamentation. Their grief was
lifted by the wind and carried across the face of Ireland until the trees bent
beneath it and the waves beating her shores receded from it. At Killaloe the
Bodhbh Dearg heard the moan in the sky and looked up in unease, knowing it

portended nothing good. This continued for minutes until Lír raised his hand, and all were silent again. And that silence was like the dropping of snow after the thunder of their grief. So then Lír said to Finola: 'At least you have your speech and your reason, so you can can come and live with us at Sídhe Fionna as if you still had your own forms.'

'No, father,' she cried, 'that is impossible too. It is part of the spell binding us that we must stay here on this lake for three hundred years and can no longer live with human people. It is true that Aoife has allowed us to keep our reason and our speech and that we have the power to make music so sweet that those who hear it will never want any other happiness. But here we must stay, for here we are bound.'

So Lír and all his followers stayed there that night and the four swans, his children, sang and made music which had the effect of calming Lír and his people and soothing their worries and cares as they listened and drifted into gentle sleep. Then, as dawn threaded its way through the night from the east, Lír came to the water's edge and told his children that he must leave in order to find Aoife.

Broken the heart in my bonded breast
That I must leave you children here
Far from where your heads sought rest;
Far from the empty halls of Lír.

I curse the day that I first saw
Aoife's smiling face that screened
A cruelty no love could thaw
Like poison in a cup concealed.

I know no rest, I know no sleep,
For through the never-ending night
I glimpse the children I would keep
Forever in my fading sight.

Finola, daughter of my heart,
Proud Aedh, than whom was none more bold,
Fiachra, gentler than the hart,
And little Conn – more dear than gold –

Oh, here on Derravarragh's shore
Trapped by Aoife's evil power . . .
Oh gods! My children! Never more
Will Lír enjoy a tranquil hour.

He drove directly to Killaloe where he was welcomed. But Lír said nothing of what he knew. Without any hint that he was aware of what she had done he greeted Aoife and the king as he would normally have done. And Aoife, who was watching him closely with narrowed eyes, relaxed and felt safe. But the Bodhbh Dearg reproached him for not bringing the four children with him. For a moment Lír didn't answer. He looked directly at Aoife, who was standing beside the Bodhbh Dearg. She met his eyes and, in that instant, realised that he knew everything. She went white and dropped her gaze as Lír turned to the king.

"Twas not I, Bodhbh Dearg, who prevented my children from coming to visit you,' he said. 'There . . .' and he raised his arm slowly and pointed a long finger at Aoife, 'is the one who has done that, your foster-child, their aunt, who has turned on them treacherously, and put a spell upon them so that they are now four swans trapped on Lough Derravarragh.'

Of course the Bodhbh Dearg was speechless at first; then angry and indignant yet all the while struggling with disbelief. But as Lír went on the doubt he'd already felt grew in his mind and overcame the frightful idea that one of his foster-children, to whom he had given such love and attention, could do such a thing. Wordlessly he turned to Aoife, seeking denial. But when he saw her face he realised that what Lír said was true. Aoife stood there knowing that the retribution Finola had foretold was about to descend on her far more quickly than she had anticipated.

The Bodhbh Dearg was terrible in his wrath, and when he spoke his voice frightened her who was not easily intimidated, low and deep though it was. 'What you have done,' he said, 'is awful. But the result will be worse for you than for those children that you have harmed. For their suffering must come to an end at last and they will eventually find happiness.' Having said that he paused and looked at Aoife through the terrible anger and justice that consumed him. And when he spoke again it was in a voice that was as implacable and as terrible as that of the angry lord of the skies, and he asked her this question: 'Of all that is on the earth, or above it, or beneath it; of all that flies or creeps or burrows, seen or unseen, horrible in itself or in its nature, what do you most hate and abhor?'

Now it may seem strange that he would ask a question and expect a truthful answer from such a person as Aoife when she stood before him knowing that her fate might depend upon it. But the truth of the matter is that she had no choice, for she was bound by a duty and obligation older than the Tuatha de Danaan themselves to answer certain questions truthfully. It was her *geasa* (gassa), her obligation, and if she did not do so the fate that would descend on her then would be worse, more terrible and unimaginable than any punishment a mere man might put on her. And so she said: 'Of all things that are most loathsome to me, there is none more dreadful than the Morrigu

(Moe-ree-goo, sometimes Moe-ree-gawn), the demons of the air.' So without further thought and in one swift motion the Bodhbh Dearg lifted his golden druidical wand, from which indeed had been carved the one Aoife herself had used on the children of Lír, and, even as he spoke, tapped her with it and transformed her into one of the dreaded Morrigu. 'Then that,' he said, 'is what you shall be.'

The Morrigu of old can take many shapes; and relishing battle and the spilling of the blood of men, is most often seen in the black and dreaded shape of a croaking raven in a battlefield, dipping its great beak in the fearful gore. Aoife was now so horrible and loathsome to see that all those in the great hall of the palace of Killaloe, except Lír and the Bodhbh Dearg alone who stood and looked at the transformation with frozen countenances, turned away or hid their faces in their cloaks. The dreadful thing she now was was crouched low on the floor a moment, flapping ugly leathery wings. Then with a scream from its mouth that gaped open, displaying curled and pointed fangs, it spread its wings and waddled past the shrinking crowd, gaining speed as it went until it reached the door. Then it jumped two, three, four times until it was airborne heavily, flapping those spread wings and slowly gaining height. It laboured blackly over the heads of those below who cringed away as it passed until it disappeared in the grey clouds in the distance. Aoife was now a demon of the air, a Morrigu; that is what she remains and will remain until the end of time.

Then the Bodhbh Dearg and Lír agreed that they would form a new court on the shores of Lough Derravarragh where all the Tuatha de Danaan of Ireland would assemble to be with the swans and listen to their wonderful music. And it is a strange thing that there, to that court, came hosts of the Milesians from Tara. They made another camp also to listen to the music of the swans. And it was said then, and written later, and passed on from mouth to mouth and from parent to child, that never before in the world or ever afterwards has music been heard that compared with that of those swans.

So it was that at the lakeside there grew and developed a community of people who shared their lives and their thoughts with the swans. Generations came and generations passed, but the swans remained. By day the swans would mingle and talk with their friends and by night they would make their incomparable music and all who heard it were assuaged of grief and sickness, pain and sorrow. They overcame their troubles and drifted into a gentle sleep from which they awoke calm and refreshed. For three hundred years the swans stayed on Derravarragh, knowing and meeting the de Danaan and Milesians who maintained these vast communities by the lake.

But at the end of that time Finola said to her brothers: 'It is time for us to go. We have been here on Derravarragh for three hundred years and have but one night left before we must leave and go to the cold sea of Moyle.' Her three brothers were not happy when they heard this for they had been as content as it was possible for them to be on the lake where the people had come to be with them. But now they faced three hundred long bitter and painful, icy years on the dark sea of Moyle, where it threshed its rough passage between Ireland and Scotland, far from human friendship. But they had no choice.

And so, early the following morning, sad and sorrowful they drifted to the shore to speak again for the last time to the de Danaan and Milesians and bid them farewell. And this is the lament they made for them as they left:

Tears are swelling in our hearts
As the lough must swell and weep
When Time lays down his hand athwart
Its waters, calm and deep,
And sunders it and blows black storms
Across its tranquil path;
For we must leave your courts and warmth
And seek the endless wrath
Of Moyle's wild sea; three hundred years
There to suffer in our fears.

Far down the twisted roads of Time
Our paths ahead are mapped;
Though men may with the Fates combine,
Our destinies are trapped;
No dreams we dream, no hopes may raise,
No laughter in tomorrow;
'Til comes that holy voice of praise
Our lives are doomed to sorrow.
But, though we go, our love remains
To ease your grief and mortal pains.

As the last notes of their song hung above the waters, the four birds, all together, began to skim over the surface of the lake, their wings and feet combining to lift them, their long necks outstretched before them. On they went until their feet were all but running on the surface and then, with powerful sweeps of their broad wings, they abandoned the lake which had been their home for so long, and rose upwards into the air, and only the tone of their passing drifted back to those below. Higher and higher they climbed making wide circles so that the sound of their beating wings continued to echo to the thousands of people gathered to watch. When they had reached a great height they could look down and see, not just Derravarragh and the camps of the men of Ireland, but much of the country around as well. They paused for a moment in their flight and then, straight and true, turned northwards and continued until they saw the bitter foam and white savagery of the sea of Moyle scouring the ocean's bed. Lower and lower they sank until they touched the first cold wave to reach up for them. Then they landed awkwardly on the cruel sea that was to be their new home.

So sad and upset were the people at their departure that they enacted a law forbidding anyone to kill a swan in Ireland from that time on. Yes; they came together, the Milesians and the Tuatha de Danaan, in a fervour of activity and energy, at Killaloe and at Tara, and made this common law. Mind you, their enthusiasm was sincere and infectious and they had the support of everyone until it became law. But once it was passed what more was there to be done? The law wouldn't bring back the children of Lír. Gradually the wild, hot enthusiasm that was there for the passing of the law died down. But still the people were proud of their new law. Yet after a while they neglected it, for people can't remain sad forever, and got on with their own affairs, and all but forgot the children of Lír except as tragic figures of the past and a salutary lesson to all, for there was little else they could do.

So, while their memories faded amongst the generations in Ireland so that they became more of an idea than a reality, more intangible than substantial, the children of Lír themselves drifted on the jagged face of Moyle, tossed from wave to wave by the growling sea. They were full of sorrow and sadness and missed the people with whom they had lived all those years in Ireland, so that when they looked at the dark green-bellied wild sea and the steep rocky, far-stretching coasts they were overwhelmed with fear and despair. And the sea was not like the warm, inland, well-stocked waters of pleasant Derravarragh, for it was cold and empty and hunger struck at them too. A biting wind swept down from the north with sleet and snow in its teeth. There was little there of food for them in that wild place, and their banishment on Derravarragh seemed like nothing compared to what they were suffering.

It was while they had lived so for a while, believing that their misery could never become greater, that one evening in winter, dark though it was, pale, milky clouds stretched coldly across the sky and the sea heaved restively beneath them. Suddenly the sky became dark and closed in threateningly. They could not tell where the sea ended and the sky began. Finola realised that a storm was coming and said: 'We are exposed where we are in the middle of this great sea, brothers. There is little doubt that the storm will separate us no matter how hard we try to stay together. So we must agree on a meeting place afterwards; otherwise we may never see each other again.'

Fiachra, who had scoured more of the sea than any of them, said: 'That is sensible. So if we are separated, let's meet after the storm at Carraignarone, which we all know well.'

They stayed huddled together for as long as they could on top of the bellowing sea, lashed by the fearful waves and the howling wind. In the middle of the night a cold wind swept the rough billows and lightning flashed from the clouds, so that the ocean itself came under attack from the sky and gathered itself to fight back. It seemed to rise from its bed and claw at the sky with angry fingers of lashing spume. As the storm worsened the swans were separated and scattered across the surface of the fighting sea so that none of them knew in what direction the others had been driven, or indeed in what direction it was being driven itself. All through the night they were tossed and hurled, whipped and blown, sometimes in the sea and sometimes in the air and sometimes in a raging mixture of the two, from one place to another place, never knowing which place they were in. It was only with the greatest courage that they managed to survive, and even when the dawn lightened the east and the storm began to abate they seemed more dead than alive.

In a dull day under heavy grey clouds the sea again seemed calm, but it had a troubled, restless look beneath, as it always has following a storm. Finola saw no sign of her brothers so she made her way to Carraignarone – properly called the rock of the seals for it is there that the seal-people congregate when the weather is welcoming – but they were not there, either on the sullen waves beating about the rock or on the craggy corners of the rock itself. She clambered onto it and looked over the desolate waste, but there was still no sign. Cold and terrified Finola believed her brothers to be dead, and began to lament them:

> There is no shelter, there is no rest,
> My heart is broken in my breast;
> Gone, my three loves in the bitter night;
> Gone all, but the deep, cold, fright
> Of despair, and life without light.
>
> My brothers are lost in the wild sea
> Where death itself would be a mercy;
> Oh, is there no pity in this place?
> Will I never see again each face
> Dearer now to me than the human race?
>
> There is no shelter, there is no rest,
> My heart is broken in my breast;
> Was not the agony we bore enough?
> Was not the cruelty, the deep trough
> Of long anguish, sufficient pain to suffer?

When she finished she collapsed onto the rock and buried her head beneath her wing. She believed that she was now alone of the four children of Lír, and only wished for death herself too. So when she had made her mind up to that she raised her head to look a last time on the bleak world. She looked out over the pale sea, now the same colour as the inhospitable sky, and there, in the far distance, what did she see but a small speck being tossed this way and that by the careless waves, but making its way towards the rock slowly and with feeble motion.

That was Conn. And Finola immediately plunged into the sea to help him towards Carraignarone. She helped Conn reach the rock and there they rested; and soon afterward they saw Fiachra limping through the waves. It took both of them a great effort to bring him to safety for he was closer to death than he was to life, and when they spoke to him he could not summon a word or any acknowledgement whatsoever in return; so Finola and Conn placed him under the warmth of their wings to bring back the heat of life to his perished body. And Conn said: 'If only Aedh were here now we would all be happy.' And, indeed, after a little while what did they see but Aedh coming towards them. But his condition was very different from that of the others, for he was swimming proudly on the lips of the ocean, his head erect and his feathers dry and radiant. The others welcomed him and he told them that he had found shelter in a Scottish cave from the fury of the storm. Between them he and Finola sheltered the other two and they were relieved and thankful to be together again. Bound by their hardship and their love for one another they lived many years and through many such storms on the sea of Moyle.

One night, there came a great, huge, unmanageable, fierce and ungovernable storm of wind and snow, sleet and frost, more severe than anything they had known before. The cold that night seemed to come from the uttermost regions of the infinite sky, and the wind from the bowels of the turning earth. Frost enveloped them like a covering of fire, and the fury of the storm broke asunder the sea where they struggled to survive. And it went on and lasted for more than one night, or two nights, or three nights, and so fearful was it that the very waters of the heaving sea itself were frozen into torn and ragged walls, grotesque and ugly all around.

They'd reached Carraignarone safely, but their feet and wings were frozen solid with high-flung spray and manacled with ice to the torn floor that was the sea, so that the skin was ripped from their feet as they moved, the quills from their wings and the protecting feathers from their battered breasts. When these cuts and wounds were penetrated by the salt from the sea, their torture was doubled. And yet they could not leave the blasted sea of Moyle for a safer place. They were forced to make their way far out across that upheaval to the channel where the water had not frozen. Wounded and torn as they were, they had little choice but to remain there in the sharp and bitter sea. They remained as close to the coast as they could until that fearful storm was past, and the feathers began to grow again on their breasts and wings. That was their worst time there, and from then on they made sure they stayed close either to the coast of Ireland or to the friendly coast of Scotland, but always on the sea of Moyle.

One day while they were swimming by the mouth of the river Bann in the northern part of Ireland what did they see when they looked towards the shore – only a great cavalcade of chiefs and lords riding from the south. All were mounted on white horses and as they came close the splendour of their cloaks blazed across the intervening distance, and their weapons glinted in the sunlight like gathered stars glinting in the night.

'Who do you think these are?' asked Finola.

'I don't know,' said Fiachra, 'unless they are Milesians, for they'd hardly be the Tuatha de Danaan riding abroad so far north in the land.'

'Why don't we go closer and find out?' asked Conn.

And so they swam together towards the river-mouth where the horses were heading. When the knights in their turn saw the swans coming towards them they changed course and came to meet them. They were indeed a party of the de Danaan, led by the two sons of the Bodhbh Dearg, Aedh and Fergus, and had been searching for the swans for many years, but had never found them although they'd traversed the coasts of the sea of Moyle backwards and forwards so long that they knew every blade of grass on its margins and every pebble that lay on its beaches. They greeted each other with unimaginable warmth, for it was the first time the children of Lír had spoken to a human since they'd come to the sea of Moyle. And at once they asked about King Lír and the Bodhbh Dearg and others of the de Danaan, and were told that they were all well (for it is necessary to understand that in those days the Tuatha de Danaan had remarkable longevity, which explains why the swans asked after their father and the Bodhbh Dearg after more than four hundred years of exile).

'They are well,' said Aedh and Fergus, 'and they and the people of the de Danaan hope to celebrate the Feast of Gabhann, and we have been searching for you on their instructions to ask you to come and share in it with us for neither they, nor ourselves, nor any of the people of the Tuatha de Danaan, have any idea of what happened to you since you left Lough Derravarragh for the Sea of Moyle.'

But of course the four swans could not return to Sídhe Fionna or to Killaloe, or, indeed, to Lough Derravarragh, so they did their best to explain the torments they'd suffered, which was not really possible. Instead they made this song and asked those who had come in search of them to take it back with them for their friends celebrating the Feast of Gabhann, which is a great occasion that ensured that the people of the Tuatha de Danaan would in time enter the Mystic

Cavalcade, the Marcra Sídhe, in the Tír Tairrnge, or Land of Promise, sometimes called Tír na nÓg, or Land of Youth. For the Feast of Gabhann is dedicated to power over sickness, decay and old age. And the lament carried back from the four swans was this:

> Though love and laughter fill the days
> Of your joyful celebration,
> Spare a thought for bygone days
> And we orphans of your nation.

> Bleak and cold the home we know.
> Our sodden down is thin and light,
> Yet we wore once – oh, long ago –
> Clothes that glittered in the night.

> Once, too, our lives were filled with laughter,
> As were our brimming cups of gold,
> Now pain and sickness follow after;
> We're lost, forgotten, in the cold.

> Our beds are rocks in wave-torn caves,
> Our lullaby the washing sea;
> No voice to hear but the tongueless waves;
> No sound but that of the pitiless sea.

You may be sure that when the Bodhbh Dearg and Lír and the hosts of the Tuatha de Danaan heard this lament they were moved to sorrow and pity again for the children of Lír.

Meanwhile, the swans returned outward onto the Sea of Moyle where they remained for many more years. But at last their time there was up and Finola told her brothers that it was time for them to leave that place and go to the west. They looked at one another, for they did not know to what fate Aoife's magic would now hurl them. Before they left Moyle they made this song:

> Three times a hundred years we've spent
> In torment here without a rest;
> Now we must leave this wild and rent
> Sea, to journey to the west.

> From this cold sea in the bitter east
> To the distant storms we fly,

That batter the west like a wild beast,
To live in the tempest's eye.

Lifting themselves from the inhospitable billows of Moyle the swans turned west across the face of Ireland. High above it they flew, without looking to see what was beneath for fear that it would distress them too much, until before them they saw the western sea peopled and dotted with islands. They flew lower and lower until they came down eventually at Iris Domhnann near Gloire. But they were little better off there than they had been on Moyle. While it was not so cold, the storms were fiercer; so that while their hardship was not the same, it was of equal intensity. While they were there at Iris Domhnann a very curious and interesting thing – and you and I might say fortuitous thing – occurred.

Close to the shore lived a young nobleman called Aebhric, who had a large tract of land covering the shore and the mountain where he would hunt and cultivate certain crops. The land in that part is poor and game is scarce so that crops need to be tended even by people from noble families. This Aebhric came to know the swans and was entranced by them so that to listen to them and their music was the greatest pleasure he had in life. And he and the four swans established a close relationship, so that they told him, from their love for him, their whole story from beginning to end. And the strange and interesting truth is that it is to this Aebhric, and him alone, that we must give thanks for knowing the story at all, for it was he who related it in the neighbourhood, and people came from far and near to hear it. But he would never allow them to meet the swans, who were now shy themselves, for fear they might do them some mischief in spite of the law of the Bodhbh Dearg from six hundred years earlier. And it was Aebhric who arranged the story – up to this point, that is – so that it was passed on from one generation to the next and so on down through the passageway of the centuries until it reached us, with the rest of it being contributed by a holy man who we will meet shortly.

In the meantime if it had not been for him the swans' plight would indeed have been desolate. Their hardship on that harsh western sea was no less than that they endured on the sea of Moyle. There was, however, one night of fearful difference that surpassed anything they'd ever known before. That night, black frost so severe, so prolonged and lacerating, fell on the land and on the sea so that the whole were frozen into one mass of coldness, with the water from Iris Domhnann to Achill frozen into a floor of ice. The snow came thick and solid in a blinding blizzard from the north-west. Throughout the centuries of their torment, no other night was so bleak and so desolate. Never was their pain so great; never such an accumulation of suffering. The three brothers were unable to stand it and made loud and bitter and pitiful complaints. Finola did her best to console them, but it was hard, for her own condition was no better than theirs. It seemed as if the end for them all was very close in that white, terrible storm, and she, too, began to lament.

But then a strange and awesome thing occurred. Through the depths of her misery and lamentation Finola felt another spirit mingle with her own. It was strange and terrifying, but also comforting and consoling. It was greater and deeper than anything she had ever experienced either of destitution or happiness. It was indescribable, intangible, mighty and yet inexplicable and full of wonder. She stopped wailing and listened to herself, or, more correctly, to what was at once both within her and without. Having listened and become sure of what it was she needed to say, she told her brothers to stop their complaining for a moment so that she might speak. When they did so, she said: 'My dear brothers there is Something here with us that I do not understand for It is past all understanding or that of any mere man. But It is so great and awe-inspiring, so manifest of Love and Goodness, of things so far beyond our comprehension, and yet for which my whole being strives, that I must believe in It, for It is Truth. It is the very Truth of the world – the earth with its fruits, and the sea with its wonders, the heavens with their infinity. Put your trust in this Truth, brothers, and It will save us.' And strange as it may seem, in these days when ugliness and material things are all that occupy the minds of men, out of their misery and hardship they said: 'We will, and we do, for we feel It too.'

And it was in that way and at that hour, we are told, when they thought themselves beyond hope from any source, that the Almighty Lord of Heaven, who had not as yet made Himself known to the people of Ireland, sent them a message of love and protection in their affliction so that neither cold nor storm, hunger nor want of any kind troubled them from that time on while they remained on the western sea, where they stayed until they had fulfilled their appointed time.

When that time came, Finola said to her brothers, 'Our time on Iris Domhnann is over, and we can leave here without let or hindrance. So let us go now and pay our respects to our father at Sídhe Fionna and to the people of the de Danaan.' Gladly they rose from the surface of that troubled sea. They cast round once over the bay they were leaving without regret – for Aebhric had long since been taken by death – and turned eastward with happiness in their hearts, swiftly flying until they reached Sídhe Fionna.

When they arrived where Sídhe Fionna should have been they were puzzled, for there was no sign of it. The great castle that had once dominated the surrounding plain where they'd spent their joyful youth was broken and tumbled. The windows gaped emptily and the mortar had fallen from between the buckling stones, many of which had themselves fallen in pyramidical piles from the once proud walls. There was nothing but sadness and desolation, to which only the wind whispered. The great courts and halls were empty, ruined

153

and overgrown with grass and weeds. The houses and villages that once flourished around the castle were gone, and nothing was left to show that they had ever been. Nothing but the ruined castle. Sadly the four swans probed with their stretching, elegant necks through the desolation for some hope or some sign of life, but there was none. They came together where the castle hall had been and sang this lament:

A wonder is this place to us
Without a home; without a house.
Bitter are our hearts to see
These halls destroyed so cruelly.
Gone; all is gone.

Our loneliness was incomplete
'Til loving homesteads 'neath our feet
Were, like this place once so dear,
Brought to ruin, the wrack of Lír.
Gone; all is gone.

Gone are the noble and stately halls,
Crumbled the pillars and tumbled the walls;
Weeds and nettles, bent and blown,
Grow where our pride was overthrown.
Gone; all is gone.

Silence fills this empty place
But for the winds that round us trace
Faint whispers of forgotten shades
Bright with rich, gay cavalcades.
Gone; all is gone.

No warriors here, no men at arms,
No tales of victory and alarms.
Heroes, chieftains, great and brave
Are still and mouldered in the grave.
Gone; all is gone.

They stayed that night in the ruins, remembering and stirring sometimes as old memories came stumbling out of crumbled corridors. They sang sweetly as their tribute to the past and what was gone. Next morning they sadly left the site of ruined Sídhe Fionna and returned to the west, but this time to a softer and gentler island called Inis Gloire (Inish Glowir), where they settled on a small lake on that island. A strange thing occurred after that. So powerful was the effect of their music on the birds and animals around that they flocked there just to hear the swans; so that from that day to this the lake is known as the Lough Ean (Ayan), the Lake of the Birds, so thickly were they crowded about it and on it and near it.

From Inis Gloire the swans flew from one place to another always returning at night to Lough Ean. They enjoyed their new freedom. They would go to Iniskea – where the lonely crane has lived in isolation since the beginning of the world and will live there until the day of judgement – or they might go to the island of Achill, or to other places along the shores of the western sea as they fancied. That is how they lived until Patrick came to Ireland bringing with him the knowledge of the true faith that had already touched them.

And what was to happen, but that one of Patrick's disciples, Caemhoch (Key-vogh) came to Inis Gloire. The night he did so the swans heard a strange sound echoing and reverberating across the waters around the island. It was a sound they'd never heard before, and they were frightened at its strange, repetitive tone. It filled them with terror so that they began to run wildly about thinking that it had some terrible portent for them. But it was only Caemhoch striking his tongueless bell for matins. It was Finola, who'd always shown herself to be the wisest and most sensible, who finally, having listened to it for a while, asked: 'Do you know what that sound is?'

The brothers said: 'No. We hear it and are afraid for we don't know what it is, or what it might mean.'

Then she said quietly: 'That is the sound we have been waiting for. The end to our suffering is close. For that is the voice of the bell which is the sign that soon we will be free of Aoife's curse.'

Then they made this song:

> Hear the reverberant boom of the bell
> Throbbing down the aisles of Time;
> The metal voice we've waited to tell
> The end is near of Aoife's crime.
>
> Listen, oh swans, to the throbbing bell
> Ringing across the shaded night;
> Rung by the priest in his lonely cell,
> Yet, for us, the voice of light.
>
> That is the bell of the Lord of all
> Ringing His faith across the world;

Be joyful, brothers, and heed that call,
For soon in His arms we'll be safely curled.

This song and the tolling notes of the bell faded together in the evening across the lake on a last lingering note. The sun, too, faded, and silence descended with the approaching night. Then they made the most beautiful music they had ever made in their long lives, and it was in praise and thanksgiving to the Almighty Creator of heaven and earth and of all things, whose disciple they knew was at hand to deliver them from their bondage.

In the distance, Caemhoch heard their music and was spellbound, for he'd never heard anything so magnificent, stealing into and filling the night, as that music in that lonely place. As quietly as he could he made his way towards the source, but was unable to see anything, for invading night had passed his own stealthy feet and it was dark before he reached Lough Ean. He stayed close and waited for the dawn because he guessed that it was the children of Lír, whom he had come specifically to find, who were making this wonderful music. In the pale dawn light he saw the four swans drifting in the water close to the shore near him, and he asked them if they were who they were. When they answered him Caemhoch said: 'Praise be to God that I have found you for that is my mission here. Come with me now and trust me and I will end your bewitchment.'

The four swans were filled with great joy when he said this and came ashore and joined him in a small group that gave and exchanged great love and affection. He told them what would have to be done and so they put themselves completely in his trust and care. He made a small house for himself and then went to one of the skilled fine metal-smiths in the district and had two chains of silver made. He put one of them between Finola and Aedh and the other between Fiachra and Conn, and so they lived with him for some time, listening to what he told them, and telling him of everything that had happened to them during the previous thousand years. For his part Caemhoch introduced them to and instructed them and taught them in the beliefs of Christianity, which they accepted joyfully. And so they lived together for a short while, the great love and tenderness between them erasing the bitter memories of their long years of misery and suffering.

Now the king who ruled Connacht at that time was called Lairgnean Mac Colman. And you can see for yourselves that there is a great mystery about this for Lairgnean lived in historical times and all the world knows about him, or they could if they wanted to. But the children of Lír had been abroad in the cold world for a thousand years and it is not an easy thing for the minds of modern men to comprehend that span of time, overlapping as it does spoken history and written history. It is a mystery from the past and let it rest so.

Lairgnean's queen was Deichte, daughter of Fíonán of Munster, the same king and queen that Aoife referred to as marking the end of their time of trouble when she put her spell on the children of Lír so long before. As kings go, Lairgnean wasn't a bad one; but when it came to queens, his wife Deichte was a different story altogether. She was proud and she was vain; and, like many another before her and after her in an exalted position, she was gracious and kindly in her behaviour towards other people (whom she considered her inferiors of course), but only so long as she was satisfied that she got her own way and was possessed of all that was best in the world for herself. She could not abide to think that there might be a thing or an attribute or a position or an opposition or a piece of this or that with any other one that she did not have or possess or control herself. And if there was a thing belonging to someone she considered beneath her station – and that was where she considered most people to be – then her torment was all the greater.

Now it so happened that the story of the four wonderful swans reached the court of Connacht and the ears of Deichte. And I needn't tell you she pricked up those ears when she heard it, and she heard it not once but many times. The more often she heard it the greater grew her desire to possess such a great and unique wonder for herself. So what did she do but what any woman in similar circumstances would do. She asked her husband to get them for her.

Now the truth of the matter was that Lairgnean had never refused her anything she asked for before – which might be as much a reflection on him as on her – but he was reluctant to do what she asked now, knowing full well that the children of Lír were neither birds nor beasts to be bought nor sold for the vainglory of any man or woman, like a common slave, but a princess and three princes who were the victims of remote and historical vengeance and misfortune. He didn't think they should be acquired as curiosities for any man or woman. Of course, I needn't tell you, he didn't put it like that to Deichte. He had some bit of tact. He just said he wasn't able.

But now, of course, there was pride as well as vanity in it as far as she was concerned because this was the first time he had ever refused her, and she became what you might call adamant for want of a stronger word. To cut a long story short, she told him that she wouldn't stop another night in his palace if he didn't do what she wanted and he could sleep in a cold bed from then on. Lairgnean had often heard this kind of thing from her before because, being what you might call, if you were a kindly disposed person, a spirited woman, she had often said the same thing in the past, but had always came round. So he paid little enough attention to her at the time. But Deichte was badly put out by his refusal to please her in this matter and she left the house within the hour and fled southwards heading for her father's palace in Munster (and that was bad for Lairgnean since the last thing he wanted was a war with Munster, which was a much more powerful kingdom, and that's what 'twould have meant).

So when he discovered she was gone he was very upset. She was a talented woman in many respects, and a cold bed is cold comfort, as they say. In spite of her faults, he loved Deichte greatly. So he sent messengers after her to tell her that he'd do what she wanted. They didn't overtake her for a while – until she was below at Killaloe as it happened – but, anyway, she returned with them to Lairgnean's palace, and as soon as she marched in the door he promised her that he'd send to Caemhoch straightaway for the swans. So round he turned the very messengers that had gone after her and sent them off to ask the priest that he'd send the swans to the queen. But, of course, Caemhoch refused to give them.

Lairgnean now became angry for it was not just his wife's pride that was at stake, but his own. In addition to that he was in need of someone on whom he could take out his anger over what Deichte had done since, of course, there was no way he could be angry with her the way things were. There are those who say that Deichte was pregnant and that that was the reason for her contrary behaviour. But whether 'tis true or false makes little difference because when Lairgnean heard Caemhoch's reply, off he stormed in a rage to the priest's house. When he got there he wasted no time in politeness and demanded from Caemhoch whether 'twas true or false that he had refused to give the swans to the queen.

'I did,' said Caemhoch. 'For I have no power to give them any more than you have the power to take them.'

When Lairgnean heard this, he puffed up like a pigeon, swelled up with a great rage inside him and, going up to the swans he grabbed hold of the two silver chains.

'No power!' he shouted. 'I'll show you whether I have power or not, priest, for they're coming with me.'

Then realising that he was making a spectacle of himself that was anything but kingly, but still holding on to the chains, he dropped his hands a little bit and asked: 'If I have no power in my own kingdom, who has?' With that he turned on his heel and walked off – but not too quickly – pulling the birds after him by their silver chains.

Caemhoch followed anxiously in case they might be hurt by the king in his anger. But that anger was dissipating quickly; and, in any case, it had little time left, for a strange and wonderful thing suddenly happened. Before the king reached his horse, which was being held by his groom, the white feathery covering of the swans began to fade and their shapes began to alter before the eyes of all those there. When he felt a drag on the chains the king stopped and turned and his mouth opened at what he saw.

Slowly, very slowly, the four children of Lír began to reassume human shape. But with what a difference! Instead of the four golden, bright, happy children who'd been the pride and great joy of the Tuatha de Danaan so long ago, the accumulation of the years and the trials and tribulations they'd undergone, were written and stamped on the features of the four as they emerged. Finola was a bent, old and extremely wrinkled woman, whose flesh was so shrivelled on her bones that she seemed to be only bones herself covered by an ancient skin, something like one of those people preserved by the mysterious properties of the bog or by the magic of Egyptian sorcerers. Only her eyes, sunken deep in her head, bore the brightness of youth about them still. Her three brothers were equally old, white-haired and wrinkled.

When Lairgnean saw them, he was petrified with fright. He dropped the chains and backed away, but had too much respect and kingliness about him to go very far. He waited and watched as Caemhoch approached the four ancient people and spoke tenderly to them.

The children of Lír were so feeble, they were unable to stand, and had nothing to cover themselves with but a small pile of feathers that lay and wafted around and about them. When Caemhoch came up to them they said: 'Oh, Caemhoch, please help us and baptise us now, for there is little time. Perhaps you'll be sorry when we are gone, but you will not be more sorry than we are to leave you. What we ask now is that you bury us together, facing one another, with our arms around each other as we often stood when we were in the world, both as people and as swans.'

And if that seems a strange request to us today, then we should remember that the custom amongst the Gaelic peoples long ago was to be buried standing. Then they sang a last song, but now they sang with old, cracked voices. Their words were beautiful, and they sang in unison:

> Come, oh priest, and stretch your hand
> Forth, over us here:
> Our long pain is over and
> Death is near.
>
> Dig a grave, oh dig it well,
> Deep and wide;
> Where we can hear the tolling bell
> Asleep inside.
>
> Lay us as we often lay,
> Four together;
> Held upright in the cold clay,
> Four together.

Place brother Aedh before my face,
Beside me stand
Conn and Fiachra. Round each place
A loving hand.

And so we'll sleep for evermore,
Children of Lír.
Come, priest, and shed your power.
Death is here.

The singing of this song drained from them all but the last feeble remnant of their strength and Caemhoch hastened to baptise them before they died. Even as he did so, blessing them with the oil and the water and the salt, their lives that had lingered for so long in torment and hardship slipped tranquilly from under his hand and their spirits departed from them. They reclined there upon a couch of bracken covered in soft skins, the enfeebled shells of the once glorious children of Lír.

Tears sprang into Caemhoch's eyes and he was moved to look up, for to continue looking at these pitiful bodies was beyond his capacity. And, strange and wonderful – and yet, perhaps not so strange in this wonderful story – what did he see above him, between him and the shimmering sky, but a vision of four beautiful children fading upwards and their faces were radiant with immense joy. They looked back at him for a long moment with love and affection in that look and then, perhaps because his own eyes were filled with tears or perhaps for some other reason beyond our understanding, the vision of these wonderful children faded from his sight. He wiped the tears from his face and when he looked again they were gone. But Caemhoch was filled with joy and gladness because he knew that the children of Lír who had suffered so much would suffer no more but live in infinite happiness. Nevertheless when he looked at the poor crumpled bodies at his feet, he was overcome with a great sadness and poignancy, and he wept.

He caused a deep, wide grave to be dug near the little church that he'd built while they were with him. And there the four children of Lír were buried as they'd asked, with Conn at the right hand of Finola, Fiachra at her left and Aedh standing in front of her. Afterwards Caemhoch performed their funeral rites and raised a burial mound above them and a tombstone with their names engraved on it. Then he made a lament and part of it is this story from the death of Aebhric to the end.

And that is the story of the fate of the children of Lír.

The Wooing of Emer

Second Period: Ultonian Cycle

This story is also from the Red Branch Cycle and has the archetypal Celtic hero Cuchulain as central character. Like many others from the oral tradition that have, perhaps, been modified by time and the 'laundering' hands of Christian recensionists, the story at first presents an apparently ill-defined outline. The main reason for this seems to be the old one of familiarity. The audiences, right down to the eighteenth century, and possibly later, were so familiar with the characters and events that filling in detail was an unnecessary and unrequired intrusion. Why trouble to explain who Conall Cearnach was when everyone knew? Why bore and irritate the listener, or even the reader, with details of consequential events and the inexorability of certain actions that were well understood? If a man broke his *geasa* retribution must surely follow; similarly if he, or a group, were overly presumptuous. The thinking is similar in many respects to that which informs Greek mythology. The actions of man are part of his destiny; but the rule of a higher order keeps him in place should he presume too much. That is what this story is about in essence. It is only for us latter-day ignoramuses, indulged as we are with push-button instant information so that it is unnecessary for us to agitate our minds with the trouble of exercise, that it becomes important to flesh out character and events from the past in order to obtain the full flavour of the story lest it be lost in a maze of epigrams and apparent *non sequiturs*.

In this tale, because of the devastating effect of his handsomeness and prowess on the noblewomen of Ulster, Cuchulain is enticed by the noblemen to seek a bride. That he might produce a son as gifted as himself is their secondary consideration. With appalling consequences their priorities are shown to be in the incorrect order. Cuchulain finds his bride and is happy and content with her, but . . .

When he was seventeen, Cuchulain, the great hero of Ulster on whose shoulders the fate of the entire province would one day rest, took arms and adopted the role of manhood with the same forcefulness and facility that marked everything he had so far done. Indeed the story of his taking arms not only indicates the profound and dedicated character of the young man, but is also a portent, if a non-specific one, of what would follow.

He had strolled beyond the ramparts of the city of Emhain Macha. Through the streets of the clay and wattle houses where the freemen lived and beyond the outer gate, past the playing fields on the *faitche* or plain of Emhain, and down by the river he went. He took a path along one bank going south, where people came to swim and catch the abundant salmon and trout and do the washing and the multitude of things for which water is an agent or an environment, and there, beneath a mighty ash tree, he saw Catha, the chief druid of Ulster whose powers of divination were beyond compare (as, for instance, when he would foretell the terrible fate that would befall Ulster following the birth of Deirdre of the Sorrows).

Catha was passing on learning and instruction to a group of students from the druidic school, and, as Cuchulain came up, one of them asked him: 'Can you tell us, *a dlui*, what is today good for? Is there anything it would be best to do today?' Catha smiled. The questioner was a favourite pupil, a small, thin, earnest boy of about thirteen from far-off Munster, whose eagerness and diligence indicated great promise (which would be justified in time).

And so Catha nodded. He rose from his seat on a large stone, a cushion under him, and stood with his back to the river. He took from his belt-wallet a small, dried segment of magic mushroom and put it in his mouth and, chewing this, stretched his arms wide and gazed eastwards towards the birthplace of the sun. Cuchulain, who'd heard the question, halted to see what would happen, but did not intrude on the group. Slowly Catha turned *deiseal*, or clockwise, following the course of the sun with his face, his arms still outstretched. The morning sun threw his shadow like an arrow towards the tree and the river and, as he turned, the shadow moved with him changing shape but not direction, until he stood with his back to the sun, facing west. When he had thus completed a full half circle, Catha raised his arms over his head and brought his palms together. Then, still joined, he lowered them directly in front of him so that his two hands pointed to the far west. Cuchulain noticed that as he had turned and done all this, his eyes had been closed; but now he opened them. His eyes seemed to probe the west, for from where Cuchulain stood he could see clearly, and it seemed to him that although Catha's eyes were open he saw neither tree nor river nor what lay beyond but something in the far-off distance, so far that it lay beyond the horizon. Catha again brought a hand to his mouth and chewed once more on a segment of dried mushroom and again extended his hands, his arms sideways, and began to complete the turning motion which would bring him back facing east.

Having completed the full circle, the druid stood for perhaps a minute – or two, or even three. Then, taking his inscribed staff inlaid with silver and gold and socketed at one end with a magnificent bronze point, he inscribed certain characters in the dusty ground where it was bare of grass and well trodden by the countless numbers of students from the druidic college who had come there and listened to Catha – and those before him – impart their wisdom. Then he took certain twigs of laurel and of oak and of yew and of ash, and dropped them, apparently randomly, on the marks, which he and his forebears, perhaps remembering the Phoenician courses taken by their ancestors, called hieroglyphs. He studied them for several minutes. Then, turning to his class, he said: 'Well, my children. Today is a very particular day . . . for any man who wants to take arms.'

Although he addressed and looked at his class, particularly the eager boy who had put the question to him, to Cuchulain it seemed, although he was outside the circle, that Catha's eyes and voice were meant for him. 'The young man,' said the druid, 'who takes arms to day, of all the men of Erin, will become the most famous for great and immortal deeds.' When he heard this, Cuchulain's heart raced with excitement. But Catha added: 'Yet his life will be short and fleeting.'

As if he had said nothing of significance Catha turned back to his class and Cuchulain, in much the same way, walked on. But he turned away from the river as soon as he was out of sight and, taking a circuitous route, began to run back to the city. All the while, his heart was beating and the blood raced through his veins with excitement and a fire glittered in his eye. Striding quickly through the outer defences and the streets of Emhain Macha he went straight to the gate in the mighty walls of the great citadel in search of the king, Conor Mac Nessa. At last he found him sitting in the corner of the *grianaan* or solarium.

'Cuchulain!' exclaimed the king. 'What can I do for you?'

'I want to take arms!'

The king looked at him for a long moment from hooded, regal eyes that gave no hint of the thoughts behind them, for kingly thoughts are laced with guile, expediency, and concern for the security of the future, since these shape the life of a king and those for whom he is responsible. Now here was Cuchulain, the extraordinary youth of prowess beyond anything imaginable, seeking the weapons of manhood. Perhaps it would serve Conor well; perhaps his ambition should be curbed. There was one way to find out.

'So be it,' said the king.

Conor ordered spears to be brought from the Speckled House, where the glitter of sunlight off the burnished spears and swords and shields gave the great armoury the appearance of a dancing ocean. Two great spears were brought and given to Cuchulain who shook them in his hand with such violence and power that the staves splintered and smashed, and he threw them aside as useless. He was given others, and still others when they broke. It was the same with the swords that he bent and broke, and the javelins and the daggers and the throwing weapons and the slings; even the chariots he smashed to pieces with the stamping of his foot, until, at last, the king's own accoutrements and chariots of war, his spears and his sword were brought to Cuchulain. And these he could not break, do what he might; so this equipment he retained. And that is how Cuchulain was armed with the weapons of manhood.

It wasn't long before he outdid the heroes of Ulster – that is, Conall Cearnach the Victorious, Ferghus Mac Ri, Laoghaire, Uadach the Triumphant, Celtchar, Duach Mac Luadach, Sceil – by his brilliance and nimbleness, in the apple feat, in the feat of the javelin and the sword edge and the other feats of a warrior. These achievements, together with his youth and handsomeness, overwhelmed the women of Ulster. Fully armoured and with his hair tied in the fillets of a warrior Cuchulain looked so fair and noble that every woman who saw him was moved by his beauty and every woman on whom he looked was bewitched by him and could think of no other man.

When this had gone on for some time, the men of Ulster became angry and fearful that he would cuckold them one after another and urged him to take a wife of his own in the hope of avoiding catastrophe. There were meetings and groups here and there which shot sidelong glances of anger and concern at Cuchulain when he passed, totally unaware of what was going on.

'He has no wife of his own,' said one.

'That doesn't stop him!' said another.

'He hasn't come near mine yet,' said a third.

'Nor mine,' said another, 'but you never know . . .'

'Will ye give over?' said a fifth. 'Hasn't he made us all uneasy and anxious? We'll have no peace of mind the way things are and it'll lead to trouble unless something is done.'

After many such uneasy conversations they held a general meeting at which it was agreed that a woman would have to be found for Cuchulain. 'A man,' they argued, 'with a wife of his own would be less likely to ruin our daughters or steal our wives.'

But there was another reason, a better one, even if it wasn't, perhaps, the foremost one in their minds, and it was this: there was the danger that Cuchulain might die young. (And when this point was made no man there met another man's eye for, while it was clear that it was possible he would die in battle, it was becoming increasingly evident that he might also die of a silent thrust from behind on a dark and jealous night.) Should that happen and if he left no son, it would be tragic, for they knew that it was only out of Cuchulain himself that his like might come again.

Accordingly, the king, Conor Mac Nessa, sent two men into every province of Ireland; two into Munster, two into Ulster, two into Connacht, two into Leinster and one to search the royal province of Meath; nine men in all. They visited every town and settlement, every castle and every fort and saw every king's daughter and the daughter of every noble and landowner that Cuchulain might take for a wife. And each one was reported back to Cuchulain and he found fault with each one. And so it went for a year.

Of this one he said, 'She has a bad temper'; of that, 'a want of grace'; 'she is weak'; 'she is vain'; 'she is not suitable to be a wife to such as myself'. He said: 'This one is not brave, and brave my wife must be for she will suffer much; this one is not gentle and she must be gentle lest I anger her. She must be fair; she must be noble; she must not only be able to pleasure me as her husband, but it is right that all men will think of her with pride so that they may say, "As Cuchulain is the first of Ulster's warriors, so is his wife the first of Ulster's women and a worthy and fitting wife for him."'

But he himself had heard of a girl called Emer, daughter of Forgall Monach, the Cunning, whose castle stood in the heart of a plain called the Gardens of Lugh, Lugh Luchta Logo, Lord of Lusca, a few miles north of Dublin. So Cuchulain called his charioteer, Laeg Mac LianGabhta, who was himself a warrior, and with his two great horses, the Grey of Macha and the Black Steed of the Glen, harnessed to his chariot, he galloped south with fire and speed so quickly that no chariot or horseman in all Ireland could have kept up with him.

Emer, who was the second daughter of Forgall the Cunning, was a girl of remarkable beauty and intelligence who had just grown to womanhood. She was fair and slender, but with no hint of weakness about her. On this day, when the sun cruised the cloudless heavens and a breeze from the south and the west gentled the land so that the bees hummed happily amongst the wild flowers that grew in profusion and festooned the gardens of the sun-god Lugh, she sat with a group of girls of her own age, daughters of her father's retainers and foster-sisters of her own, in the *grianaan* or solarium of her father's castle, embroidering a great *brath*, or wall-hanging, for the castle. It was spread out between them as they worked and they sang and told stories and gossiped amongst themselves and giggled as girls of that age have ever done and ever will.

Emer, whose golden hair was rolled in braids about her head and whose green eyes were soft and gentle now with pleasant humour (but which could flash with dangerous anger when she was so moved), was the most skilful of the girls there; or at any rate she took the lead as she did in most things. What is more, her father, Forgall, was a hated and feared man. But if he loved anything in this world it was his second daughter Emer, and he had sworn that none under a king or ruling price would marry her, and any who dared the attempt, unless he was a king or a prince, would die forthwith. This he laid upon his three sons and made them swear upon their swords, upon the wind and the sea and the air and the earth, that any but a king or a prince who should come to woo Emer would never leave his castle alive.

As Emer and her friends sat in the *grianaan*, in the distance they heard what at first they thought was the rumblings of thunder. But the noise came closer and Emer, surprised to hear thunder on such a sunny and cloudless day, looked at the other girls in wonder. The noise came closer and louder as if it was a great troop of horsemen and warriors in iron-shod chariots bearing down on them at a full gallop. Forgall was away from home and Emer was concerned, so she asked one of her girls to go to the ramparts of the castle and see what was causing this unsettling commotion. As soon as the girl got to the parapets Emer called out:

'What do you see?'

'A chariot in the distance.'

'*One* chariot?'

'One!'

'Then it must truly be some great prince or king who is coming,' said Emer, 'for his chariot to make such a thunder.' For, as everyone knows, the rumbling and creaking, the crashing and the roaring of a chariot designates the status of the hero within until a king's chariot comes like the thunder of the angry gods or the roar of the unsettled sea.

Then the girl said:

> At first my eyes are strange and feel the distance –
> But now, far off, I see
> Racing swiftly on the plain, as though the winds
> Themselves did hasten it and thrust it on
> A rampant chariot.
> And now I see a splendid chief within, whose bearing
> Is a king's.

'Who?' cried the girls. 'What else?'

> I cannot tell who it might be,
> But round his head
> As if the hero's light were shining there,
> His gleaming helmet is like a beacon through the dust-cloud
> Sometimes veiling both his horses and himself. A charioteer
> Of giant build restrains the war-steeds in their rush.

'Who can it be?' cried Emer.
'Now I can see,' cried the girl on the ramparts.

> His hair is russet-gold and flies
> In braids beneath his helmet to keep it from his eyes.
> Magnificent
> The pair he drives. Two steeds of equal size are they
> Like night and day. Curling their manes
> And long. And as they come, foam from their curbed jaws
> Leaps and flies so strain and bound they forward.
> Beneath their feet the turf is thrown
> So high around it seems as though a flock
> Of darting birds are following them. Before it all
> The blood-flecked nostrils and the eyes
> Of each great steed are stretched and strained as they
> Bear upon us.
> On one side, broad and strong, his head outstretched, a grey,
> That swift and wild and thundering as he goes
> Moves madly o'er the plain.
> The other, firm and slender, is a black,
> And as he moves
> His muscles ripple in the shimmering sun
> And pound the fearful earth beneath his hooves.
> Oh! – Now I see! Worthy the chariot in which he rides
> Is he who sits within. Youthful he seems and yet,
> I think his face and form are older than his years.

'Go on! Go on!'

> About his shoulders, held there by
> A silver brooch, a rich five-folded mantle
> Flares about his white and gold-embroidered shirt.
> Upon his thigh there hangs a massive sword . . .
> And yet I think he comes not here to fight.

When she heard this, Emer stood and turned towards the castle walls. 'There is only one warrior of whom we have heard who answers that description,' she said, 'Cuchulain.'

And with that she went to a side gate that led from the *grianaan* to the *faitche* outside the castle and there she saw Cuchulain leap from the chariot even before Laeg hauled back on the traces and brought the two great steeds to a roaring standstill in a cloud of dust and a slide of the chariot wheels. Laeg, indeed, leaned so far back that he was almost parallel to the ground as he pulled and hauled. But Cuchulain was already striding across the *faitche* towards Emer whom he immediately recognised.

They turned and walked beside each other as if it was the most natural thing in the world – as indeed it was. And during that short walk Cuchulain told her of his love for her and that he would marry her. But she in reply told him about her father and the restrictions he had placed upon her and the promises he had exacted from his sons to defend her against all comers in case she should marry against his will.

Although Emer knew it was Cuchulain whom she had sought and dreamed of in her inner eye, she was sufficiently a woman to want to test him a little in the way that women sometimes do; but not too much, for it has been known that women who tested me who were true and devoted did so overmuch, so that their men did not know what they were doing and thus each lost the other for want of simple talk. Nevertheless Emer decided that it was right to test Cuchulain a little, not because she did not know him for the great warrior he was, but so that she might be sure of his love for her. And it is a strange thing that women, who are themselves by nature fickle and forever alert to the possibility of some new man around the corner and who frequently test each newcomer against that expectancy, are forever fearful of a similar attitude in the men they love – who, mostly, have no notion of such a thing.

So, after they had exchanged their greetings and she had softly said, 'May the gods make smooth the path before your feet,' and he had replied, 'And may you be safe from every harm,' she asked, although she knew full well, 'where have you come from?'

'From Conor's court at Emhain Macha,' he replied.

Emer looked a him. 'I am Forgall's daughter. And as you know he is called the Cunning One. He is cunning in mind and cunning in power. He is stronger than any man known here around, more learned than a druid, more sharp and clever than any *ollamh*. Men cannot number the multitude of his warlike deeds and he has given me a bodyguard of twenty men, with my brother, Conn, as their captain. I am well protected and no man can come near me but that Forgall will hear of it. If it were not that he were gone today on an expedition and these men with him I am afraid he would have met you with the point of a spear.'

Cuchulain looked at her blankly. 'Why are you telling me this?' he asked. 'Do you not know who I am? I know no fear.'

Emer looked at the ground for fear she would betray herself. 'If I knew who you were and your exploits,' she said, 'then I could, perhaps, take account of them. But, before now,' she lied, 'I have never heard of you.'

'Then,' said Cuchulain, piqued, 'you will hear of me now.'

'Well,' said Emer, 'what is your standing amongst the noblemen of Ulster?'

'This,' said Cuchulain. 'When I am at my weakest, I can defend myself alone against twenty. On a normal day, I could cope with forty; and under my protection, at my best a hundred are secure. The greatest warriors avoid me in the battlefield.'

'It seems to me,' said Emer softly, 'that you are boasting.'

Now Cuchulain was more than piqued; he was quite annoyed. 'King Conor himself was my foster-father. I was reared amongst the chariot-chiefs and champions of Ulster, with poets and learned men. And it was among the northern nobles of Ulster that I learned my courage and skill. I am a match for any chief and I direct the councils of Ulster. At my own fort at Dun Dealgan the king comes to me for entertainment.'

He looked her full in the eye and drew himself up, his face assuming a stern and yet handsome appearance, so that her heart turned over in her bosom. 'Not as one of the common herd have I come here today,' he cried, 'but as a champion of Ulster. Lugh,' he went on, fixing her lovely green eye with his grey one, 'is my protector. I am of the race of the great gods and his especial concern.'

Emer, who had the six gifts of womanhood – the gift of beauty, the gift of poise, the gift of sweet speech, the gift of needlework, the gift of wisdom and the gift of chastity – looked at him and smiled. Immediately Cuchulain's sternness evaporated. 'Is it not clear,' he said, 'that I love you? We must be married.'

Then it was that Emer almost went too far. 'But perhaps you are already married,' she said.

'No!' said Cuchulain. 'I swear I am not.'

'What a pity,' said Emer. 'You are a fine man and should have a wife. And look, here is Fial, my sister. I should not marry before my older sister. She is excellent in every way, particularly in handiwork. Clever and an excellent needlewoman. Why don't you marry her? I'll call her over.'

Then Cuchulain became angry again. 'By the gods,' he said, 'I do not love Fial, but you. And if I don't marry you, then I never will marry at all.'

She lifted up her face and again their eyes locked and gently Cuchulain said: 'May the apple of your eye see only good.'

For a while they spoke together in riddles such as the druids had taught them both. And Cuchulain was delighted, for this was the first woman he had ever met who understood the secret language of the druids and they spoke and riddled with each other and laughed for a long time. And as they did so, Cuchulain's love grew and he felt certain that so did Emer's love for him.

Then she bent to pick a flower. He caught sight of her breasts above the top of her dress. 'Ah!' he said. 'I see a sweet and pleasant country. I could rest my weapon there.'

Emer looked at him and said: 'No man will rest in that country until he has killed a hundred men at every ford between Ailbine and Feidm's Leap,' which was a druidic way of saying that he must prove himself as vigorously in mind as in body so that the nobility of his heart as well as of his weapons stood out above those of other men.

Cuchulain nodded. 'Then in that sweet country I will rest my weapon,' he said.

'No man will rest in this country,' Emer went on, 'until he has done the salmon leap feat carrying twice his weight in gold and has struck down three groups of nine men with a single stroke leaving the middle man of each nine standing unharmed'; which, once again, was a druidic way of referring to combined qualities of mind and spirit and body, this time to proving skill and valour in chess.

'Then in that sweet country I'll rest my weapon,' said Cuchulain.

Again she said no man would rest in that country unless he had done other feats of ennoblement and again she looked at him so that the longing for him to rest there and the longing for him to prove himself shone from her eyes.

Cuchulain looked into her eyes and nodded: 'It is said and it is done.'

That night he returned to Emhain Macha, but before he went she had promised him that if he was away for a year and performed the tests she had outlined and came back again she would then become his wife. But she warned him against her father for she knew that he would try to kill Cuchulain if he got the opportunity.

That night when Forgall Monach returned to his castle he was informed of what had happened. He summoned his daughters Emer and Fial and asked them. And, being truthful – and also, perhaps, because Emer could not prevaricate in case Fial, out of envy or for some other reason, coloured the story even more highly than it was – she told him.

'Clearly,' said Forgall, 'it was the warped one from Emhain Macha.' By this he referred to the manner in which Cuchulain changed and altered fearsomely when his battle-fury was on him and he went into the warp-spasm that twisted his body into a monstrous thing of pulsing muscle, and from the crown of his head – or so 'twas said – a pillar of blood shot upwards for forty feet, his eyes became glazed and his body so hot that it would take many buckets and vats of cold water to cool it again.

'I see,' said Forgall. 'So he and you have talked about love. Well,' he went on, 'I'll put an end to that.' But there was more to Forgall's protectiveness of Emer now than there had been. He knew well who Cuchulain was and also that, brave and powerful as he himself was, he was no match for the young warrior. Therefore he devised a plan which should bring about Cuchulain's death, but without his hand showing in the matter.

Disguising himself as a merchant from Gaul he went to Emhain Macha with wine and other Gaulish produce for the king. While there he was introduced to many of the Ulster warriors, including Cuchulain, whom he acknowledged, in his wily way, to be the best, but with room for improvement. He said that if only Cuchulain were to visit Scatach of the Land of Shadows, the mysterious home of the Scythians, and studied the warriors' art with her, he would be the most powerful warrior in the world. If Forgall expected this to light a fire in Cuchulain's mind he was more than correct. Cuchulain leaped at the idea and was so eager to be off that he wanted to leave immediately. In spite of protests from his friends and from his foster-father, King Conor, that he was over-young for such a journey, Cuchulain was fired with enthusiasm. And that is what he did.

First he went to the land of Alban in the east where a fierce woman warrior called Donald the Soldierly, Donal Mildemail, and her daughter, Big Fist, lived near a dark and gloomy shore. They were both hideous, both huge, and had large eyes and black faces and rough, bright red hair. They were so cruel and vengeful that it was held extremely dangerous to quarrel with either. But they were skilled in the use of arms and even more skilled in teaching them; and Cuchulain stayed with them until he had learned all that they knew. But at the end of that time he was anxious to leave, having learned from Donald the feat of the Pierced Flagstone with the Bellows under it and the Hero's Coil and the Spikes of Spears and many other wonderful feats with arms until he was perfect in all that she knew to teach him. 'And now,' said Donald, 'it is time for you to go to Scatach in Scythia.'

So Cuchulain travelled across Alban and thence to Gaul and thence to the city of Nyrax from whence had come his ancestors, and thence further east until he reached the great Plain of Ill Luck, today called the Wallachian Plain, where he could not cross without being mired in its bottomless bogs or sticky clay. And while he was standing there looking eastwards and wondering what to do, what should he see coming towards him but a young hero with a face shining like the sun. And although Cuchulain didn't know it, this was his own relation Lugh Lamh Fada, the god, who sometimes walked amongst men and always protected his own, and now his look of cheerfulness and hope went to Cuchulain's heart. Lugh gave Cuchulain a wheel with instructions to roll it before him across the plain and follow it carefully wherever it went, and if he did so he would reach the other side. So Cuchulain set the wheel rolling and followed the path it took through the bogs and marshy places, and as it rolled before him water shot like rays from its rim and blazed in the sunlight so that it looked as if it was made of silver and gold as it made a firm path across the great bog for Cuchulain to follow in safety.

Cuchulain survived many other adventures before he reached the last bastion before the land where Scatach lived, which was the Bridge of Leaps. And before it he found many young lords and nobles from Ireland who had gone before him, being older, to learn the feats of war from Scatach. Among them were Naisi and his two brothers, the sons of Usna,[1] and Cuchulain's friend, Ferdia, son of the Firbolg, Daman. When he had told them all the news of Ireland, Cuchulain asked Ferdia how he could find Scatach. For answer, Ferdia pointed to a great gorge that dropped sheer from the plain on which they stood to the ocean far below. Through it swung the tides of a boiling sea in one tempestuous welter of foam from one end of this precipitous gorge to the other.

'She lives,' said he, 'on the island on the other side of that gorge.'

'And how do I cross the gorge?' asked Cuchulain.

Ferdia looked at him and grinned. 'Like the rest of us,' said he, 'you cannot cross it until Scatach comes to teach us how to do so.'

'How is that?' asked Cuchulain.

'There are two feats that Scatach teaches last. One of them is the thrust of the *Gae-Bolga* – and isn't it a cruel irony that it was from Ferdia himself that Cuchulain first heard of the terrible body-spear, or belly-spear as some call it, which was the weapon with which he killed Ferdia in the battle of the Ford years hence? – 'and the other is the leap across the bridge, for she comes here every day to teach us varied feats of arms. But if a man steps on one end of that bridge, the middle straightaway rises up and flings him back, and if he leaps upon it he might miss his footing altogether and fall into the gulf where the sea monsters are waiting for him below.'

And with that Cuchulain approached the edge of the cliff and looked down and sure enough, where the sea boiled and roared through the narrow passage, the monsters of the deep rose to the surface and gaped aloft with fearful fangs.

Beside him, Ferdia said: 'You may well look down. But I'm telling you if you stand on one end of that bridge the other will throw you back again. Not one of us has crossed the bridge so far – nor will we until she is satisfied that we have learned everything else. And I might as well tell you,' he added, 'that while she might teach some of us the leap of the bridge, she will teach only one of her pupils, namely the champion who excels in all other feats, and the one she likes best, the feat of the *Gae-Bolga*. And I have every intention of being that one,' he went on with a grin.

Cuchulain looked down and then he looked at his friend and he said: 'Tell me, Ferdia, how Scatach herself crosses the bridge when she comes to teach you?'

'By two leaps,' said Ferdia. 'That is the only way the bridge can be crossed. She leaps to the very centre of the bridge and from there to the ground beyond without a pause. But if you miss the exact centre, and that is very likely, you would be hurled to the gulf.'

With that Cuchulain looked, first at the bridge, then at the foaming gorge and the open-mouthed monsters and the tossing waves, and then he turned back and walked towards the others with Ferdia beside him. He rested for the remainder of that day to recover his strength and when the evening came he stood up and gathered himself and ran at the bridge from a distance striving to leap for the middle. The far end rose up and threw him back again. Three times he leaped and three times it rose against him and flung him back. His companions, who had come up to watch, mocked him and laughed because he would not wait to be taught by Scatach, until Cuchulain became angry and with that he went into his warp-spasm. When they saw that the others drew back silently.

He stepped to the edge of the gorge and sprang off in his hero's salmon-leap right to the middle of the bridge and again he leaped and reached the far end so quickly that it had no time to fly at him. Then he sprang onto the solid ground of the island and went straight up to the fort where Scatach lived. He looked back at his companions and then he struck the gate of the fort with his spear-point and broke straight through the gate.

When Scatach heard the sound of the timber splintering from the blow, she was astonished and sent her daughter, Utach the Fearful, to bring in and welcome to her fort whoever it was who knocked so grandly. 'By the gods,' she said, 'this must be some exceptional warrior to have achieved this.'

When Utach saw Cuchulain she was overcome by desire for him. And so powerful was this emotion that she, who was called Fearful not from any infirmity of hers by way of nervousness or appearance, but because she could inspire fear with the boldness of her manner and the brazenness of her tongue, was struck dumb and awed into silence by his manly beauty. Silently and with round and distant eyes she went back to her mother whom she told, rather haltingly, what she had seen.

Scatach smiled at her with amusement. 'I can see he pleases you,' she said.

'Indeed he does,' sighed the girl.

'Then,' said her mother, who was forthright in all things and had long wished her daughter to become star-struck with a man rather than batter him to pieces with her tongue, 'take him to bed with you tonight and sleep with him if that's what you want.'

'Indeed,' said Utach, 'it would be no hardship, if he would like to.'

And so, afraid that Cuchulain might have heard of her and of her reputation, Utach pretended to be a servant, and welcomed and entertained him and provided him with food and water and other things which it is better not to go into here. And this she did for three days and at the end of that time they pleased one another so much that Utach felt she could safely tell Cuchulain who she was.

Cuchulain was surprised – there was no doubt about that – but, on the other hand, he said: 'I knew by your manner that you were no servant girl. But it never occurred to me that you were Utach the Fearful I had heard about. Either,' he said, 'your reputation is unwarranted or you have changed considerably.'

''Tis you've changed me, Cuchulain,' said Utach, 'and I can tell you I feel all the better for it. And now listen to me, and if you do you will become the greatest warrior in the world. I can do that for you in return.'

She told him that he should go to where Scatach was teaching her two sons, Cuar and Cat, in private in the centre of a sacred grove, a *nemeidh* of yew trees. No one but Scatach and those she invited into it were permitted there. Utach told Cuchulain that he must make his salmon-leap into the high branches of one of the yew trees and from thence into the sacred grove. 'And when you get there,' she said, 'what you must do is put the point of your sword between her two breasts and make her promise you three things.' She looked at him fiercely in the two eyes and said: 'Thoroughness in your training; prophecies for your future; and a dowry for your marriage.'

With that she looked even more intently at Cuchulain. But he failed to notice the meaning in her look for his mind was already racing to the *nemeidh*, and the rest of him followed swiftly. He made the leap Utach had told him to, and another.

Then he stood before Scatach, bared his sword and put the point to her breast and said, 'Death is in the air above you.'

She looked back at him without a flicker of emotion – and it may well be she had foreseen this was going to happen – and said: 'You can have the three things your heart most desires if you can ask them in the one breath.'

And so Cuchulain said what Utach had told him to and made Scatach give her promise. From that on until he returned to Ireland (except for a small while we'll come to shortly), Utach and Cuchulain lived together and Scatach taught him all she knew of the craft and trade of arms. She also taught Ferdia Mac Daman and he and Cuchulain became great and inseparable friends. But in the end of all, she taught both of them everything except the feat of the *Gae-Bolga* – which she would teach only to Cuchulain, refusing Ferdia's request that she teach him too, for she wanted Cuchulain to be invincible and to have one battle feat known only to himself.

But because Cuchulain was the younger and because they were such close friends, Cuchulain became arms bearer to Ferdia while they were under Scatach's training and together they went through every danger and every peril, and swore by the heavens above them and the earth beneath them and the sea round about them that unless the sky should fall with its showers of stars on the ground where they were, unless the earth should be rent by an earthquake, and the waves of the blue sea come over the forests of the living world, they would never betray or contest with one another. And as they made this oath, if they could have seen the future they would have blenched and turned pale and sealed up their lips . . . and their hearts too, maybe. Or maybe not!

The *Gae-Bolga* was a fearsome weapon. Cast with the foot and aimed at the belly of the enemy – hence its name, 'belly spear' – it was cast from the fork of the toe and was often fired secretly from the running water of a stream. It entered a man with a single wound like a javelin and then opened into thirty barbs. Only by cutting away the flesh could it be taken out of that man's body.

Scatach taught Cuchulain everything she knew and so increased his power and skill that, before his time was rightly up and young though he was, he was acknowledged by all as the greatest hero and champion that ever was trained at her war school. And speaking of war, didn't it so happen that a deadly enemy of Scatach's, a Cichloiste or Amazon by the name of Aoifa (the fiercest and strongest of the women warriors of the world so that even Scatach was cautious about meeting her in battle), had her army in the vicinity. And Scatach's ambition overcame her caution and the armies of these two princesses drew up in battle array and faced one another where their territories joined.

Scatach, who loved Cuchulain as much as her daughter, Utach, was concerned that he might be killed or injured in battle before he made his mark in the world, for all the prophecies and omens agreed that he would die young. Accordingly, on the night before the battle, she made a powerful soporific that she had mixed herself from the juice of herbs and tree bark with his drink. 'Twas so strong she calculated that he wouldn't wake for at least twenty-four hours, by which time the battle would be over. Moreover, while he was asleep she tied him up as an added precaution, and then took her place at the head of her troops to await the dawn and the battle it would bring. But the concoction that would have stretched any other man dead asleep for a night and a day encumbered Cuchulain for only an hour. And when the time was up he woke up and, finding himself tied, understood what was going to happen. Putting forth his strength he burst asunder the bonds that tied him and leaped to his feet looking for his weapons. Arming himself for war Cuchulain followed Scatach's hosts at a run by the chariot tracks until he came up with them. When Scatach looked back and saw him racing after her hosts, she sighed, knowing that there was nothing she could do to prevent Cuchulain taking part in the battle.

But before the battle proper commenced there were, of course, challenges issued from one side to the other for single combat. And three of Aoifa's warriors, the three daughters of Ilsuanach, stood out before their host and jeered and challenged Scatach's two sons, Cuar and Cat, to come and fight them. They shook their spears and struck their shields with them crying: '*Buail mo sciath* – I strike my shield at you.' They turned their backs on Scatach's hosts and raised their skirts – for that was the type of garment they wore – and displayed their bare backsides in a sign of contempt. And as if that wasn't enough they danced three times in a circle to the left all the while calling cowardice and misfortune against the sons of Scatach.

'You are well named Cat,' cried one of them, 'for your battle-cry is like the mewling of a kitten.'

'And you, Cuar,' cried another, 'for a more crooked and perverse looking eejit never put foot on a battlefield.' (Cuar means 'crooked', and it was the name by which Scatach's second son was called because he was afflicted with the curiosity of having one eye probing east while the other, simultaneously, probed west.)

This was too much for the two sons of Scatach who, although night was drawing fast and there were only the two of them against the three Cichloiste, leaped from the ranks of the hosts and charged towards those of their scoffers. Seeing that there were two against three – and not being aware of the fact that the enemy were women, for they were bigger and stronger and uglier than most men and, after the fashion of most Amazons, had cut off their right breasts as an encumbrance to sword-work, and strapped the other up behind their jerkin – Cuchulain followed after. Being quicker and fleeter of foot than any man he passed the two sons of Scatach before they were halfway towards their enemies and reached them while they were still laughing at the youth who was charging at them. Without pause or alteration in the rhythm of his stride, and with one blow of his great sword, Cuchulain swept the three heads of the daughters of Ilsuanach from their shoulders and, before their bodies had fallen, had grabbed the heads by the forelocks with his left hand and was racing back towards the hosts of Scatach. As he passed the two sons of Scatach he tossed a still grinning head to each one (keeping one for himself) and so brought them, triumphantly, back to his own side.

Next morning himself and Scatach's two sons went out and faced three more of Aoifa's soldiers, Ceri and Biri and Blaicne, the sons of Eis Enchenn, the Bird-Headed, who had challenged them as the dawn broke – and it goes to show that not all warriors in the Amazon army were women. And, although these three warriors claimed to be the greatest in Aoifa's forces, their heads too were brought back by Cuchulain to Scatach's troops. Then Aoifa challenged Scatach herself to single combat. But Cuchulain said 'no', and that he would meet Aoifa, who was called the Fair Fury, himself instead.

But first he asked Scatach: 'Tell me, what does Aoifa prize above all else?'

'Her horses,' answered Scatach, somewhat puzzled. 'Her horses, her chariot and her charioteer.'

Cuchulain nodded, saying nothing. He took his weapons, settled his helmet firmly on his head, and went out to meet Aoifa in single combat. They fought for hours, Cuchulain and the Fair Fury, Queen of the Cichloiste. At first they circled one another cautiously watched by the hosts of both armies. And then with a terrible clash they closed on one another and fought ceaselessly and without pause for several hours. Every champion's feat and skill in battle that they knew they tried on one another in vain until at last a mighty blow of Aoifa's battleaxe smashed Cuchulain's sword at the hilt and he was left with nothing bigger than a piece the size of his fist in his grasp.

In the instant Cuchulain leaped back, the sweat running off him, and locked his eyes on hers as she moved in on him, her axe held wide for the death-swing. His own arms were outstretched as he crouched and moved slowly backwards. Then he flickered his eyes over her shoulder and allowed them to widen and smile. 'Hi-i-i,' he roared, casting his voice in the direction of Scatach's troops behind him. 'Look where Aoifa's horses and chariot, her charioteer and all are going over the cliffs. Good man Ferdia!'

In spite of herself, Aoifa took her eyes off him and glanced over her shoulder. But when she did so, Cuchulain flew inside her axe, leaped on her and seized her by the two breasts (which goes to show that it wasn't every Amazon who cut off the right one), threw her over his back like a sack, and carried her back to Scatach's army like that, roaring and screaming with rage until she realised 'twas no use and she quietened down. When they reached Scatach, Cuchulain threw her on the ground, knelt astride her, and put his knife to her throat.

But she had herself well recovered by that time and she looked up at him as bold as you like and there was no trace of fear in her lovely eyes. Her two breasts, which were rising and falling with her breathing – which, fair enough, was a bit faster than normal, and why wouldn't it? – clearly showed the marks of Cuchulain's fingers where he carried her, and she said: 'A life for a life, Cuchulain.'

He looked down at her. He saw a beautiful woman, and the finest warrior he had ever struggled with. His blood stirred in him, and along with it a thought for the future, and he said: 'I have three demands.'

Then Aoifa repeated the formula of commitment Scatach had already put him under about the other matter: 'What you can ask in one breath you may have,' she said.

'Well,' said Cuchulain, leaning on her and looking into her eyes, 'this is what you must promise; that you'll have lasting peace with Scatach, give her hostages, and will never attack her again.'

He paused, and she nodded. Now he looked at her for a good long moment, and her lips parted, but her eyes – although they widened – stayed locked on his own. He went on; 'The pleasure of your company tonight in your own bed.'

He paused again, looking at her; she looked back at him a moment and then nodded. He eased his weight now off her wrists that he had been holding and said in a gentler voice: 'And to be the mother of my son.'

This time her eyes wavered after a moment and the lids dropped. Her breast heaved. Then she looked up at him again. Now childbearing was supposed to be anathema to Cichloiste. But when Aoifa thought of their battle and struggles –

and maybe her life – something profound stirred in her too as she looked up at Cuchulain. 'It is done,' she said.

So Cuchulain returned with Aoifa to her own camp and they spent that night together and loved each other and he stayed with her for a number of weeks until she told him that she was with child. 'Moreover,' she said, 'I know it will be a boy. I can feel it in my womb.'

Then Cuchulain knew it was time for him to return to Ireland. Before he left he gave Aoifa a gold arm ring and told her to give it to their son, and when he was old enough so that it would stay over his wrist she must send him to Ireland to find him. Then thinking of what lay before himself in Ireland when he got back, and, also, that his son, the child of the two greatest warriors in the world, would be the greatest of all; and thinking of the situation that could arise; that his enemies would do all they could to kill his son if they ever discovered about him, he said: 'I put this *geasa* on you, and you must put it on him.'

But when he gave his *geasa* he was so busy thinking of those things that he failed to consider well enough the meaning of his words and, so, with fearful consequences, he said, 'He must not make himself known to *anyone* that he is my son; he must never turn aside for any man; he must never refuse a combat. Lastly, he is to be called Connla, meaning "bright and glittering constancy".'

Having said that and made a tender farewell with Aoifa, Cuchulain went back to Scatach's castle, returning the way he came. The route was by a very narrow path through the mountains. On one side rose a cliff and on the other was a sheer fall. And right smack in the middle of it what did he meet coming towards him but a hideous, one-eyed hag, who snarled at him to get out of the way? Mildly enough – for he was ever polite, at first anyway – he pointed out that this would leave him no room; and if he was to move aside it meant either climbing the cliff which was overhanging and therefore impossible, or descending the cliff to the sea, which was impossible too. But if she didn't beg and plead and squint at him with her one eye from where she was crunched and scrunched on the path and crawling along it, to make way for her somehow, for she couldn't go back (though 'twas the easier road for her) and, so, wasn't he moved with pity? What did he do only brace himself against the overhang with his two outstretched hands and move his two heels back over the precipice, clinging only with his toes, so that he made an arch over the path so that she could pass beneath. Well, if he did, didn't the old biddy strike with a rock she had concealed in her fist at his bare toes where they stuck out of his Greek sandals so that he stepped backwards involuntarily to escape the blows, and over the edge of the cliff with him and the old hag cackling and screaming with unnatural glee. But, as you know, Cuchulain was no ordinary man and didn't he grip the rocky edge of path with his hands and with a great heave throw himself back up again? A remarkable feat! The hag lunged at him, but with a blow of the new sword given to him as a parting gift by Aoifa he cut off her head. It flew from her screaming shoulders out from under the shawl that had been draped about her, and fell to the path before rolling over the precipice edge. Before it vanished he recognised it as that of Eis Enchenn, the bird-headed mother of the three warriors he had killed in single combat before the battle with Aoifa. She had watched him all these weeks and had waited in ambush to kill him, knowing that he had to return by this route.

When he again reached Scatach's castle Cuchulain told her that it was time for him to return to Ireland as she had taught him everything she knew. 'And,' he went on, taking her arms, 'much more. You have taught me the apple-feat with nine steel apple-missiles in the air at one time; the thunder-feat from my chariot; all the feats of sword-play and shield-work; the strike of the cat; perfected the salmon-leap; the great feat of the chariot-pole at full gallop; the spurt of speed; the mouth of a wolf and the hero's scream; the stun-shot and all the other feats of war and martial arts. But now 'tis time for me to go.'

Then Scatach, the seer, prophesied his future. She described the battles, the torment and destruction that would afflict Ireland because of the desire of Maeve of Connacht to possess the brown bull of Cooley. She told how, when all of Ulster's heroes would lie sick from a magical affliction, he alone, Cuchulain (because he was not an Ulsterman), would stand against the entire army of Maeve. Staring with a wide, fixed gaze into the flames of a small bronze brazier that stood on three tall legs, and speaking in a high, sing-song, she cried:

Crimson battle's violent roar
Sweeps over landscapes stained with gore
Through with the mordant ravens seek
Riven flesh with blood-stained beak.
'Tis you'll defend the lands and maids
Of Ulster from these Connacht raids.
Alone you'll stand blood-ringed and brave
Against the warring hosts of Maeve.
While you roam Muirthemne's plain
Many champions will be slain.
But when your blood and strength are wasted,
Then at last will death be tasted.
I see it all. For thirty years
A hero's deeds inspire great fears.
But after that I see no more.
Beyond it stands a shuttered door.
Yet in the meantime, too, you'll know
Love and Triumph as you go.

There's heartbreak too, for I can see
The single twig crushed by the tree.

After that Cuchulain left Scatach and returned to Ireland, heading for Emhain Macha. When he landed, below in Wexford, he hired a chariot and charioteer to take him north. But on the way, anxious to put the skills he'd acquired in the east to good use, he made a detour and drove along the marches between Connacht and Ulster, where there had always been turmoil. He came to the territory of Nachtan and his sons.

'And are they,' asked Cuchulain of his charioteer, 'the sons of Nachtan of whom it is said that more of the men of Ulster have fallen by their hands than are still living?'

'The same,' said the charioteer, 'a fearsome tribe altogether. You'd be well advised to steer well clear of them.' And with that he pulled the trace to turn the horses' heads east.

But Cuchulain stopped him. 'Hold hard. Turn west there and drive to the *faitche* beyond. We'll pay them a visit.'

'But —' began the charioteer, until Cuchulain looked at him.

Then he shrugged, flicked the reins and pulled the horses' heads round to the west, but I can tell you his heart wasn't in it, for those sons of Nachtan were no respecters of persons and were as likely to shorten a charioteer by a foot or so as anyone else. Anyway Cuchulain charged down upon the great Dun of the sons of Nachtan and there, on the *faichte* before the castle, he saw a pillar-stone and round it was a collar of bronze on which was written that any man of an age to bear arms who should come to that green was obliged under *geasa* not to proceed without having challenged one of the dwellers in the dun to single combat.

When Cuchulain read this he flung his arms around the pillar-stone and, wrenching it this way and that, tugged it and heaved at it until at last he pulled it out of the ground and flung it, collar and all, into the river that ran close by. 'Well,' said the hired charioteer gloomily, 'there's no doubt! Ordinary men go out of their way to avoid meeting death, but I have the luck not to be hired by one and nothing else will do him but to go running at it with his arms wide open.'

Well, the words were no sooner out of his mouth than Foill, one of Nachtan's sons, came out of the castle. But when he saw that Cuchulain was little more than a boy, he was so annoyed and disgusted that he turned back again, spitting out as he went. Only Cuchulain called after him: 'If you're going back inside don't come out again without your weapons and your armour, for I won't kill *giollas* or gofers or unarmed men.' When he heard that Foill went back into the castle in a rage to fetch his weapons.

'Whisper,' said the charioteer in Cuchulain's ear, 'you'll have a hard job killing that fella. He's protected by some magic of his own patent against the point or the edge of any blade, and I can tell you dam' the thing you'll poke him with or strike him with will do him the smallest bit of harm' – (and what he had was a suit from far in the eastern world made out of the finest, tightly woven and well-padded silk ever was seen. And it could turn the point of an edge in the most extraordinary fashion).

Cuchulain nodded and put a ball of tempered iron in his sling – a trick he learned from Scatach who had it from some obscure tribe of the Seleucid kingdom south-east of Scythia beyond Armenia, whose king, Daithi, or David in their own language, employed the same feat against a Phoenician hero. And when Foill appeared Cuchulain plugged him with the ball through the forehead. Cuchulain cut off his head and tied it to the rim of his chariot. The other two sons of Nachtan who had been watching came out running in a rage. Cuchulain fought the two of them and killed one of them with his sword and the other with a spear. Then he set fire to the dun and left it blazing and drove on, delighted with himself, the heads swinging from the rim of his chariot. The charioteer felt better too. He couldn't say enough in praise of Cuchulain and tried to get as much noise as he could out of the chariot, so they were both well pleased with themselves as they rattled along.

Indeed Cuchulain was so pleased with his exploit that when he saw a flock of wild swans whooping above him on the way he cast so expertly at them with his sling that he brought sixteen down alive. Then he tied them to his chariot with long leather thongs, so that they flew above him as he advanced. When he saw a herd of wild deer he went after them in his chariot, but the horses couldn't overtake them. At that he leaped out of the chariot and chased them himself on foot 'til he caught two stags. And he tied these to his chariot with thongs and ropes and went on towards Emhain Macha.

Well, King Conor was sitting in his great hall when one of his scouts came running in a sweat and collapsed before him. 'What ails you at all,' asked Conor, 'to come galloping in here like a hare with a hound after it and fall down like that on your face before me – the proper position for you, I might add?'

'Lord,' babbled the scout, 'the queerest thing you ever saw is charging down on top of us over the plain. A single chariot and all above it are white birds fluttering and wild stags are racing beside it and the bleeding heads of enemies are bouncing on its rim like baubles on the bosom of an excited maiden.'

When he heard that Conor had a fair good idea who might be in it and he jumped to his feet and went out onto the battlements of Emhain Macha to look out over the plain. Sure enough what else did he see but exactly what the scout had told him – a chariot charging with the birds and the stags and the thunder of hooves and the rattle and crash and clang of a hero's war-chariot howling out

181

of the dust with the sods flying behind him and the bleeding heads grinning and bouncing on the chariot rim. 'The gods between us and all harm,' said Conor, 'that's Cuchulain in his battle-fury and the divil and all won't stop him when he gets here but he'll kill every man-jack of the lot of us.'

But he wasn't a king for nothing, and hadn't he inherited his share of his mother's wisdom and cuteness (she who was responsible for his being king at all).[2] And one of the qualifications of a king that makes him different from other men is that when there is a problem, no matter how big it is or at what time it presents itself, he finds an immediate solution to it. Accordingly, Conor hastily gave the order that as many of the women of Emhain as could be found in the time should go out fast to meet Cuchulain before he reached the city and stand before him as the gods had made them *in*, so to speak, *puris naturalibus*, as the Romans say.

And so while the chariot tore down on Emhain Macha a group of a dozen or so women ran out of the gates shedding their garments as they ran, to stand in front of the oncoming chariot in all their naked loveliness, and a strange and wonderful sight indeed it must have been to see: the rattling chariot, the battle-crazed hero and the wild charioteer lashing the foaming horses to a thundering gallop of furious speed, the wild birds and animals flying and streaking through the sky and alongside them, with only twelve or fifteen trembling and naked women standing between that and the gates of the city. When Cuchulain saw the women standing in the way of his chariot, the battle-lust began to die in his eye and the rage became tempered in his blood. He was overcome with shame and bowed his head on the chariot rim that he might not behold the nakedness of the women of Emhain Macha. The grateful charioteer brought the chariot to a halt and Conor's men took hold of Cuchulain and plunged him into a great bath of cold water outside one of the sweat houses. But if they did the water boiled around him and they had to whip him out again and plunge him into another, and yet another until, at last, his fury left him entirely and his natural form and aspect were restored. Then he was dressed in fresh clothing and welcomed by the king to a feast in the banqueting hall. And that is how Cuchulain returned to Emhain Macha.

On the next day Cuchulain decided to go again to the castle of Forgall the Cunning and claim Emer as his bride. His own chariot was harnessed and he drove south to Lusk like a champion, measured in the noise of his oncoming chariot, for noise was the distinguishing mark of a great king or hero. On the way he did a thunder-feat that slew three hundred and nine of Forgall's men according to the chroniclers of the event (who might have been biased, being Ulstermen, for others say it was only three hundred, and others that it was still less). When he reached the castle he made a salmon-leap across the three enclosures to the middle of the castle where Forgall's bodyguards attacked him from all sides. But he let go three strokes with his spear at the three groups of them and with each stroke he killed eight men and left one man standing in the middle of each group, and they were Emer's three brothers.

When Cuchulain saw that Forgall tried to escape in terror, he pursued him across the ramparts. And in his fright didn't Forgall slip and fall from the highest point of the highest battlement and kill himself? With that Cuchulain carried off Emer and her foster-sister and their full weight of gold and silver, thus fulfilling another of Emer's edicts. Out with them from the castle across the ramparts with shrieks and cries rising on every side. At every ford between Lusk and Emhain Macha he was attacked by the great hosts of Forgall and at every ford he left a hundred dead behind him. And so he accomplished everything Emer had laid on him.

When they reached Emhain Macha, Emer was brought into the Craebh Rua to be made welcome by Conor and the other Ulster nobles. There, too, was the sharp-tongued hosteller Bricriu, who liked to sow dissention and, looking up as if it was no business of his – which it wasn't – he observed to the ceiling in a voice loud enough to be heard by anyone who cared to listen: 'I don't suppose,' he said, 'Cuchulain will find tonight's doings very much to his taste. Isn't it a fact,' he went on, 'that this woman he has brought here must sleep tonight with Conor or,' he asked innocently, 'am I mistaken in thinking that the first forcing of girls in Ulster is always the king's?'

When Cuchulain heard this, his eyes started to blaze and he trembled so hard that the cushion burst under him and the feathers flew around the house. He was hard put to it to keep his temper. He knew, too, that if he did lose it his battle-fury would come on him and he'd slaughter all round him indiscriminately so he rushed out of the palace and stamped up and down outside in the night to cool himself.

'Hmmm . . .' said Catha the druid, 'if this isn't the tricky business! 'Tis a pity Bricriu brought it up; but now he has the king can't very well refuse to do what he says. On the other hand,' he mused, 'Cuchulain will surely destroy any man who sleeps with his bride.'

And here again Conor showed what it is to be a king. He told his steward to shake the *craobh sida* or branch of peace for silence – the *craobh sida* being in the likeness of a tree branch in silver hung with bells to be rattled when the king wanted order; there was another yoke, the *Slabra Estechta* or chain of silence which is used in other places for the same purpose – and, when all was quiet and everyone was looking at him, he said calmly: 'Go out one of ye and call back Cuchulain. We'll see if we can't cool his fever.'

When Cuchulain came in, Conor said to him: 'Cuchulain, I have a small job for you. Let you go up into Slieve Fuad and bring me back all the herds which are wandering there, like a good lad.'

Cuchulain wasn't too happy about this in view of what had gone before, but the king was the king and he couldn't very well refuse, so off he went to gather together the swine, the cattle, the deer and every other kind of an animal or wild flying creature he could find on Slieve Fuad, and drive them back again in one flock to Emhain Macha. When that was done his anger was quenched.

Meanwhile the men of Ulster had discussed the problem and, on Conor's prompting, came up with the decision that Emer would sleep all right that night in Conor's bed, but Fergus and Catha would sleep there too to protect Cuchulain's honour. When Cuchulain came back in the morning with all those flocks and herds outside on the *faitche* of Emhain Macha they told him what the decision was and added that the whole of Ulster would bless the pair of them – that is himself and Emer, not himself and Conor – if he accepted. Cuchulain was relieved and thought it was a good plan and accepted it and that is what was done. Next day, Conor paid Emer a dowry and Cuchulain was given his honour price, and after that he slept every night with his wife and they were never parted again until he died (that is, if you don't count his time in the other world for which he wasn't responsible but that's another story).

And while that is the end and the determination of the story of the wooing of Emer, it is by no means the end or conclusion of the events that occurred during its course, so we'll go on.

Seven years after that, Aoife discovered that the arm-ring Cuchulain had left for his son would no longer fall off his wrist and so 'twas time for him to go to his father, Cuchulain, who, by virtue of his bravery and exploits, had, by this time, been appointed the official Champion of Ulster.

It so happened that at that time the nobles of Ulster were gathered by the seashore on a strand that came to be known as Tragh Eise, the Strand of the Footprints, from what was about to happen. Cuchulain was below in his own place at Dun Dealgan enjoying himself with his wife and wasn't with them. When their business was done (for they were adjudicating and making judgements on some matters pertaining to the colonies in the wild land of the Picts, Alban), they relaxed and talked or walked, or played this game or that game on the beach, for all the world as peaceful and tranquil a sight as one might expect where a group of nobles were gathered together: their horses tethered behind on the coarse grass beside their chariots, nibbling the pink and white clover. The coloured tents and awnings threw formal shades on the white sand, and the pennants on standards hung limply in the golden air as they discoursed and disported themselves. Then, far out on the shimmering sea, what did they see coming towards them but a small boat of beaten bronze guided by servants pulling gilded oars, and in it a small lad absorbed in feats of the most extraordinary skill. For instance he would fit a stone in a sling and fire it with such prowess, humming, at the wild seabirds that soared above him that he brought them down alive at his feet, whereupon he would toss each in the air again to fly free and fire another stone at another that fell in the same fashion, only to be set free as before. That, and other feats of extraordinary skill he performed far beyond his years and, indeed, far beyond the ability of most grown men.

All the nobles gathered around King Conor and watched this. Conor didn't look at them, but nodded slowly and thoughtfully stroked his beard. 'Well,' he said, 'I don't know. I don't know at all. I don't know where the divil he comes from, but I know this much: if one of their young lads can do that, what would a grown man do to us? Go on out and meet him some of ye, but whatever ye do don't let him put a foot or a finger ashore until I say so.'

'Who'll go?'

'Who else,' snapped Conor irritably, for – and 'tis an important matter to know, for some, anyway – those around a king are supposed to know such things as are in his mind without being told, 'but Condaire Mac Echach? Hasn't he more common sense and eloquence than the rest of ye out together? Condaire is the man for the job.'

'Well,' said Condaire cautiously, 'I make no promises, but I'll see what I can do.'

Conor nodded and off went Condaire along the shore to meet the boy. He arrived just as the boat put its nose into the beach.

'Eh,' said Condaire, 'you've travelled a while, young man.'

'I have,' replied the child.

'Eh, well,' said Condaire, summoning all the resources of tact and eloquence for which he was renowned, 'you've travelled as far as you're going now in this direction. Until we find out who you are and where you came from and who your people are there's no chance of your setting foot here.'

'Is that a fact?' said the boy.

'It is,' said Condaire.

'Well now,' said the boy – and in another it might be taken as a piece of impudence for one so young to speak in that fashion to a respected senior; but there was about him a firmness and a calmness that did away with impertinence (and that surprised Condaire) – 'I'll tell you the way it is. I'll give my name to no man, and I'll make way for no man either.'

'You can't land,' repeated Condaire, 'until you tell us who you are and where you come from.'

'I'll go where I'm going,' said the boy determinedly, and stepped off the boat and went to pass Condaire up the beach.

Out of the corner of his eye, Condaire saw a general movement and a rustle of unease among the nobles behind him and pity stirred him. The last thing he wanted was to use force.

'Hold up, *avic* (my son),' he said quietly, ''tis easy to see you're no ordinary boy, but someone of exceptional gifts from some foreign part, and whether you or it is the more remarkable, none of us can tell. And we all acknowledge your great gifts and wonder at them.'

'You're right about that,' said the boy.

'So tell me who you are and where you come from and I'll see what I can do,' said Condaire.

The boy didn't reply.

'Look,' said Condaire, his patience wearing thin – and he was a man not much used to it, by today's standards anyway – 'can't you be sensible? Do you want blood spilt?'

The boy turned, said nothing, only shook his head.

Condaire said: 'Look, son, I have my instructions. I'm sworn to stop you one way or another. Do you want me to use force?'

'You're a kind man and well spoken,' said the boy, 'but I'm telling you now I have sworn my own oath and if you had the strength of a hundred men you couldn't stop me.'

Condaire was upset by this for he liked the look and the spirit of the lad and nothing would persuade him to tackle him, order or no order. 'I won't have the blood of this little boyeen on my hands,' he said to himself. He shrugged. 'Very well, so,' he said, 'let someone else talk to you.'

He went back to the king and the nobles and told them what had happened. 'Well the divil fire you!' said King Conor when he had heard him out. 'Why didn't you do what I told you?'

He turned to the others, his irritated eye searching. After some hesitation it lighted on the champion, Conall Cearnach, Conall the Victorious, who was paying no attention to what was going on at all, well satisfied that he was too mighty and important a person to be troubled by the king over a matter as insignificant as a precocious boy. He was absently gnawing on a leg of mutton that he held in one hand and picking his teeth with his *sgian* that he held in the other.

'For the love and honour of the gods, Conall, will you go down and give that young fella a skelp on the arse and send him on his road away about his business or back wherever he came from?'

'Who?' exclaimed Conall (who, apart from Cuchulain, was the most powerful warrior in Ulster) with both his jaw and his *sgian* suspended in wonder. 'Me, is it?'

'You!' said the king; so there could be no argument.

Conall glowered. The anger rose up in his throat to be sent on an errand against a *gorsoon*, a little boy. But, throwing the remains of the leg of mutton behind him on the sand-dunes (where it was descended on by a handful of squalling gulls), sheathing his *sgian* in his boot and wiping the two sides of bacon he called hands on his substantial hind-quarters, he stumped off down the strand towards the little figure in the distance. And when he looked, what was the boy doing but practising his games and his feats? One would have thought that he had no purpose in life other than to perfect himself in games he had already mastered to immaculate perfection. When Conall came up to him, what he was doing was an apple-blowing feat with little golden balls suspended in the air where they danced and sparkled in the sun while he sang. And he would tune his voice in tone and pitch so that the balls danced up and down in answer to his singing.

Conall stopped in front of him, put his two fists on his hips and glared at the boy for a good fifteen seconds without saying anything. Then, 'Will you get on away home, little boy, and don't be bothering decent people with your fancy games!'

The boy looked at him sideways, which was a neat trick in itself as he was still doing the feat, and between breaths so that the balls leaped up and down the scales, said: 'I'll go where I'm going.'

Conall decided to change his approach. 'That's a fancy game, boyeen,' he growled.

'I have one to work just as nicely on you,' said the boy, neatly dropping the balls into his hand and putting them away in the wallet at his waist. He turned to face Conall, and with that fitted a stone larger than before in his sling and let fly so that it whipped and cracked past Conall with the sound of a thunderbolt and Conall fell to the ground in a state of shock. Before he could rise the boy leaped on him and hogtied him with three whips of his shield cord so he couldn't move.

When the nobles of Ulster saw Conall Cearnach on his back and trussed up like a *bonhamh* or piglet for a feast, they were dismayed. Conor frowned and stroked his beard rapidly in perplexity. 'Go now let one of ye summon Cuchulain,' he said quietly, 'for no one else can contain this boy. Tell him that the honour of Ulster is at stake and that Ulster is in danger of being put to shame before the world.'

When the messenger reported this to Cuchulain, he simply said: 'Go on before me. I'll be on my way as soon as I'm armed.'

But his mind was troubled, no more so than that of his wife Emer, though, who was with him and had heard what the messenger said. And it was she who noticed his own concern. She put her arms around his neck and looked at him and said: 'Cuchulain, don't go. I know what's in your mind. You have an old pledge of love and friendship with Conall and you have sworn to help each other in trouble! But think, Cuchulain. Who might this boy be, if he is not your own son by Aoife? Who else could perform these marvellous feats described to us?

187

'Tis now seven years since your return. Will you go down and murder your own marvellous son? Remember what Scatach foretold and do not damage the twig from your own tree.'

But Cuchulain shrugged away saying: 'What can I do? They have put the honour of Ulster on me. If it is my own son itself, as the champion of Ulster, what choice do I have?' And he shouted for Laeg, his renowned charioteer, to harness his chariot and fit it with his weapons.

But Emer tried again to persuade him saying: 'Cuchulain, listen to me; listen to reason. We know who it must be. You told me yourself he cannot and must not tell his name to anyone or turn aside from any man. Is not that this boy's stand? Who else can it be but your own son?'

But Cuchulain, tormented, answered her: 'No matter who he is I have no choice in the matter. If Scatach's prophecy is to be fulfilled, then let it be fulfilled.'

So he rode in his chariot in all his panoply of war to meet the boy whom he found on the strand performing his game feats as he had been doing since he arrived.

'You're good at the games, *a mhach*, my son,' said Cuchulain. 'Now tell me who you are and where you come from.'

'I may not,' said the boy.

'Perhaps you were meant to meet me,' said Cuchulain.

'So be it,' said the boy; and he drew his sword and went for Cuchulain.

Laughing, Cuchulain parried the blow. But soon his laughter faded when he found out the ferociousness with which the boy attacked him and realised that not only was he no novice at swordplay, but that he was one of the most dangerous and brilliant opponents he had ever fought. Indeed in the middle of their battle the boy brought a blush of shame to Cuchulain's face when, with the speed of a swallow or a kingfisher, or a flash of light on a broken ring of water, he sheered a braided lock from Cuchulain's head with the Sword-feat of Shame, and Cuchulain stood back in disgust and anger looking at the braid where it had fallen on the ground. 'Enough of this tomfoolery,' he said. 'Let us wrestle to see who is the better,' thinking to best the boy with ease in that fashion.

But when the boy came to stand before Cuchulain he barely reached to his midriff and he looked up at Cuchulain and said: 'This won't do at all. Sure I can't reach you at this level.'

With that he climbed on two standing stones that were nearby and grappled with Cuchulain from there. So firmly had he planted his feet that try as he might Cuchulain could not move him and in their struggle the lad's two feet sank deep into the stone and left their imprints upon them which is how the strand got its name, Tragh Eise, the Strand of the Footprints. Without moving a foot, three times the boy thrust Cuchulain between the two stones, but neither could best the other.

Then they went down to the sea to continue their fight. At first the boy got Cuchulain down and held his head beneath the waves so that it seemed he'd suffocate. Then, his head reeling and his body struggling and fighting for life, what did the mighty Cuchulain do but fire the *Gae-Bolga* that Scatach had taught to no one but him. It sped under the water and through the belly of the boy, and ripped up his bowels, bringing them down around his feet so that the water of the ocean was stained with red blood.

'Ah!' cried the lad. 'This is what Scatach never taught me.'

And 'Ah!' cried Cuchulain, throwing his arms around his son. 'We are both wounded and tragedy has overtaken us.'

Gently he lifted the dying boy and carried him to the shore and laid him down before the nobles of Ulster. As he did so the bracelet he'd given Aoife to give to his son slipped down upon the boy's wrist and Cuchulain saw it. He looked up at the king and those around him and he cried in a broken voice; 'Here, oh men of Ulster, is the son of mine that you wanted.'

And with his last breath the boy gasped: ''Tis true. It is a pity. If I had only five more years longer among you I would have slaughtered the warriors of the world for you and you would be king of the world as far as Rome. But since I am dying, just point out to me the heroes of Ulster so that I can know them to say farewell to them.'

Then they all came around him, and one after another the boy put his arms around the neck of each one and kissed him, and then once more he put his arms around the neck of Cuchulain, his father. And then he died.

This was the only son Cuchulain ever had, and he killed him. When Cuchulain saw that his son was dead, a burst of anguish and lamentation broke from him and the others all joined in. And they made a grave for him and put a gravestone above it and for three nights and three days they mourned him as they would have mourned a king and no calf in the land was allowed to go to its cow because of the death of Connla.

That is the story of the wooing of Emer and the death of Cuchulain's only son.

FOOTNOTES

1 See 'Deirdre and the Sons of Usna'.
2 See 'Deirdre and the Sons of Usna'.

Mac Datho's Boar

Second Period: Ultonian Cycle

Mac Datho's Boar is straightforward story-telling, without concealed or subtle meaning unless it is to emphasise the status and, incidentally, the wisdom of a *brudir* or hosteller. He was an important man in ancient Ireland, but not – or not always – a nobleman. He was, however, often very wealthy. Indeed wealth was a necessary condition of his status, which was graded. There were greater and lesser *brudirs*. Five were greatest of all, national *brudeanna*. This story concerns one of these.

A *brúden* – or 'hostel', for want of a better word – was much more than a hotel. It was a vital social institution essential to the peace and stability of a restless and incohesive community. It even possessed a legal function. It was, therefore, important at several levels and there were laws and controls governing it and all concerned with it, which the various regal administrations and authorities recognised and supported. It was an institution where food, rest, sanctuary and peace were guaranteed to the traveller, both king and beggar alike.

Such places were entrusted to no ordinary men. However, in spite of his influence and wealth, a *brudir* was sometimes subject to the whims of his noble patrons. That is the subject matter of this tale.

In many ways, the story almost seems to belong to a later period. It has a homeliness absent from most of the stories of the Ultonian Cycle. Mac Datho's reliance on his wife's advice is so earthy as almost to smack of the later, significantly more tellurian Fianna Cycle.

A powerful and wealthy man named Mesroda Mac Datho was lord of one of the six great *brúden* of Ireland. That was in the time of King Conor Mac Nessa of the Red Branch of Ulster. Mac Datho's *brúden* was in Leinster; and the other five were the Brúden Da Derga, which was situated, like all *brudeanna*, where two roads crossed on the River Dodder where the Bohernabreena – the road to the Bruidne or 'Breen' in the vernacular – crossed the Slee Cualann on its way south towards Bray, at a place called Donnybrook; the Brúden Da Choca (where Cormac, Conor's son, was later killed), a few miles from Athlone; the Brúden Fergal at Lusk north of Dublin which was run by Cuchulain's father-in-law; the Brúden Blai Briuga in Ulster; and the Brúden Mic Gareo in Breffny. Every *brúden*, whether it was one of these great six *brúden* or a smaller, was a place of refuge and sanctuary where even a man of red weapons, that is a manslayer, could claim protection from the pursuit and vengeance of his victim's friends and family until he could be tried before a court of law. These were the six refuge *brúdens* of Ireland and there were three hundred and eight *brúden* or public hostelries, ninety of them in Connacht, eighty-nine in Ulster, eighty-nine in Leinster, and one hundred and thirty in Munster.

Hospitality and generosity were greatly esteemed virtues in Ireland at this time and these *brúden* offered free entertainment, food and lodging to every traveller. Indeed so great a place was given to these attributes that the law itself provided the occasions where a *brughaidh* (or *brudir*), that is a hosteller, might be excused a deficiency of food if, for instance, a large number of guests arrived unexpectedly or a tributary lord failed to contribute his due to the food supply of the *brúden*. It was said of anyone who found himself unable to discharge the due rights of hospitality that his face would become suffused with a *ruice* (ricka) or blush of shame. Accordingly, *brughaidhs* took care to ensure that they had no reason to blush and if it should happen that one of them fell short of provisions before visitors and had reason to feel ashamed of his scanty table, a defaulter had to pay him a compensation called the 'blush-fine'. Moreover, chieftains were bound to entertain guests without asking questions: who he was, or what his business was or whither he was bound and so forth, although the *feine* (perhaps *feini* or farmers) were not so bound and might make reasonable enquiries of their guests before entertaining them. But once a guest had eaten in a house, his host was bound to abstain from offering him any violence or disrespect under any circumstances whatsoever.

Below the six great *brúden* of Ireland, there were two other classes of *brughaidh* out of the hundreds mentioned which would entertain and keep open houses for kings, poets, *brehons* and travellers. The lowest class of *brughaidh* was the *brughaidh-cedach*, or hundred hospitaller, who had at least a hundred head of each kind of cattle, a hundred labourers and corresponding provision for feeding and lodging guests. Greater than him was the *brughaidh-lethech*, who had two hundred of each kind of cattle and labourers and so forth. He was not allowed to borrow and should have been able to entertain a hundred guests at a time, including providing them with beds.

That they might be able to receive visitors at all times, a *brughaidh* of whatever class was bound to have three kinds of meat cooked and ready to be served up at all times to all who came; moreover he had to have three kinds of raw meat ready for cooking and animals ready for killing. The law described him as 'a man of three snouts' – that is, the snout of a live hog rooting in the field to break the blushes off his face, the snout of a dead hog on the hooks cooking, and the pointed snout of a plough – meaning that he had plenty of live animals, of meat cooked and uncooked, and a plough and other necessary tillage appliances. And he was also 'a man of three sacks', required to have always in his house a sack of malt for brewing, a sack of salt for curing, and a sack of charcoal for cooking and for heating iron. His kitchen fire never went out, his cauldron was never taken off the fire, and it was never empty. He was obliged to have a man upon each of the roads, four or more, leading past his *brughaidh* so that not a traveller should pass without being invited to enjoy his hospitality; and at night he maintained a light on the *faitche* or lawn before his house to guide travellers from a distance. But as he was bound by law so was he protected by it; and his furniture and other property was defended against possible injury and the penalties and compensations for them were great. A *brughaidh* was also a judge entitled to hold minor court.

Thus Mac Datho's *brúden* was one of the 'six great courts of hospitality in Ireland'. (And, remember, a *brughaidh* though often the friend and entertainer of kings and nobles – and often wealthier and more powerful than some, and as powerful as many of those he entertained – was seldom himself either king or noble; and, though he might mingle with them, he could not sit with them.) Besides the great attributes of a powerful *brúden* – many acres, hundreds of cattle and a multitude of retainers – Mac Datho had two other possessions the fame of which had gone throughout all Ireland. The first of these was a boar. It was held to be the finest and greatest in size ever seen, standing at the shoulder as high as a pony, but twice the weight. A fearsome animal and the wonder and delight of many a sow, the progenitor of an unaccountable number of *bonamhs*. The second was a hound by the name of Ailbe, which could outrun every other hound and wild beast in Ireland. Of these two animals it was written:

> To Mesroda Mac Datho belonged a great boar
> With tusks like a *fiorlainn*[1] and as broad as a door;
> And a hound he called Ailbe – so great was its fame,
> It – no word of a lie – gave Magh Ailbhe its name.

By one of those coincidences upon which the fate of men and their generations sometimes hinges, didn't both Queen Maeve of Connacht and King Conor of Ulster become simultaneously afflicted with a passion of greed for possession of the hound? Each of them sent messengers to Mac Datho offering to buy the animal – and, as anyone with half an eye in his head and sense enough to make water with the wind behind him knows, from such as these mighty personages an 'offer' was no less than a command so far as the likes of a *brughaidh* was concerned. Of course the coincidence that each of them, the Queen of the West and the King of the North, conceived their desire and sent their messengers at the same time, so that the heralds of each arrived at Mac Datho's *brúden* together, is part of the story and no doubt is true: a minor version of the Tain Bo Cuailgne, if you like, for weren't they forever trying to get the better of one another after they broke up, and you may be sure that if one of them heard the other was after something, he, or she, would do his or her best to get it first.

Anyway, Mac Datho's *brúden* was a great place: seven doors to it and seven passages running through it. Within were seven mighty cauldrons and in each one of them the finest of the flesh of swine. Every traveller who came into the *brúden* after a journey would strike his fork into a cauldron and whatever he brought out at the first thrust, that was what he had to eat. If he got nothing at the first try he was not allowed a second attempt; and, you may be sure, everyone was pretty careful with his stab.

To go back to our story: when the heralds of the two monarchs arrived they were brought in to Mac Datho straightaway, even before they ate, which was unusual. And it was unusual for two reasons: firstly it was unusual because the laws of hospitality required that a traveller should be fed before anything else; and secondly it was unusual because of the *geasa* upon the lord of each of the six great *brúden* that they would not ask for information from any of the travellers who came to their hostelries. But in this case it wasn't Mac Datho's fault, for the heralds insisted, no less, that they see Mac Datho first off.

The Connachtman spoke first. 'Mac Datho,' said he, 'lord among the *brúdens* of Ireland, I am the messenger of Maeve, mistress of Connacht, and of her husband Ailill, and I am sent by them that I might ask for your hound, Ailbe.'

Mac Datho looked at them from where he sat, but said nothing. The only change in his expression was that his right eyelid dropped a little over his eye. The messenger went on: 'In exchange for this hound, Mac Datho, I am instructed to tell you that you can have six hundred milch cows, a travelling chariot with the best pair of horses to be had in Connacht and, moreover, at the end of a year you will be entitled to the same again.'

The herald from Ulster shot this fellow a sideways glance from out of his eye and looked back at Mac Datho whose expression hadn't changed.

'King Conor will give you no less, Mac Datho,' said he. 'And, moreover,' he added, 'he will give you his friendship and protection – which might be no small thing and you considerably closer to Ulster than you are to Connacht,' (which wasn't entirely true), he added with a kind of meaningful suggestion in his voice that anyone else might have taken as a threat. 'And another thing,' he went on, 'the pick of the litter.'

Mesroda Mac Datho looked at the two men for a while without saying anything. His left eyelid sank over his left eye to parallel the right one. His nostrils widened a bit to help him to breathe and the skin at the corners of his mouth, if you could have seen it for his beard, went a bit whiter. 'You must be hungry, men,' he said, waving a hand away from himself. 'Go and eat now after your long journeys and I'll talk to you by and by.'

And indeed it was later before he talked to them two – I'm telling a lie! – three days later. And in that time he tossed and he turned; he ate nothing; he hardly slept; and not one, single, solitary iotam of a word passed his lips. His wife, who turned out to be his greatest treasure, unknown to himself, though he wouldn't have thanked you for saying so beforehand, and who was an observant class of a woman, happened to notice this.

'What ails you?' she asked. 'There's food all around you and you won't eat it. You haven't slept for three nights with your face to the wall and your backside to me, and you haven't a word to throw to a dog. Are you sickening for something, or what? Do you need a dose? Will I make you a *deoch* (potion), and clear you out?'

With that Mac Datho spoke for the first time in three days. 'There is a saying,' he said lugubriously, 'never trust a slave with money or a woman with a secret. But if I don't talk to someone I'll burst.'

'Huh!' said his wife. 'The one time a man should talk to a woman is when there's something wrong. A bad tenant is better out than in, as they say after eating the beans.'

With that Mac Datho told his wife of the demands from Ulster and from Connacht. 'And if I please one of them,' said he, 'won't I offend the other? And if I am paid with cattle by one, won't the other harry my cattle and slay my people?' He had good cause to be frightened. The redoubtable Connacht warrior, Cet Mac Margach, was known to be roaming the western fringes of Leinster, and the whole world knew that King Conor of Ulster was not a man who could be lightly crossed.

His wife thought for a while, and then she said: 'Listen to me and you'll be all right. There's no way you can keep the dog. That much is clear. So this is what you must do; tell the two of them they can have it, but that they must come themselves to fetch it on a certain day. Tell them both the same thing the way they'll arrive together; and, if there is killing and murder to be done, let them do it to themselves.'

Mac Datho looked at her with admiration and wonder. 'Well,' he said, 'there's no doubt that the women have brains too – some of them,' he added quickly, in case he'd gone too far, 'for some things. I'll do that.' He rose from his *lepad*, or couch, and shook himself. He smiled and looked at his wife and said: 'That it may fall out well for us.' With that he summoned food and drink for himself and then, since the three days of hospitality which he was obliged to provide were up, he sent for the messenger from Connacht.

When the herald came to him, Mac Datho said: 'I have been vexed and bothered with confusion and doubt over what to do these last three days.' He glanced at the herald who remained unmoved for he was a good messenger. 'And now,' said Mac Datho, 'I have come to a decision and it is that Ailbe is a fitting animal – if you could call him an animal at all for he is more like a human than many who walk on two legs – for a great queen like Maeve. So let you go back to Connacht and tell them to come for it with splendour and all their hosts, for isn't he a king of dogs and well worth the honour? I'll provide a feast for you here the like of which has never been seen before in this dun. And on your way out,' he added, 'let you be careful what way you go for I don't want you spreading the word to the Ulsterman befear he'd ambush and kill you before you got home with the good news.' The herald was naturally very pleased at this (having been told to come back with the dog on a leash or his head on a stick), and returned to Connacht delighted with himself.

No sooner was he out the door than Mac Datho sent for Mac Nessa's herald. 'My good man,' said he, 'I have been racking and tormenting my wretched brains these past two nights or three to know what should I do about this matter of the hound, Ailbe, and the requests I got. But, sure, wasn't the answer staring me in the face the whole time?'

He didn't, you should know, tell him what the answer was. Instead he said: 'My hound, Ailbe, as you well know, is the finest hound ever. A king of hounds fit for a monarch himself and therefore it is only right and fitting that if he must leave my proprietorship that he should go to the greatest monarch in the land. So leave you go back now to Ulster, like a good man, and tell that to King Conor and if he wants the hound let him come hither for it with his army and panoply so that he may, if he wants, take him back to Ulster in splendour and in safety from any attempt by the Connachtmen to capture him.' And, of course, as his wife had advised him, he told him to tell Conor to come on the same day as he told the Connacht herald and that he'd have a great feast ready for them when they came. No less than had his western counterpart, the Ulster herald returned happily to the north secure in the knowledge that his standing would be increased and that his stature, happily for another while, might continue to be what it had been up to now, with his neck supporting his head in its customary position atop his somewhat narrow shoulders and not be gone off somewhere else by itself.

And so, when the appointed day arrived, two great armies, one from the north and one from the west, bore down upon the dun of Mac Datho. They advanced with banners and chariots, with trumpets and drums and with many hundreds of marching warriors, so that the air was filled with the slap and the clap and the clang and the crash of the flags and the emblems, the weapons and harnesses, and the brazen notes of marching music. Two floating clouds of dust rose where these armies passed, for 'twas dry summer, and finally the great hosts and all their panoply were assembled on the *faitche* before the dun and Mac Datho went out to speak with Maeve and Conor who had accompanied their warriors and who ignored each other's forces with studied indifference – no mean feat when you come to think of it and the size of their two armies all crowded together on the *faitche*!

'Well now,' said Mac Datho, 'ye are welcome, even though we weren't prepared for two armies. Never mind, there's enough and to spare. Let ye come into my *brúden* now and make ye'reselves comfortable.'

Now even a blind man could see that the situation was unusual, to say the least. For three hundred years the men of Connacht and the men of Ulster had been at continuous war. And now here was an army of each, with the king of one and the queen of the other at Mac Datho's *brúden*. 'Twas only because they were on the *faitche* (which, as I told you, was a sanctuary and a sacred place) that they didn't fall to murdering and killing one another there and then. As it was there was a fearful lot of surliness and muttering and bitter glances between the two assemblies. If a man was that way inclined and had the gift, you might say that he could 'feel' the tension passing between them. Stamping of feet, and shuffling, black looks and nasty exclamations meant to be heard by the other side, if you know what I mean. So, when Mac Datho invited the king and the queen in there was a fair bit of perplexity and misgiving, I needn't tell you. But, anyway, the king and queen and the leaders and chief men of the two armies filed in, grudging and muttering, through one or more of the seven open doors. Between each of these doors there were numerous *lepads* or couches, each of which would seat three men – or four if they weren't too big – so that most of those who went in were accommodated in the great hall and those who wouldn't fit were accommodated elsewhere, while the two armies were brought food and drink by the cart- and barrel-load outside. And it didn't take them long, I can tell you, to stack their spears and their shields and their hand-stones and tuck their swords under their tail ends and sit down to the finest of bread and meat and wine and mead they ever saw or tasted. And so the enemies sat facing one another, the chiefs across the entire length of this huge hall, and the fighting men outside on the *faitche*.

The nobles and leaders were plied with drinks of one kind or another, beer and wine and hazel mead that is called the nectar of kings, with little plates of nuts and fruit and cooked delicacies to whet their appetite. While they were at that what did Mac Datho do but direct that the great boar should be killed. For seven years it had been reared on the milk of fifty cows. No other boar in the history of man had ever lived as it had lived, cosseted and fed and plied with apples to nurture and feed it throughout the year, and with sows in plenty as the need arose. And now it was going to be killed and eaten; but indeed, as was later remarked, it might as well have been reared on venom and gall so great was the murder and mischief that came from the carving of it.

When it was properly cooked – and that took some time, so that 'twas dark when 'twas ready and the guests were well on, if you take my meaning – it was brought in with forty sheep and deer as side dishes and every other kind of food that one could think of besides. Instead of an apple, which would have been lost in its gob, it had a pumpkin between its jaws and fifteen men carried it on a great shield around the hall and presented it to Mac Datho who nodded and stood up and cried: 'I bid ye all welcome. The boar that lies before you has no match and there is ample of venison and mutton and other meat, the best of Leinster, besides. Moreover if there is anything lacking or something that you want that isn't here you have but to name it and I'll get it.'

''Tis a mighty boar indeed,' said Conor.

'Indeed,' said Ailill, Maeve's consort, 'and the only question, Mac Datho,' said he, 'is how 'twill be divided between us.'

At this a kind of a silence fell over the assembly. For that question brought them near to the heart of the matter that had laid tension on them since they first entered the house. Men exchanged meaningful looks with their companions on either side, then looked across the two tables and the intervening space between them at their enemies, who did the same thing. Now Mac Datho was after dismissing his *rachaire*, or house-steward, whose important function it was to allot to every guest his proper place. The greatest care had to be given to this taking account of rank and deeds, parts and families, grades, arts, and customs so that no man might say he had been slighted or placed below his station. Now in those times it was the custom for the choicest cuts and joints to be reserved for certain chiefs, officials and professional men according to their rank. Moreover it was the particular custom to assign the choicest joint of the finest animal of the whole banquet to the greatest hero among those present; he who was acknowledged by general consent to have performed the bravest and greatest exploit. And this is where the trouble now began.

I needn't tell you that this piece, the *curath-mir* or hero's portion, was keenly coveted. Where there was no dispute as to who was the outstanding hero the host would take his knife in his right hand, and with his left hand holding the joint, cut it and present it to him. In this case, as you can see, there were obvious difficulties. Having said his say, Mac Datho, on the advice of his wife, merged into the background as best he could. Mind you since he had acquired the habit of testing personally, every day, what he had to offer his guests, he wasn't exactly a thin class of a man; and since he happened to be standing on a high chair in the middle of the hall at the time, it was no easy matter.

Now, as if things weren't bad enough the way they were, wasn't there amongst the Ulstermen present a man called Bricriu (whose talent, which he delighted in exercising, was to foment strife, argument and bitterness amongst those with whom he found himself. Indeed, wasn't he the cause of another famous dispute at a feast he gave himself that is called after him, Bricriu's feast, that has gone down in history too? 'How else should it be divided?' asked Bricriu, 'only that the best of us should take the best of it? Aren't the best men of Ireland here today, and is there any one of ye hasn't belted any other of ye some time or another?'

'Fair enough,' said Ailill. 'That's what we'll do.'

'All right,' said Conor, 'we've plenty hardy lads here have scoured Connacht often enough.'

'Huh,' said an old warrior called Senlaeth, a charioteer from the far west, 'if you have you may need them. Much good may they do you if they're the ones I left sprawled on their arses while I harried their cattle.'

'Well now,' cried Munremur (Moon-raymer) of Ulster, 'is that a fact? 'Twas some queer bullock you left behind you in your brother the last time you tried. He was best meat west sure enough, but he never got back to the west.'

'If he didn't,' shouted Lughaidh of Munster, 'Echbal left a bigger and better man dead at Tara Luachra when he killed Irloth Mac Fergus.'

'Echbal?' bellowed Celtchar of Ulster. 'I remember him. He had the makings of a hero all right . . . 'til I whipped the head off his shoulders.'

The insults and the fury grew hotter and faster so that there was hardly a *ridire gaisce* (that is a champion who had proven his worth in battle, most of who were entitled to wear the *nascniadh*, the champion's collar of gold won in the battlefield for some exceptional exploit) who wasn't red-faced and pop-eyed with rage. The insults and tumult continued for a while along these lines and tempers were getting very short with them, so it seemed it was only a matter of time before one of them would leap from his place into the space between the tables and, sanctuary or no sanctuary, roar a challenge at one of those on the other side. But the final hand was stayed.

But then one man, who had remained silent up to that (but who, it might be noted, hung his weapons higher than those of anyone else), stood up slowly, almost ponderously, took his *sgian* or knife in his hand and sauntered silently over to the boar and stood beside it. A class of a silence had fallen when he did so. But every eye was on him. He was Cet Mac Margach, the great warrior champion of Connacht. Taking hold of the boar by one of his ears he lifted his knife and said, quietly enough, mind you: 'If there is a man amongst ye,' addressing the Ulstermen, 'who can match myself for deeds and renown, let you stand out here now or else hold ye peace and leave me carve this animal here.'

The silence that followed seemed even deeper and more profound than that which fell when he first picked up the boar's ear and held his knife over it. After a moment Laoire the Triumphant stood up and said to his fellow Ulstermen – carefully keeping his shoulders towards Cet: 'I, for one, won't have Cet carve this boar in the face of us all.'

'Oho!' said Cet. 'Is that yourself Laoire? You won't mind if I remind you of something?' The thing is it was the custom that when every young Ulster nobleman first took arms he was expected to go on a raid into Connacht and bring back cattle or some other booty or, if he couldn't do that, the head of a Connachtman. It was to this custom that Cet was going to refer.

'I remember,' he said, smiling at Laoire, 'the time you first took up arms, Laoire. Wasn't that when you rode into Connacht looking for valour? It was, to be sure. And do you know what, didn't you have the fierce misfortune – depending on your point of view, of course; 'twas fortunate enough for me – but as I say, wasn't it your misfortune to meet me? Do you know what, I think I still have that fine chariot and horses you kindly donated to me at the time. I suppose you still have a little bit of trouble from the wound in the ribs my spear gave you? Have you it still? The spear I mean. I'd like it back sometime when you're finished with it, if you please. I don't think, somehow,' he went on with a smile, 'you're the man to take the boar from me.'

Laoire sat down.

But no sooner was he seated again than another fair-haired warrior whose face was as red with anger as his head of hair was fair from the sun bounded down the hall towards Cet, shouting: 'Never will Cet divide that boar!'

Cet looked at him: 'And who have we here?' he asked calmly.

'A better man than you,' shouted the other. 'Aengus Mac Lamha Gabhaid (Hand-in-Danger).'

'Well,' exclaimed Cet, 'is that a fact? So you're the son of Lamha Gabhaid! Well, I'll tell you what, let you, or anyone else for that matter, tell us why your father is called that.'

Aengus stopped, uncertainly, the other's calmness and obvious and unmoved authority slowing him. He looked at the floor. Then he looked at Cet again. His brows drew together. He muttered something, but other than that it was an indication that he didn't know the answer to the question; 'twas no more than a mumble.

Unperturbed Cet looked round the Ulstermen. 'Anyone else?' he asked amiably. A general mutter came from the Ulster ranks, followed by a silence, and it all added up to the fact that nobody knew the answer.

'Well, I'll tell you,' said Cet. 'Once – 'twas a good while ago now – I went abroad on a bit of a raid east into Ulster and carelessness or some other little thing that had my attention from where it should have been . . . Now that I think about it, it might have been a girl; yes, that's what it was! I was just rolled over on my back looking at a cloud . . . Anyway wasn't I attacked by a troop of Ulstermen who came rushing at me out of the furze? I needn't tell you my attention returned dam' quick. And just in time for who was one of the troop – only Lamha Gabhaidh. Of course he had a different name that time. What did he do only fling his lance at me, and it would have spitted my windpipe if I hadn't ducked and caught it going past. Well, of course, I threw it back at him with the hero's throw, and didn't it take off the hand that threw it first? What do you think of that? I can see it still; the hand, I mean, lying there on the ground – twitching! And is it that man's son that comes to challenge me?'

Aengus went back and sat down.

'Any more,' asked Cet, 'or will I divide the boar?'

'Naw!' growled another Ulster warrior, lumbering to his feet.

Cet swung his eyes towards him, the knife still held loosely in his right hand. 'And who have we here?' he asked.

'Eoghan, son of Duach,' cried several Ulster voices, 'Eoghan Mor of Fern Mala. He's the man for you.'

'Eoghan?' said Cet. 'Haven't I met you before?' He eyed the other benevolently.

Eoghan glared at him from his single eye. 'Where?' he roared. 'I never saw you before in my life.'

'Well, now,' said Cet, 'I'll tell you: the way it is, you had two eyes at the time, but maybe you didn't see as well with the two as with the one you have now. 'Twas in front of your own castle. I was borrowing a few of your cattle at the time and didn't some unfortunate member of your own people take exception to it, the poor man? But he raised a cry out of him before he died and didn't you and your bodyguard come roaring out of the castle and, fair dues to you, you put a spear through my shield. But, the way it was, I already had two good spears and I didn't need another, so I threw it back to you. But – and you might remember this – didn't you catch it with your eye instead of your hand?'

Eoghan sat down.

'Is there a man amongst ye at all,' asked Cet, 'will contest this pig with me?'

Now as may easily be judged the Ulstermen's tempers were pretty high by this time. But they were hard put to it to bring forth anyone who could match Cet. Triscatal, King Conor's champion, a mighty, broad-fronted, shaggy-haired man, with thighs as thick as an ordinary man's body, who wore a thick leather apron from his armpits down and bare limbs, and whose aspect was so fierce that he killed men with his very look, was misfortunately in Emhain Macha. Cuchulain was abroad chasing a lady somewhere (or maybe being chased by one) and Conall Cearnach was missing, no one knew where. But in the face of Cet's taunting they kept on trying.

Munremur shouted at him: 'You haven't yet won the right!'

'Is that yourself, Munremur?' cried Cet.

'It is,' roared the men of Ulster hopefully.

'Well,' said Cet, 'I'm told you've been away from home this last week or so, Munremur, so I have news for you. You'll find when you get back that didn't four of your best warriors lose their heads entirely three days ago through carelessness, I suppose, or some other thing. One of them was your eldest son, I'm sorry to tell you.'

Munremur sat down.

And so it went on, the Ulstermen putting up one hero after another and each of them finding that he, or his family in the past, had been shamed and mortified by Cet, whose arrogance seemed to increase with each new revelation that demonstrated there wasn't an Ulsterman in the hall fit to challenge him. Mend, whose father was called Salcholcam (Sword Heel) rose to challenge only to sit down again when Cet told him that it was he who had put both the nickname and the scar on his father when he cut off his heel so that he walked with a limp thereafter. Again he threw out his challenge and again he was answered, this time by Celtachar, now fuming with rage at the insults being heaped on Ulster.

'Whisha, hold on, Celtachar,' said Cet; and he reminded him of how they had met in a ravine in front of Celtachar's own castle, the outcome of which was that Cet's spear had taken the kidneys of life from Celtachar so that he had neither son nor child to follow him from that out. Celtachar sat down.

Well, no sooner was he down and Cet was issuing his challenge again when a young Ulsterman rose to his feet and cried in a terrible voice: 'I – I – I – cha – ch – ch –'

'Who have we here?' asked Cet.

'Cuscuid!' cried the Ulstermen.

'Ah-ah!' said Cet. 'Cuscuid! Of the line of a king. Isn't it a great pity that when you made your foray against Connacht you met me and left a third of those who accompanied you dead behind you. And you went back with my javelin through your throat so you can no longer talk right, Cuscuid the Stammerer!'

Cuscuid, his fury dampened, sat down.

Again Cet looked round and issued his challenge and this time there was no response. He raised his knife to plunge it triumphantly into the boar, when there was a tremendous clatter outside one of the seven huge doors. Then it burst open and Conall Cearnach of the Victories, strode into the hall wrapped in his great cloak and walked straight to King Conor. A shout of exaltation rose from the Ulstermen and the king himself took his crown from his head and raised it high to greet Conall.

Conall had a great beam on his craggy face as he looked around and saw that everything was ready for the feast. Whether mischievously or not no one will ever know but his words were: 'Well, I arrived just in time. And who is it is carving the boar for us?' he asked.

'Cet Mac Margach,' cried the Ulstermen. 'There is no one,' came a solitary voice, 'able to contest the place of honour with him.'

'Is that a fact, Cet?' asked Conall Cearnach mildly.

'Not a word of a lie,' said Cet, not a bit put out; and he made a poem on the spot for Conall Cearnach, which was one of the true signs of any hero.

> Conall, you're welcome
> There's iron in your heart
> And fire in your blood
> You're a man set apart!
>
> You glitter like frost
> Sharp, keen and bright,
> When your battle-rage bursts
> You have victory in sight.

'And now,' said Cet, 'let you sit down with the others 'til I carve this pig for us all.'

'Ah, now,' said Conall. 'I couldn't do that. Sure haven't I got a poem for you?'

> Good day to you, Cet
> There's no doubt we're well met,
>
> You bull amongst chiefs,
> You purveyor of griefs.
>
> You're as cold as black ice,
> No man troubles you twice,
> Like the sea's stormy wave,
> You're both powerful and brave.

'There now,' he said benevolently when he was finished, 'let you rise up from the board and give my rightful place.'

Cet looked at him in surprise. 'Why so?' he asked.

Conall's brows darkened slightly. 'Are you looking to fight me?' he asked in wonder. 'Let you mind yourself, Cet. You may not know it but I swear by all the gods, by the wind and the sea, and the air and the earth and all the four elements, that since I first ever took weapons in my hand no day has ever passed that I didn't kill a man from Connacht, nor a night that I haven't slept without the head of a Connachtman under my cloak.' As he spoke, Conall's voice became firmer and his gaze was fixed compellingly on Cet.

'If that is so,' said Cet, 'and,' he added, 'I have no reason to doubt it, then there is no doubt that you are a better man than I am and I yield the boar to you. But I would like to say this: if only my brother Anluan was here, he's the man would match you deed for deed, and it is my shame and my sorrow that he's not here.'

'Ah, but he is here!' cried Conall, and with that from under his great cloak he pulled the head of Anluan and threw it at Cet so that it struck him on his chest and a glob of blood flew in his face.

That, of course, put the fox amongst the geese, as they say, and the whole hall of warriors jumped to their feet and reached for their swords.

'Now,' roared Conall, 'is there anyone here who'll challenge me?'

The Ulstermen raised their shields around Conall in case there was a stray spear flung at him while he divided the boar. He took the great tail in his mouth – and it as big as the leg of man – and spat out the bones of it as he divided the carcase. And he divided it in such a way that there was nothing for the men of Connacht except the two forelegs – which wasn't very much when you come to think of it.

And with that insult, the two halves of the hall – the Connacht half and the Ulster half – flew at each other with flashing weapons so that the bodies heaped inside the house as high as the side wall and rivers of blood flowed under the seven doors. The fighting warriors broke through the doors onto the *faitche* outside where the battle continued until the men of Connacht turned and flew before those of Ulster.

With that Mac Datho let loose his great hound. It was his intention just to see which side the hound would join (which doesn't seem too bright of him – but then he didn't have his wife to advise him this time), and the hound, true to its instincts, took off like its namesake from hell after the Connachtmen and it was therefore decided that it had joined the Ulster army. Together with the men of Ulster it pursued the Connachtmen westwards across the country (and outstripped most of them), until it caught up with the chariot of Maeve and Ailill on the plain near the little town today called Emly and fastened his teeth on the pole of the chariot and hung on to it. Ailill's charioteer, Ferloga, whipped the head off the hound with a blow of his sword so that the body fell beside the flashing wheels as they raced on, but the great jaw of the hound still gripped the chariot pole and remained there until the mad career across the plain came to an end. It is for that reason, so they say, that the plain got its name, Magh Ailbhe, the plain of Ailbe, the name of the hound. North past the rolling hills of Ballaghmoon, over the mid-Boyne ford, and the ridge of Drumcriocht at Kildare, by Rathdangan in the forest of Gabla, and on by Mac Luna's ford over the ridge of the two plains 'til they came to the Bridge of Cairpre across the Boyne; and it was at a ford there, ever since known as the Ford of the Hound's Head, in Westmeath, that the dog's head at last fell from the chariot which rolled to a stop.

The first chariot behind them was that of Conor, who was so fired with the pursuit that he wasn't paying enough attention to where he was going; and Ferloga, who had landed in the rushes when his chariot overturned, sprang up behind the king and seized him by the throat. 'You have a choice,' he said, 'Conor. You can give me your life or give over the pursuit.'

'Well now,' said Conor, and, as you might imagine, his voice was a little strained, 'that's not the hardest choice in the world to make because I value my life above most things. Is that it?'

'No,' said Ferloga, 'I want you to take me with you to Emhain Macha and let me live there in peace and comfort and tranquillity as long as I want and that you order the most beautiful women of the court to serenade me at night whenever I want them to.'

'Done,' said the king. And so he took Ferloga back to Emhain Macha with him and the charioteer lived there for a year and a day having the best of food and drink and with the most beautiful women of Ulster to serenade him whenever he wanted it – and he must have been fierce fond of music for not a night passed (and the odd day too), but he was summoning them in ones, and sometimes twos, to serenade him, if you please.

At the end of the year he decided to return to Connacht. In spite of the finest of food and drink the poor man had lost weight and didn't look too good in himself. The northern air didn't agree with him, I suppose. Anyway, Conor escorted him as far as the border and bade him a kind farewell giving him two of the finest horses of his stables bridled with gold – but no women – to take back to Connacht with him.

And that's the story of Mac Datho's boar if it isn't the story of Mac Datho, since no more is heard of him and we may assume that he lived quietly and contentedly with his wise wife even if he no longer had the finest hound or the greatest boar in Ireland.

FOOTNOTES

1 Curved spearheads or short swords allegedly of Fomorian design. Specimens in the National Museum of Ireland.
2 See 'The Wooing of Emer'.

The Vengeance of Mesgedra

Second Period: Ultonian Cycle

This story is interesting because of the clear and demonstrable evidence it provides of the 'wedding' between pagan tradition and imported Christian teaching. The main thrust of the story develops and interweaves with stylish skill that of the avaricious Athairne, that of the vengeance of Mesgedra himself, and that of the regal and difficult decision to be made by King Conor Mac Nessa. The inexorable progress towards a typically Celtic retributive conflict of choice, so beloved by them in their stories and riddles, may, in an original pre-Christian version, have satisfactorily provided an explanation for Conor's sudden and dramatic death, here provided by the news of the Crucifixion. The Gaelic love of the mystic triune could well, with again typical Celtic fondness for consequential drama, have accommodated the difficult and fatal decision. In some cases, Christian 'laundering' or adaptation appears to have interrupted the sequence or rhythm of a story, if it hasn't swamped them altogether, in a pietistic – and often incongruous – interpolation. Not so in this case: the ending is adapted with great skill that does little or no violence to the rhythm, sequential integrity, and, so far as we may judge, the structure of the original; and it apparently accommodates to it with remarkable validity.

The story belongs to the Ulster or Red Branch Cycle and, so, falls into the intermediate category where mythology and folk memory mix and mingle in a legendary world of human passions. Athairne's concupiscent arrogance is well delineated, as are the derived lusts and arrogance of his sons and the shocked immobility of the young queen when faced with them. Only Conor's dilemma and its resolution properly belongs, undiluted, to the 'grand' scale and period of Celtic romance. But what a scale it is and with what penetrating insight it pierces to the heart of a human conflict of majestic proportions! For Conor to have undertaken, even with the support of the nobles and in the face of blatant abuse, reforms of the scope and magnitude indicated was a profound matter measurable today, perhaps, in terms of a proposal to reform religion and abandon representative democracy. It would take a book of its own to discuss and assess the social and moral implications. It is sufficient to say that they were great. We are not concerned with them here. 'The Vengeance of Mesgedra' is first and last an excellent story, as it was when it was first told by adults for the entertainment of their peers.

It was that time when Conor Mac Nessa was King of Ulster and Athairne was its chief poet. This story concerns the death of one and the malignancy of the other. And it should be noted that, although these things were certainly connected by circumstances, they were by no means directly connected; and yet you may be certain that, while the death of the one would sooner or later undoubtedly have occurred, it would not have happened when it did if it had not been for the malignancy of the other.

Athairne was second only to Conor in power and in position in Ulster. Besides being chief poet, he was also chief satirist, which made him a *dlui* – or 'druid' as the British Celts had it – and an *ollamh* or master of that art as well: one who could call down curses and perform the *glawm-dicenn* against an enemy by going against the sun with one arm tied, one eye closed and standing on one leg to encourage the malevolence of unity and disrupt the triune strength of the enemy as, it is held, the Fomorians had done in past ages. But whereas Conor's power was that of King of Ulster and one of the Pentarchy – one of the five great kings of Ireland (no matter how he achieved it) – Athairne's was a different power. As chief poet his rank was such that no man in all Ulster stood higher. He sat beside the king himself; and his power came from the general recognition of this and also from fear. It was not the fear of might, or of force, or of troops, or of any of those things that try to knock fear into a man's stomach to frighten him or to make his blood race and rise up in him so as not to be afraid, like a man going to battle, but something deadlier; fear of the power of poets that lay in their calling and in their craft and that penetrated a man's bones and his mind and his soul with the most fearful thing of all, the unknown.

In those times in Ireland learning, wisdom and knowledge, but especially the art of poetry, were held in esteem. So much was poetry regarded and so high was the honour given to poets – not just any bard or versifier, but those of the Order of Poets who spent a minimum of twenty-seven years mastering their craft, which few achieved – that kings themselves went in awe of them . . . or in fear of them, if the truth be told. And the reason is this: many poets were also satirists and strangely – even laughable though it may seem today when their power is curbed by things such as the law of libel (and it might be well to remember that!) – by satire poets had the power to demean a man beyond measure should he displease them for any reason. It is said that a poet could – and sometimes did – satirise to death a man who offended him. It was not uncommon for them to raise on the faces of those they satirised three blisters – of shame, blemish and disgrace (about which we will hear more shortly). That was the way of it and that is why Athairne was feared; and, let me tell you, blisteringly did he employ this power. As a matter of fact 'tis said that it was he started the rot in the Order of Poets so that they came to abuse their position out of all reason and knowledge. But it wasn't for nearly another six hundred years after the events described below that they came near to being abolished altogether because of their arrogance.[1] They were only rescued then by Saint Colmcille himself (he wasn't a saint then, of course), himself a poet of note.

While we're on it, there's another thing; wasn't it only with the threat of getting her chief poet to raise blisters of shame and disgrace to disfigure him that Queen Maeve of Connacht was able to blackmail Ferdia to fight Cuchulain at the battle of the Ford? That, now, will give you some small idea of the sort of carry-on there was with the poets. You can judge for yourself the level of disgrace there could be in a simple thing from this short satire against a man who displeased a poet by not giving him what he thought he ought to get for a poem:

> No wrong
> When said he won't give a horse for a song:
> But what one would expect from him anyhow,
> A cow!
> (*Ro-cúala*
> *Ní tabair eochu ar dúana do-beir*
> *a n-í as dúthaig do,*
> *bó.*)

That was the poets' standing and their power. And even before the poison was as widespread as it became, Athairne was in it up to his oxters. His heart was full of greed and arrogance and those of his sons along with him; 'like father . . .' and you know the rest. No one, king or noble, dared refuse him whatever reward he asked for his poems for fear of the shame and disgrace he could heap on them if they did. He became the scourge of the country at a time when it was held shameful to refuse a poet whatever he might ask as a reward. (It only goes to show 'twas Athairne and his likes who put poets in the low place and low esteem they're in today – worse than shopkeepers and doctors.) But in general the poets were honourable and asked – if they asked – only what was considered proper, or, as was more often the case, accepted gratefully enough what was offered, if it wasn't too mean altogether. But Athairne and his sons were the other kind. Mean out! They asked without shame and, signs on it, their greed would be their destruction. But it came too late for Ulster or for the Order of Poets itself.

'Tis said that Athairne once demanded of King Eochy Mac Luchta, a man noted for his hospitality and generosity, the one thing he most desired to keep – namely his eye, for he had but the one. So great was Eochy's generosity – or his fear – that he plucked it out by the roots and gave it to the poet, which was a great disappointment to the latter who had hoped the king would ransom his eye for a great price. But it was a great tragedy for the king, who lost the kingship because of the blemish. That will show you the sort Athairne was.

Now, in addition to being satirists, poets in those days also held a monopoly of legal knowledge. This monopoly was broken by Conor and, I needn't tell you, that didn't endear him to the poets either, even though he was a great patron of learning and the arts and protected them when the nobles rose up against them. His decision that learning should be thrown open to all followed a controversy between two poets which no one could understand except themselves. In order to prevent anyone else dabbling in it hadn't the poets wrapped the law in an ancient language so obsolete and complicated that no one could understand it but themselves – a system that came back afterwards with the lawyers, I might add. The main idea was to shut out any but their own families from the legal profession (and, of course, to impress the uninitiated). Anyway Conor ordered that plain language was to be the order of the day from then on and that the professions were no longer to be in the keeping of their few families only. That's how, at a stroke, he deprived the poets of the private ownership of the law and opened the profession to all freemen; and 'tis a pity there aren't a few more like him around today.

At this time, Conor was very powerful and warlike and overawed many of the other kingdoms of Ireland. This description of him by the herald, MacRoth, that he made for the benefit of Queen Maeve of Connacht, who had been Conor's first wife, is as good as any: 'A tall, graceful champion of noble, polished and proud bearing stood at the head of his troops with all the signs of obedience, superiority and command. He had a great head of curling, golden hair falling to his shoulders and a pleasant, bronzed countenance. His eye were deep and blue and piercing, and his forked golden beard curled upon his chin. He wore a crimson deep-bordered, five-folded mantle held by a golden brooch at the breast and a brilliant white shift, woven with threads of red gold beneath it.' That was Conor.

Now, round about this time, he fixed his ambitious eye on the kingdom of Leinster, which was rich and worth plundering, but he needed an excuse to have a go at it. It occurred to him that he might kill two birds with one stone by sending Athairne to visit the Leinster King, Mesgedra, who might, with some luck, dispose of him for his insolent demands. If that happened, wouldn't it rid Conor conveniently enough of Athairne, and at the same time give him the excuse he needed to invade Leinster to avenge his poet?

He sent for Athairne. 'I think,' said Conor, stroking first one and then the other side of his forked beard to keep it neat, and looking at his poet over his hand, 'you should go to Naas and see King Mesgedra of Leinster.'

Athairne, who was no fool, knew the king, and if not well, fairly thoroughly so far as he himself was concerned, and that knowledge had this difference to it from similar knowledge of other men: it made him uneasy. 'Why should I do that?' he enquired, his lean, many ringed hands spreading themselves out like the useless wings of a scrawny and flightless bird. 'Amn't I content here with you?' he smirked at Conor.

209

And Conor smiled back at him with his mouth. His eyes were another matter.
'Well, now,' he said, 'I've been thinking. Mesgedra's is the richest kingdom in the
east. He has all the trade with Britain and the great fattening plain of Kildare
where his multitudes of cattle grow heavy with the sweetest grazing in Ireland by
the countless thousand. You could gather information for me. None better.
Moreover,' he added, 'he has not been visited by a truly great poet for many a
year, let alone the greatest.'

Now Conor had no notion if this was so, but he knew that if Athairne
thought so he would immediately start calculating the vast gifts and oblations
that would be there for the picking in the absence of a visit of one such as
himself. And he was right.

'No visits?'

'Not a visit!'

'Hmm!' said Athairne.

'They say he is the richest king in Ireland,' said Conor.

'Lies,' said Athairne automatically as if he were throwing a bad poem at a
beggar, 'that's you. You know they do say Leinster is a beautiful place.'

'They do,' said Conor. 'The mountains there are purple and the skies over
them rich with white clouds.'

'Is that a fact?' asked Athairne, as if 'twas different in Ulster.

'It is,' said Conor, 'mountains of the richest colours.'

'And the fields around them rich with fat cattle,' murmured Athairne.

'You could maybe write a poem there,' suggested Conor.

'A masterpiece,' said Athairne, 'at least!'

'At least,' said Conor.

And so Athairne went to Leinster. Accompanied by his huge train of sub-
poets, harpers, fiddlers, scribblers, scribes, bards, servants and gillies, Athairne
arrived at the great dun of Mesgedra, king of Leinster, at Naas in Kildare not
long after. For a year, twelve of the longest months Mesgedra ever knew, he
stayed in the king's palace wasting the substance of the Leinstermen. But Conor's
plan failed. Mesgedra was too shrewd and too wily to be caught either by his
fellow king or by the importunities of the greedy poet. Accordingly, at the end
of a year Athairne decided to get what he might from Mesgedra and go back to
Ulster and he went to the king to demand his fee.

With his *coir sainnte,* or pot of avarice, in which donations were to be put –
but which was no more than a symbol at that time, like the bag on the back of
a lawyer in our own – borne behind him he strode past the assembled lords and
went straight to where the king sat at the end of his great hall facing south.
Athairne's *coir sainnte*, unlike that of other poets who were content with a simple
bag of leather or of material, was of silver and it hung by nine chains of *finn-
drinne* or white bronze from golden hooks which were on the points of nine

spears carried by nine men of the poet's company. As Athairne stopped before Mesgedra, the men who bore the *coir sainnte* moved around him and stood in front of him before the king chorusing a poem of praise – a short poem and not very good – which Mesgedra chanted. When they were finished, Athairne demanded his poet's fee.

Mesgedra looked at him with hooded eyes so that his dislike would not be too evident. Addressing himself somewhere to the left of Athairne's right shoulder he enquired; 'What is it you require for your fee, Athairne?'

'Eight hundred cattle,' said the poet tentatively, watching the king like a hawk.

'You have it,' said Mesgedra.

'And six hundred sheep,' added Athairne before the king had finished breathing.

'That too,' said the king.

'Twenty ounces of gold,' went on Athairne, now that he had judged the king's mood to be for peace (as he thought), 'and coloured silks out of the east enough to make tunics for my followers.' He gazed hard at the king from little eyes buried under his hood to see how this was going down.

'You shall have it,' said the king tonelessly.

'And forty-five —' said Athairne. And then he paused and waited until the king's eyes finally locked with his own before proceeding: 'forty-five,' said he, 'of the fairest virgins of Leinster to grind my corn and be my tallywomen in my castle.'

The gasps that had greeted his earlier demands were nothing at all to the roar of anger that burst from the assembled nobles in the king's hall when they heard this. Some of them leaped to their feet brandishing their fists (for weapons were not allowed to be carried in the great hall, though they hung behind each lord and noble and a few of them turned to their pages as if to reach for them). The king raised his hand and his steward shook the Branch of Bells for silence. He never took his eyes from Athairne, but his voice was low and his gaze was baleful as he said: 'You shall have them.'

With that Athairne retired quickly and returned to the guest quarters, well satisfied with his work, though he was naturally worried and concerned, as, indeed, he had every right to be. He had pushed too hard, perhaps. By no means had he expected the king to agree to all these demands, especially for the women. The king and the nobles of Leinster did not seem to him like people on whom shameful conditions could be laid, and what he had in mind all along, of course, was a good ransom for the gifts. Mind you the gifts themselves were better than any ransom, no doubt about that. But gold was easier to shift than cattle or women.

Now he was uneasy. Mesgedra had given in too easily. He would give what he had been asked, but how long would Athairne be allowed to keep them? That's what bothered him now. When they hadn't offered to ransom the women he knew he had cause to worry. Ransom was what he had expected and hoped for (being long past the age and condition when he might hope to entertain, with any purpose for any significant length of time, one tallywoman, let alone forty-five of the fairest women of Leinster). Something was up and he guessed that the Leinstermen planned to attack him and recover their gifts once he was beyond the borders of their kingdom and the bounds of their hospitality. He therefore sent a fast rider to Conor urging him to come and meet him with as strong an escort as possible at the borders of north Leinster and Ulster.

Next day, with all his retinue and the great plunder of cattle and sheep, gold and silk, and forty-five of the most beautiful women of Leinster, he left Naas, aiming for the Slee Cualann where it crossed the river Liffey in the district of Emania. But when he reached there, the river was so swollen with rain that the ford near the Black Pool, Dubh Linn (or Dublin), could not be crossed. There was a small *baile*, or town, there with some nice old buildings in it. But the chiefs of that place were an oafish and vulgar crowd who had hidden them with horrible sod houses – wicker pigsties and the like of that – for their own use. So didn't Athairne, in a panic with the Leinstermen behind him, order these torn down and also order a great number of hazel rods which grew in abundance all over the area to be cut. And with these he made large hurdles of wattle with blood, mud and dung made into a mortar and set them in the river at intervals. Over them he laid a causeway of the fencing and logs and more mortar so that his cattle and sheep and his people came safely across as dry-shod as if they walked on solid turf. Then he camped on the far side and it is a notorious fact that down to this very day that place is called Baile Atha Cliath, or the town of the Ford of the Hurdles. Tearing down those pigsties was the one good thing Athairne ever did, and he didn't know it at the time. (But, whisht! Aren't the descendants of the oafs who ran that place just as bad as – and worse than – their forefathers, for haven't they built concrete pigsties to block out one of the finest buildings there now! For themselves! With the people's money! Beat that in two throws!)

The following day, a few miles north, Athairne met the Ulstermen along the marches of the border. But even as he did, the troops of Mesgedra burst from behind and descended on them, driving Athairne and the Ulstermen who had come to meet him back across the neck of land separating Ben Eadair (Howth) from the Plain of Sorrows near a place called Cluain Tarbh and very close to what had been Tuireann's stronghold in bygone days.[2] Here Conor and his troops built a fortification across the neck of land and took refuge behind it. They were besieged for several days. They managed, however, to send messengers north to inform Ulster of their distress. But to add to their plight was the galling fact that, although they had retained the cattle, the gold and most of the other booty, hadn't the Leinstermen recovered their women in the first onslaught?

When Conor had rushed to Leinster to meet Athairne, Conall Cearnach the

Victorious, as was usual in the absence of the king, remained behind in Ulster as *Tanaiste* or regent. When the messengers from Howth reached him, he assembled the army and marched as soon as possible. This host came on the men of Leinster from the north and behind, and many were killed on both sides in the ensuing battle. The Leinstermen, who were caught between two forces, were getting the worst of it now. Mesgedra, like Nuada before him,[3] lost his hand, only in his case 'twas his left, and himself and his army were routed and fled southward before Conall Cearnach and the men of Ulster.

Mesgedra wrapped the bleeding stump of his arm, first in soft moss and then in a cloth. He bypassed Baile Atha Cliath and the new hurdle bridge, making for the old ford that crossed the Liffey at Clane nearer Naas. What's more, there was a *nineadh*, or sacred grove, there, which provided sanctuary under the shadow of the ash and yew trees bordering it. The enemy were close behind when Mesgedra took refuge in it, satisfied that he would not be killed so long as he stayed inside.

Conall Cearnach, who was in the van of the pursuit, drove his chariot straight towards the *nineadh* and had his charioteer haul back on the reins so that the foaming steeds champed and stamped on the very threshold of the sacred place. Leaping to his chariot-pole, Conall Cearnach shouted to Mesgedra to come out and fight or be called a coward amongst the kings of Ireland.

But Mesgedra called back: 'I the coward? Or is it just that the champions of Ulster prefer to challenge one-armed men?'

Growling, Conall Cearnach instructed his charioteer to bind one of his arms to his side. Then he again climbed on his chariot-pole and shouted at Mesgedra to come out and fight. Ignoring the pain in his stump, Mesgedra drew his sword and with a short run leaped the boundary of the *nineadh* and swung to face Conall Cearnach even as the other rushed on him with his drawn sword raised. They fought there on the river bank, hacking and slashing until the river flowed red with their blood. At last a chance blow from Mesgedra severed the bonds that bound Conall's left arm and with that the king stood back panting.

Conall Cearnach glared at him and growled: 'On your own head be it if you do that again.' Then he had his arm rebound and no sooner was that done than they rushed on one and the other again with flailing swords. After some time the thongs binding Conall's arm were cut once more and it fell free. 'The gods themselves have damned you,' shouted Conall, and he rushed on Mesgedra two-handed, and in no time had mortally wounded the king.

As Mesgedra lay on the ground with his life's blood ebbing from him, he looked at Conall and said: 'You may take my head to add my glory to yours, but you may rest assured your great feat –' he spat and coughed, 'won't go unavenged by me.' With that, a spasm of coughing shook him, blood came up from his mouth, spilled out on the ground, and he died.

Then Conall cut off Mesgedra's head and put it in his chariot. Hitching the king's chariot behind his own he turned north. Before long, he saw a cloud of dust ahead and, when he came closer, saw that it proved to be thrown up by a train of four-wheeled canopied chariots with fifty women as their guards. In the lead chariot sat Buan, Mesgedra's wife and Queen of Leinster. She was returning from royal Tara where she had been visiting the wife of the Ri-Eireann.

Though he knew well who she was, Conall the Victorious shouted at her as he came abreast: 'Who are you, woman?'

She drew herself up on the seat and turned to look at this proud warrior who addressed her so informally, and replied with dignity: 'I am Buan, wife of Mesgedra the King.'

'Then,' cried Conall with a sneer, 'you may come with me.'

Buan looked at him frostily. 'By whose order?'

'Can you not see that I have your husband's chariot and his horses?' asked Conall.

'He is a generous man who will give gifts to – anyone,' replied Buan, looking at him with distaste. 'That you have those things means no more to me than that.'

Then Conall reached down and grasped the head of Mesgedra by the hair and held it aloft, still dripping from the neck, so that it faced his queen. 'This is my authority,' he shouted at her, 'widow of Mesgedra.'

In spite of her shock and distress, Buan was a queen. She controlled her emotions as best she might, but could not prevent a tear from starting in her eye and rolling down her cheek, or keep her throat from tightening so that she found it difficult to speak. 'It is enough,' she whispered, 'but allow me to *caoine* (lament) him before we go.'

Then she stood, and all her women with her. She raised for Mesgedra a *caoine* and wail of sorrow so loud and so intense, so pitiful and so loving, so soul-searching and so tormented that her heart broke – and she fell backwards dead on the road. Conall Cearnach buried her there at Clane beside the Liffey and from her grave grew a hazel tree which has ever since been called the Hazel Tree of Buan.

However, in order to preserve his strength before he buried Mesgedra's head, Conall took the brain out and mixed it with lime, blood and mud to make a bullet for a *tathlum* or stick-sling, which was one of the most powerful missiles, both in fact and because of the awesome components from which it was fashioned, that can be imagined. Called brain-balls, such missiles were deadly. Then Leinster was burned and plundered by the invading Ulstermen who eventually withdrew with as much booty and women, cattle, gold and slaves as they could carry; and when they reached Emhain Macha the brain-ball was laid in the Speckled Hall, the armoury of the Knights of the Red Branch.

Now it so happened that Conor was a marrying kind of man. He had once been married to the strong, aggressive Maeve, then Queen of Connacht, who later became his great enemy. Even when they were married there was forever fire between these two powerful people and Conor had to put her aside (which was before she took up with the king of Connacht, I needn't tell you). Then he took in her place her sister Eithne, and she was a different story altogether. 'Eithne' means 'sweet kernel of nut', and she was truly gentle and sweet. But Eithne didn't last either, for she died, and in time Conor married the young and beautiful Luaine (of whom more in a moment) who was his queen at this time.

After that battle with Leinster there were years of peace and plenty and an absence of warfare, during which Ulster prospered. All those who had taken part in the battle with Leinster found that they had to strain their memories a bit to recall the details. Forgotten entirely was Mesgedra's threat (before Conall removed his head) to have vengeance. No one thought of it, much less remembered it, not even Conall. Indeed it might be that he had never told anyone, for who would credit a dead man's threat or pay it any attention except to laugh at it?

When these gentle years were in their fullness didn't a warrior and a killer from Connacht named Cet Mac Margach and known as the Wolf of Connacht, disguise himself and penetrate Ulster in search of prey. Eventually he reached Emhain Macha and there he saw two youngsters of the court of King Conor on the *faitche* before the palace, playing with the brain-ball of Mesgedra. They were throwing it from one to the other, as children do, having surreptitiously 'borrowed' if from the Speckled Hall (so called because the glint of sunlight from the multitude of arms and armour within danced upon the walls as it dances upon the waves of the sea on a brilliant summer's day). Cet knew it for what it was and intercepted a throw, hiding it while the boys searched for it. Thereafter Cet carried it with him wherever he went, hoping for an opportunity to enhance his reputation by destroying some great warrior of Ulster.

A little later he was involved in a cattle raid on the borders of Ulster, but before he and his men could return to Connacht with their spoils they were intercepted by Conor and a party of his men who had been hunting. Both groups got ready for battle, braiding their hair, cleaning their weapons, and adorning themselves before the onset, and while they were at that reinforcements came up to both sides. A river, namely the Brosna, ran between the armies and the women of the Connacht host assembled themselves on the western bank, led by their noblewomen, where they were engaged in cleaning and sharpening the weapons of their men.

In those days, the women of Ireland were forthright and passionate, and also noble and independent minded, but, above all, they were womanly and dignified – qualities well matched and balanced, which might give some of their latter-day descendants something to think about now and then when their aggression gets the better of them. And if they had some customs that seem strange to us, you may be sure that we have plenty that would seem dam' queer to them! Since he had married the earth,[4] it was the custom for a great king to display himself to women at their request for his own glorification and to their satisfaction that they had seen such a king and, of course, that they might be fruitful and strong. Indeed it was in such circumstances that King Niall of the Nine Hostages subsequently met his death in Gaul nearly five hundred years later.[5] In any event the women of Connacht let it be known that they desired to look on the King of Ulster, who, as we have already noted, had a royal and stately bearing. Enemies though they were, to refuse was impossible. Accordingly, wearing only his cloak, Conor walked towards them on his side of the river while the Connachtwomen assembled on theirs.

Meanwhile, Cet, who was aware of the arrangement and of the Connachtwomen's request, concealed himself in the bushes near the women and, contrary to all honour and nobility, lay there in ambush with a deadly *tathlum*, a stick-sling which hurls a bullet with great force, while on his own side of the river. Conor, seeing no one but women on the far bank, opened his cloak that they might see his shape. Then Cet, leaping up, hurled Mesgedra's brain-ball from his *tathlum*. It struck Conor on the temple, felling him like a dead man. The warriors of his court hurried to carry him away. Connacht troops crossed the river in a mad rush and broke upon the ranks of the retreating Ulstermen slaying many and driving the remainder back across the land. Forever after, this place was called Cath Ath-nuachar, the battle of the Ford of the Sling-cast.

But when Conor, still prostrate, reached Emhain Macha, Fingen, the chief physician of the court, discovered that the ball, though half buried in his temple, was not fatal. 'If it is removed,' he said, ''twill kill him. But if it remains where it is, he'll live – but he will bear the blemish of it.'

Now this was an important matter for it was an ancient law that a noble who was blemished could not be a king. The lords of Ulster decided to make an exception in Conor's case because he was held in such high esteem. 'Blemish or no blemish,' they said, 'that is a small matter beside the death of a king.'

Accordingly, Fingen dressed the wound and stitched it over, brain-ball and all, with threads of gold to match Conor's hair; and when the king recovered his senses, instructed him to keep himself from all strenuous movement and passion, and to avoid horseback riding or other violent exercise, and he would live. Reluctantly Conor agreed. But it was, at the beginning, a sore trial to him until he had accommodated himself to it, for he was a man of great vitality who loved sport and gaming and action of all kinds. It was during this time too, taking advantage of it, I suppose, and of the king's enforced quiescence in every way, so to speak, that Athairne, and his sons, overreached themselves.

Conor, as I told you, had married the beautiful young Luaine. Well, now, the two sons of Athairne were poets themselves – not in their father's class of course – indeed 'twas said they only made it through the poets' school because of who he was – but they were also of a venomous disposition, need I say? Didn't they conceive the warped and depraved idea of solacing the young queen and, what was worse, decided to act on it. Coming on her one day in the *grianaan* or solarium, they smirked and sidled towards her until one of them sat on one side of her and other on the other, and, surrounded by her women though she was, they whispered in her ear obscene proposals, restraining her when she wished to rise and go, so that, young as she was, she was covered with confusion and embarrassment, and because of it dared not show it to her maidens who, naturally, from her reaction, nevertheless guessed that something was wrong, without knowing what.

'If you don't let us,' hissed the eldest son, 'we will make a *glawm-dicenn* on you.'

'Leave me,' gasped the young queen, turning her head only to find herself facing the other son who whispered sibilantly: 'Come with us now and enjoy what we'll do or it will be the worse for you. Anyway,' he went on, 'you must be dying for it by now the way he is.'

This was too much and the queen stood and walked from the *grianaan* followed by her women, all of them trembling and as indignant as she was. But the two poets, God help us, were drunk with power and blind to consequences. They put their threat into execution and performed the left-handed, one-eyed, one-legged, one-armed *glawm-dicenn* and made three *aers*, that is, hauntings, which raised three *bolga* or blisters on her face; a black blister called *om*, or stain; a red blister called *ainm*, or blemish; and a white blister called *aithis*, or defect; and these so disfigured and hurt the young queen that she died of grief and disgrace within twenty-four hours.

However, it was the crowning and final iniquity of Athairne and his family. The rage that overcame Conor when he heard of it bid fair to burst his brain, but he restrained himself. At his urging, however, the Ulstermen rose up and slew the whole family of Athairne and destroyed their dun and not, when you come to think of it, before time. There are still a few so-called *olilamhs* around could get similar treatment to everyone's benefit.

Towards the end of the seven peaceful years an extraordinary phenomenon occurred for which there was no accounting. In broad daylight the sky darkened, the gloom of night spread across the world, the earth was sundered so that those long dead seemed to step forth where they stood, and thunder roared in the heavens. The people became terrified before the calamity portended. The earth shook and lightning pierced the darkness. Death was in the skies. While this was taking place, Conor summoned his chief druid, by name Bacarach, and asked him what was causing these awful events. And although the druid went to a *nineadh* of ash and yew and performed rites of all kinds, he could not penetrate the darkness. Eventually it passed.

But, some time later, the Roman consul Althus, from Britain on a visit to Emhain Macha, revealed to Conor what had happened on that day. Standing before Conor with his plumed helmet under his left arm and leaning lightly on a *pilum* – which was purely for effect since he was not a common soldier – Althus said: "Twas very strange. I am told, and my seers confirm it, that in the city of Jerusalem on that day and at that time three men were crucified on a hill. 'Tis said that one of them was a great prophet and a seer, but was nevertheless executed.'

'And were there not Romans there,' asked Conor, 'who might have prevented it?'

'Indeed,' replied Althus, 'but it was they who executed him.'

'Then he was a criminal,' said Conor.

'No,' replied Althus. 'On the contrary. I believe that he epitomised holiness and innocence and truth on earth and in heaven and it was for this that he was condemned. And for this too that the heavens darkened in anger.'

And this, it is said, was too much for Conor, who leaped up in a fury and grabbed his sword shouting: 'Had I been there with the hosts of Ulster they would not have killed Him. Had I been there I would have scattered His foes and saved the world and the Light and the Truth.' And with that he began to hack and slash and stab at the trees and the bushes around the *grianaan*.

And in the heat of his passion the brain-ball burst from his head through the golden stitching. Conor fell to the ground and was still – and was dead. That is how the vengeance of Mesgedra against Conor Mac Nessa, King of Ulster, was fulfilled.

FOOTNOTES

1 See *Crucible* Donal O'Neill (Macdonald/Futura)
2 See 'The Sons of Tuireann'.
3 See 'The Sons of Tuireann'.
4 See 'Introduction'.
5 See *Crucible* Donal O'Neill (Macdonald/Futura)

The Castle of the Rowan Trees

Third Period: Fianna Cycle

The Fianna tales relate to a period of proto-history in which known historical figures may, however faintly, be discerned. The period is also one which, while historically indeterminate, nonetheless verges on that of recorded history. Their time of action is, therefore, set in a reasonably specific time in the past. Accordingly, they might have some claim to being classified as sagas rather than myths.

This magnificent story of the Fianna and the intrigues of Midac ending with the onslaught from Sinsear of the Battles, King of Greece, 'King of the World', and his followers, like many of the Fianna tales, demonstrates the influence and values of the much later 'Viking' period, but with no evidence of the Christian ethic that has been introduced into some of these tales. It is partly this 'historical' ambivalence that makes many of the Fianna tales so vivid and narratively heroic, as if they represented the folk-history of the Norse period as much as the heroic tales of legendary figures from a remoter past; rather like defiant and thinly disguised eighteenth-century nationalistic ballads. Here the admixture makes for a fine story in which necessary suspension of the critical faculty seems to be almost directly proportionate to the nineteenth-century 'heroic' input.

It is important to remember that the listeners were intimately familiar with all the characters in these stories and did not need to have their individual characteristics filled in. What appear to the modern eye as cryptic remarks, even total *non sequiturs*, become explicit and integral to the plot and story-line when interpreted in the wider context of the understood nature of the individual or event concerned. Thus bald Conán Maol, one of the best-drawn of all the Fianna heroes, is known as a coward and a glutton and is a figure of fun – though tinged with caution – for he can be vicious and, worse, is a noted and dangerous satirist. The folk element emerges strongly in this interpretation and, for that reason, the Fianna stories are amplified and recounted in that idiom. The result seems to enhance their validity and integrity as stories as well as the narrative quality without doing violence to the essential tradition.

To purists who would disagree with this approach, I put the question: 'What "purity" is being defended?' These tales were originally oral. No one today knows how they were recounted, much less how they were modified by events. The only thing one can be reasonably sure of is that they were popular, and devotion to rigid and undefined 'purity' is no criterion of popularity. Popularity, almost by definition, implies that they were contemporaneously relevant. I am confident that in giving them a contemporary, or near contemporary, idiom and in fleshing out the narrative and characters, no violence to the essential spirit of the story is being done. On the contrary I hope that this form brings the story closer to the original in intent than might otherwise be the case. There are some clear allegories, of course, which defy rationalisation, but which are an acceptable part of folk narration and tradition. Perhaps the most obvious one in this story is the synonym for death and/or disease brought by the foreigners which magically renders Fionn and his companions helpless in the Castle of the Rowan Trees, and for which release is obtainable only by the posthumous magic of the same foreigners.

The King of Lochlann, which is away to the north and east of Ireland and is today the southern part of Norway and Sweden and the northern part of Denmark, was a man called Colga of the Hard Weapons. He was brave and brutal, big and loud, and in general not the sort of person you would be inclined to have an argument with or to meet in a dark place. Every now and then he would call together his nobles and chief people and discuss with them whatever was on his mind (though maybe 'discuss' is too strong a word for it since his normal method of dealing with those foolish enough to disagree with him was to cut off his eyelids and a few other appendages that he stuffed in his mouth, while at the same time feeding in a few hot pebbles out of the fire at the other end to help convince him of his erroneous thinking, before he did him any serious hurt and after that he pierced his eyes with hot needles; that treatment often cured argumentative people and those given to pointless disputation). Colga usually held his meetings on the *faitche*, or plain, that extended out from his palace before his city of Berva.

On one occasion when all were gathered together and he sat high on his throne made of hard pinewood and the tusks of sea monsters, he addressed them in a very loud and clear voice, asking a kind of question that had something in it to indicate that it was a trick question and only he knew the answer. Of course this made all the lords and nobles a bit uneasy for Colga had a well-developed sense of humour and could think of many ways to trap men with questions for which they would have to pay a forfeit, like surrendering their lands, or their gold, or sitting for an hour seven feet up on a pointed pole fixed upright in the ground, or to spend the night tied up in a tidal pool and up to the neck in water before the tide was in — that class of thing. So they looked uneasily at one another when he asked: 'Tell me, does any of ye know of anything at all in me, as your king and lord, deserving of blame?'

Naturally, no one was inclined to say 'yes', whatever they might think in private. On the other hand, not knowing the mood he was in, they were cautious about saying 'no' too. They had an uneasy feeling that he wouldn't have asked the question if there wasn't something on his mind. So, knowing the kind of man he was, they all took the sensible course and a chorus of grunts, coughs and shuffling rose from the front until from the back where the speaker couldn't be identified a voice rose up: 'Not a fault nor the sign, or trace of a fault whatever, in the wide world.'

Colga looked at them sort of coldly for a moment. Then his face assumed an expression of sadness, so that, for a number of reasons — few of them to do with Colga's mien — many of them felt like groaning and quite a few surreptitiously wiped the sweat from their foreheads while wondering rapidly: 'What is it? Did he learn this, or that or the other — or what?'

Having gazed at them thus for a minute, Colga said: 'If that's the way you see matters, then you don't see them as I do.'

He paused. He waited for a moment to see if anyone would say anything, at the same time quelling the possibility with a glare from his drooping eye. Then he went on. 'Am I not called the King of the Four Tribes of Lochlann *and*,' he emphasised, 'of the Islands of the Sea?'

Here they knew the form. As one man the multitude roared: 'Yes!'

'Well then,' he said, 'is it not also true that there is one island that does not acknowledge my rule?'

There came mutters and queries from amongst the nobles until they all fell silent again and looked back uneasily at the king. 'Ireland of the green hills,' Colga cried in a fearfully angry voice, 'refuses me; refuses tribute and expels my emissaries.'

Now they had it. A load – almost visible – lifted off them. They stopped sweating and became red and angry. There was much loud muttering.

Colga went on, enjoying the proceedings: 'You all know that our forefathers, the Fomorians, ruled there[1] until the people of Ireland rose up against them and drove them out at the battle of Moytura, where many of our brave ancestors fell dead or were driven off. The great King Balor died there, killed by his own grandson, the Il-Dana. Bres, who was regent of Ireland was killed there. Balor's wife, Caitlin, was killed there. And many others, too numerous for me to name. And ever since these haughty Irish have ignored our messengers and refused to pay tribute and have threatened war on us.'

The muttering rose to a growl, and the growl to a sullen and angry rumble with a louder voice here and there rising above it until Colga raised his arm and stopped it, well satisfied with the effect he was producing. He went on: 'I have decided that we will sail with a fleet and an army to Ireland, bring it under our control either by consent or by force, and exact the tributes that are due to us by right. And thereafter we will hold the island in subjection 'til the end of the world.' With that there was a great roar and a shout of approval and the meeting ended.

After that scouts and messengers went all over Lochlann summoning the fighting men of the land. They came in groups from all quarters until they had assembled a great army at Berva. While they were being summoned, assembling and coming in, their slender, sweeping, curved-flank white-sailed ships and their strong, gliding boats were being made ready so that the army had not long to wait before it embarked. And when they did so they raised their sails and plied their oars and cleft the billowy, briny sea. The clear, cold wind whistled in their rigging and filled their bosomy sails to drive them across the ocean to the drumbeats of the ships' masters, so that they never paused nor stopped 'til they drew up on the shores of the north of Ireland.

Now the King of Ireland at that time was Cormac Mac Art (Curr-muck Moc Awrt) – which means it was round about a hundred and fifty years before the coming of Saint Patrick. Cormac was one of the most illustrious kings who ever sat in Tara. He was the grandson of Conn Céad Cath, Conn the Hundred Fighter, and was renowned for his learning and wisdom. It was he, Cormac Mac Art, who wrote the *Teagasc Rí*, or *Instructions for Kings*, the rules by which a king might govern[2] not only his people, but himself, with justice and wisdom. He codified the law in one great volume and had the records of Ireland collated and written. He established three schools at Tara, one for military science, one for law, and one for history.

When Cormac heard that a great enemy fleet had come to Ireland and landed an army, he immediately sent news of the invasion to the hill of Allen in Kildare, which was the headquarters of the Fianna, which, as everyone knows, was the standing army established by Cormac's grandfather, Conn. (But it was under Cormac that they achieved their greatest glory, only to see it wither and die when he retired from the kingship to devote the last years of his life to study in a monastery – but that is another story.) While each province had its own battalions of the Fianna, all were under the command of one general-in-chief. The most distinguished of these was Fionn MacCumhail and Allen was his headquarters.

Fionn was a great commander and was, according to many, gifted with the power of divination, which he had acquired through tasting the Salmon of Knowledge that he had caught at the Well of Sergeis, the source of the seven great rivers of Ireland, which is overhung by the nine Hazels of Wisdom. The hazel nuts dropped into the well and caused bubbles of mystic inspiration to form on the streams that issued from it. These were eaten by the Salmon of Knowledge, and whoever first tasted the Salmon obtained the gifts of the seer and the poet and the art of divination. Fionn tasted the Salmon by accident – but that is another story too – nonetheless it is well to remember that his name, Mac Cuil, means Son of Hazel. He was formidable both as friend and foe and could be implacable in his enmity. Oisín, the great poet, was his son.[3] Oisín's son, Oscar, one of the most handsome of men, was also one of the most valiant and kind-hearted of the Fianna. Diarmuid O Dyna, who eloped with Grainne, Fionn's bride, was known as the bravest of the brave. Coilte Mac Ronan was Fionn's nephew and was distinguished for his fleetness of foot.

Amongst the Fianna was Goll Mac Morna, the leader of Clann Morna, who was one of the mightiest of all the heroes of the Fianna. Although he served under Fionn, the two chieftains had no love for each other; and Goll had, in fact, killed Fionn's father in years gone by at the great battle of Cnoc Adh, Castleknock, near Dublin, and these two men were great rivals. And sure, eventually, weren't they the cause of the destruction of the Fianna? Conán Maol, or Conán the Bald, was a great warrior, a great boaster, a great coward and a great glutton with a great and venomous tongue. He was the son of Goll Mac Morna and was forever mocking the Clann Baiscne, which was Fionn's clan.

When the messengers reached Fionn, he immediately sent heralds to summon the battalions of the Fianna to meet him some miles short of the enemy camp. In the meantime he led the Fianna of Leinster north immediately. When both armies were assembled the battle took place. All day long the clash and clang of weapons and the screams of wounded men despoiled the plain. By mid-afternoon, it looked as if the Lochlannaigh would be successful, for they pressed on the Fianna who gave before them.

Then the powerful Oscar, son of Oisín, seeing what was happening, and with his own men in support, drove mightily for the Lochlann centre towards the standard of Colga, dealing havoc and slaughter on any that stood in his way. Oscar burst through the shield of spears to where Colga stood waiting for him, for he had seen him coming. Eyeing one another and with deadly tread they circled to the left and then leaped at each other in hand-to-hand combat. Both armies stopped and dropped their weapons to watch the battle between these two. Soon their shields were rent, their helmets dented from great blows, their armour pierced, and the blood flowed from fresh wounds. Both men staggered from exhaustion after each blow and their striking at one another was like the weary, alternate rise and fall of a mechanical arm. Their swords dragged on the ground after each blow. One struck as the other tried to recover his strength and balance. But, in spite of the exhaustion it epitomises, the struggle was all the more deadly, for one man had to die – and that man was Colga. A blow by Oscar struck him on the neck and he fell to his knees. Another blow severed his head. When the Lochlannaigh saw Colga fall they lost heart and, fighting desultorily, they fled the field and returned to their ships.

Most remarkable is the fact that of all the lords and nobles of Lochlann who sailed to Ireland on that expedition only one remained alive, and that was the youngest son of King Colga, whose name was Midac. He was fifteen years old. Because he was who he was he was brought to Fionn before execution. But, because of his youth and station, Fionn, in a burst of generosity, spared him and offered to bring him up as his foster-son in his own house.

After the battle, the Fianna rested and bathed in baths with healing herbs, sweated in sweat houses, and buried their dead standing, facing Lochlann. And having done all that, they turned and marched slowly south bringing with them their sick and their wounded. When they again reached Allen, Fionn introduced Midac to his household as a prince, and gave him servants and teachers who were instructed to prepare him to become a member of the Fianna. And so things went on for several years.

Midac grew to manhood and lived with Fionn at Allen, and hunted and feasted with the Fianna and fought with them if they were required to fight. But he was withdrawn and reticent, yet most observant. He walked alone and spent much of his time alone getting to know the paths and fortresses of the Fianna, their methods and habits, and in particular their manner of going to war.

When he was about eighteen years old it happened one day that Fionn and certain of the elders of the Fianna were sitting together in council as they did from time to time considering matters of concern to the Fianna. Each commander was expected to give a report and advance his comments or opinions or advice on any matter being debated at the meeting. After the matters on the official agenda had been dealt with and the meeting was about to relax before concluding, Conán Maol (Co-nawn Mwail), the son of Goll Mac Morna (Gowl Moc More-nuh), stood up and addressed the meeting. He spread his feet, put his two fists on his hips – which meant that they were well separated – and looked round slowly, the poll of his bald head glistening and shining as if it had been rubbed with butter.

Then he said, slowly and meaningfully, as they say: 'I've been thinking: and it seems to me, Fionn, that you, me, and the whole of Fianna, are in a dangerous situation. I'll go further, I'd say outright we're in danger.'

A rustle swept the hall the way you'd think you were in a wood on a day in October. Men weren't sure if he was serious or not; or if they ought to laugh, thinking it might be one of Conán Maol's jokes. But when they saw no flicker of slyness or amusement about his mouth and that his eyes were hard, the nature of the mutter changed to one of surprise and they wondered what he'd say next. When there was silence Conán looked directly at Fionn.

Then he continued: 'In your house, and mixing with your own people, there's a man with very good reason to be your enemy. You know who I mean – Midac. You were responsible for killing his father, *and* his brothers, and many of his friends along with them.'

He looked round and then waved an expansive hand. 'So what about it, you ask? That was long ago and he's not the first to be taken in and reared by his father's killer,' he said deliberately.

He turned back to Fionn. 'I'm sorry if that offends you, but that's the way it was. And if you have a stem of sense you'll listen to me. Let you take a good look at the ferret you've got in your nest. Look at him!' Conán looked round intently. 'He talks to no one. He mixes with no one. He spends his time watching and listening. There's nothing he doesn't know about any one of us. I don't trust him and you'd be a fool to trust him either. Don't you know as well as I that he has plenty of friends and relations in Lochlann; more like his father and himself, and the ships and armies to go with them? Let me tell you, the day will come when he'll use that knowledge against us.'

He looked round. Several heads nodded agreement. He looked back at Fionn, and Fionn was nodding too, and biting his upper lip with his lower teeth.

'There's a lot in what you say, Conán Maol,' said Fionn. 'The question is what should be done about it?'

'I'll tell you what should be done about it,' said Conán. 'That fella shouldn't be here at all. He should be shown the door from Allen and sent some place where he can do no damage.'

'We can't just throw him out,' said Fionn, 'having offered him our hospitality.'

'If you said we can't separate his head from the rest of him for that reason I might go so far as to agree with you,' said Conán. 'But there's more ways of killing a cat than choking it with butter. Here's what you'll do. Tell him, now he's a man, that he's entitled to the rights and responsibilities of a man. Let him build his own castle on a piece of land in some other part of Ireland and have servants and the like of that, and let him go away off by himself and we'll be shut of him. That way you'll save your honour, we'll be free of him, and he won't be sticking his long nose into all our affairs or learning all our secrets.' Having said that Conán Maol sat down and folded his arms.

'That doesn't seem like a bad idea,' said Fionn, to a general murmur of approval from the assembly. And so Fionn sent for Midac, spoke along the lines suggested by Conán Maol (offering him two *cantreds* of the best land in Ireland and all the help he needed with servants and cattle to set up on his own). Midac listened quietly and coldly, showing no emotion; and when Fionn was finished, simply said it was a fair proposal and that he accepted. Having said that he chose the *cantred* of Kerry on the Shannon and the *cantred* of the islands lying next to it to the north on the other side of the river.

And let me tell you he had good reason for choosing those two *cantreds*. Doesn't the Shannon open out between them like a sea and aren't there a multitude of islands there with the divil knows what bays and harbours in them to shelter ships? Oh, he had had his eye on this place all right for some time and he could hardly believe his luck when he got the opportunity to select it for himself. No better place to hide a fleet or introduce an army to move out from the centre of Ireland and destroy it. So I can tell you he was a well-contented man when he got the offer and more so when he was given cattle and silver and gold and timber and servants and what all else besides to go and build and stock and furnish his new holding. *Bhí sé ag gáire* – he was laughing! And when he was finished, wasn't he a rich and wealthy prince in his own right thanks to the generosity of Fionn? Anyway, he shut himself off in his own place from contact with everyone and for fourteen years developed and built and ruled from his two castles until he was a man of considerable and secret power. And in all that time he never invited one of the Fianna to visit him or offered them hospitality of any kind; and, besides that, in all that time weren't visitors and messengers and heralds going secretly between himself and Lochlann disguised as merchants from Gaul or Spain or the like?

At the end of the fourteen years, Fionn and the Fianna were hunting one day on the plains of Croom near what was to become Limerick, not far from Kerry,

Midac's territory. While the main body of the Fianna hunted across the plain, Fionn and a few of his companions went to the top of the hill of Knockfierna which is conspicuous in that area. The servants put up his tent and the tents of his companions and made couches for them from the rushes and the heather and the ferns and dug cooking pits, while the nobles lay down and rested and talked and drank wine and mead and the usual kind of thing customary on such occasions.

And while they were at that, what did they see coming up the hill towards them but a tall, powerful warrior in full battle harness? He had a fine coat of mail in the Lochlann style on him and over it a cloak in five colours to show his rank. A shield cut from one piece of alder covered with glittering bronze hung over his left shoulder. And his magnificent bronze helmet gleamed in the sunlight as he came on towards them. From his left side hung a long sword and its cross-shaped hilt was worked with gold and enamel, and in his right hand he carried two long, smooth, polished, deadly spears. He was tall and majestic looking and when he came up he saluted Fionn courteously. Fionn replied just as courteously and the two of them spoke for a little while in the secret language of the druids, so Fionn knew at once that this was no ordinary warrior. He was quick that way!

'Tell me,' he asked, 'where do you come from?'

'That's a small thing of no consequence,' said the stranger. But he went on: 'The fact of the matter is I'm an *Áes Dána* (Man of Learning) and, hearing you were in the district, I thought I'd make a poem for you.'

'Well,' said Fionn, who fancied himself as a bit of a poet, 'that's very nice of you, I suppose; and while you may be an *Áes Dána* and a poet, from the look of you I'd be more inclined to the view that you are more familiar with the handling of a sword and with the music of battle than with the sharpening of quills and the music of melodious words.'

'You can think what you like,' said the stranger, but without giving offence, though he came near enough to it, I suppose. 'But I am an *Áes Dána,* whether or which, and, if you don't mind, I'll prove it by reciting my poem.'

'Well,' said Fionn, not too pleased with the reply or with the idea of having bad poetry spouted at him when he was trying to enjoy himself, 'a mountain top isn't the best place for poetry. Moreover,' he went on when he saw that the stranger was about to interrupt, 'I won't have the chance now because myself and these gentlemen with me came up here so that we can sit down at our ease and watch the chase and listen to it and see what's going on below.'

The stranger opened his mouth to protest and Fionn held up his hand to stop him. 'Look,' he said, 'I'll tell you what I'll do. Sit down there and be quiet until the hunt is over. After that you can come with us to one of our castles and we'll have a bit of a banquet and that'd be a better place altogether for poetry. I'll listen to your poem there; and if you're as good as you say you are, I'll give you an appropriate gift, whatever it might be.' That way, thought Fionn to himself, we can decide if he's good enough to come with us and I can decide if he's any good at all.

But the stranger wasn't having that. 'No,' he said to Fionn, looking at him in the eye – and there was a clash of wills if ever there was one – 'that doesn't suit me at all. I don't want to go to your castle. And now I'm putting you under *geasa*, a solemn vow and injunction, which you cannot refuse without loss of honour and reputation, to grant me my reasonable request and listen to my poem and discover its meaning if you are able.'

This speech had several effects on Fionn. It started off by making him angry naturally enough for being thwarted, and went on to make him indignant at having a *geasa* put on him, and it ended up by making him curious to know if he could solve the riddle since he fancied himself a very clever man, which he was. So he said: 'Well, if that's the way of it, it's got to be. Get on with your job and recite your poem.'

The stranger drew himself up and, in keeping with his flamboyant class of a nature, struck a pose. He planted the two butts of his spears in the ground, leaned against them with his extended arm and, putting the other arm on his hip, let fly:

> A castle shines by a verdant stream,
> Renowned its name has ever been.
> Richer its treasures than one might dream,
> With gold and crystal its rafters gleam.
>
> But, though 'tis open to all who come,
> Lord or reiver, thief or whore,
> Safe its treasures from any one,
> Its lord is master of magic lore.
>
> Fire will never break its walls,
> Nor torrents flood its ancient halls,
> Now if you read my riddle right,
> Name this mansion I describe.

Fionn's temper wasn't one bit improved by this simple conundrum. Wasn't he a poet himself? And like all poets he was much given to composing riddles and poetical puzzles and that class of thing for champions to try to explain. I needn't tell you it was a mark of great and acute intelligence in a champion to be able to do that with facility. But this riddle was so obvious that Fionn was annoyed the other thought it worth putting to him. 'Ah,' he said in disgust, 'sure that's Newgrange, the Brugh of the Boyne, the palace of Aengus Ogue. It's open to all.

It cannot be burned; it cannot be drowned; or spoiled by robbers because of the power of Aengus who keeps his doors open to welcome every man, woman and child.[4] If that's the best you can do, we're wasting our time.' And he turned away.

'I have another for you,' said the stranger. 'Let's see if you can explain this one.' Again he declaimed, in proper poetical fashion, as follows:

> Looking south I saw a queen,
> Her bed was crystal, her room was green,
> He numerous children, swift and small,
> Within her you could see them all.
>
> Stately elegance marks her course
> But yet she's swifter than a horse.
> That riddle's tested many a man.
> Solve it for me if you can.

Fionn looked at him again with disgust. 'Do you take me for an ordinary sort of person or what?' he asked. 'Or is it that you're trying to trick me with two riddles from the same place? Your queen is the river Boyne which flows beside the Brugh. Looking south from Tara you saw her. The crystal couch is the sandy bed of the river and her robe of green the verdant plain of Bregia it flows through. The children you can see through her skin are the silver salmon and the lively trout and all the other fish in the clear waters of the river. And while your queen flows slowly its waters cover the whole world in seven years, which is more than the fastest horse can do.'

'Well,' said the stranger, 'you answered my riddle.'

'If I have,' said Fionn, 'having listened to it and, I might add, not thought much of it, the least you can do is to have the good manners to tell us who you are and where you come from. For it seems to me very strange that such a champion as yourself could live in any of the four worldly provinces of Ireland, let alone the fifth, without being known to me or my companions.'

Conán Maol looked at Fionn, a sort of sneer lifting his lips, and he said: 'I don't know, Fionn, whether you've having us on, or if it is the way your powers are deserting you; for the way it is, any one of the Fianna would have unravelled harder poems than that before breakfast. It seems very strange to me too that you don't recognise this man you brought up in your own house and afterwards made rich, or that you can't tell friend from foe. Because I can tell you, and you know the state of affairs between us, that this man is an enemy of yours and an enemy of all of ours for that matter. This is Midac. And he has lived here for the past fourteen years without sign nor sight of the Fianna during all that time, or the hand of friendship extended towards us. And although he is one of the

Fianna, none of us has ever crossed his threshold or eaten a bite of his or got so much as a sup of water from him.'

Then Midac – for that's who it was all right – said: 'If you, Fionn, and the Fianna – and, of course, Conán Maol, who seems to have some kind of a grudge against me as well as against everybody else – haven't feasted with me that's not my fault. My castle has never been without a banquet fit for a king or chief, lord or noble, but the divil a one of any of ye ever came near me. True enough I never sent you an invitation, but then if I never went near you, none of you ever came near me either. It seems to me that you might have come to me before I came to you seeing that I was one of the Fianna and was brought up in your own house – and, when it suited you, put out of it too. However, that's enough of that. I have a feast down below ready for eating worthy of a king. Now I'm putting you and all of you here,' he turned to look at them one by one, 'under *geasa* that you come on down tonight to my castle, that I call the Castle of the Rowan Trees because 'tis surrounded by them, and eat that banquet with me.'

They all agreed – Conán Maol first, his greed overcoming his doubt, which was usual enough with him where food or gold or getting anything for nothing was concerned – and Midac, having shown them the quickest way down to the castle, went on ahead to have everything ready against their arrival.

Fionn and his men waited until Midac was out of earshot (and out of sight as well) and then they had a hurried consultation, and the result of that was that they decided Oisín and five other nobles would stay behind and keep an eye out for the main body. But that was only a part of it, because they also decided that Fionn would send back word to Oisín when they reached Midac's castle to say how matters stood and whether they should follow on or not. When all was decided, Fionn went off with Goll Mac Morna and twelve companions. Diarmuid O Dyna, Caoilte Mac Ronan, and three other younger nobles stayed back with Oisín.

Well, Fionn and his party faithfully followed the directions Midac gave them and when they came to the Castle of the Rowan Trees, the Lord save us, they were amazed outright at the size and splendour of it. They couldn't understand why it was they had never seen it before, or heard of it for that matter. But there it was, standing on a broad, wide *faitche*, surrounded by as fine a plantation of rowan trees as ever you saw, each one of them thickly covered with blazing clusters of scarlet berries – which goes to show that all of this happened in the mystic month of *Lunasa*, or August. There was a broad river with round, tumbled rocks marked grey and green with lichen and black at the water-line, tumbled and jumbled together on one side of the *faitche*. A steep path led down through it to a ford, and that's how they crossed over. They stood outside this fine palace, looking at it, for not a sinner was there to welcome them.

What surprised them more than anything else was the silence, the stillness of the place. Not a living soul anywhere nor sound to be heard; not of bird or of the wind in the elongated leaves of the trees; nothing! Fearing something was wrong (and who'd blame him in the circumstances), Fionn would have turned back again only for his *geasa* and his promise. He looked at the others doubtfully. Then he looked at the castle, and then he shook his head. But the great, wide door of the castle was open.

The sunlight streamed invitingly through it and this was too much for Conán Maol, and he could no longer prevent himself going in to see what awaited him inside in the way of food and entertainment. After a minute or two he came out again. There was a smile on his face, enough for the others to know that what he'd seen was to his satisfaction. The leg of some bird, well browned and dripping fat, was in his left fist, and his cheek bulged as he chewed and shifted what was in his mouth from side to side before speaking.

He waved his other arm at them. He wasted no time praising the magnificence of the building, or the trappings, or the fine workmanship of the furnishings. 'Come in quick,' he cried, having pushed the food in his mouth more or less aside, ''til ye see what's before us. I wouldn't believe it myself if I didn't see it with my own two eyes.' Mind you, 'twas hard enough to understand him the way things were, but his meaning was clear.

Well, anyway, they all went in, some of them laughing and some of them silent, some of them slowly and some of them confident – and away out in front on Conán's heels. When they got in, they stopped and looked round in astonishment for what Conán might have said – but didn't – was true: no other king or noble in all of Ireland had a banqueting hall to match that of Midac, son of Colga. But . . . there was no sign of anyone within. Sight nor sign of a Christian, if you'll pardon the word, or a Mithraist or a decent follower of the gods, was not to be seen; neither host, other guests, nor servants.

An enormous fire burned brightly, dancing in the centre of the hall with little smoke – and what there was of it was drawn up through a cunningly contrived apparatus in the ceiling that disposed of it outside after the fashion of the Romans. Whatever timber was on the fire gave out a sweet perfume that filled the whole room with a fragrance and added to the growing cheerfulness of the Fianna leaders. Comfortable-looking couches covered with cushions, rugs, and soft gleaming furs were here and there around the place. The timber wall shone with the best of yew wood closely jointed so that you could not see the junction and polished so that the different colours of the timber glowed in the firelight.

Still no one came into view or presented himself to welcome them. So they sat down on the couches, but without touching the unbelievably lavish and sumptuous banquet that occupied the whole of the huge table that circled the fire – and waited. It was, of course, too hard and difficult a wait for Conán Maol, who had to be restrained from any additional breach of etiquette by reaching for something else before the host was present.

Presently a door opened and Midac walked into the room. He held the door with one hand without greeting them or offering them a word of welcome, and looked at each one of them in turn, coldly and dispassionately without so much as a muscle twitching in his face, or the blink of an eyelid. Then he turned round and went out, shutting the door behind him.

But, wonder of wonders, if he did, didn't he take a great deal more along with him? A gloom that was not there before descended on the hall and it took the heroes a moment or two for their eyes to get accustomed to it. And when they did! Well, they were as surprised as they had been before, I can tell you, but if the surprise they had the first time was of wonder and amazement at the unprecedented lavishness, that they felt now was of a mighty different sort entirely. 'Twas composed of anger and horror and dismay at what they now saw about them.

The fire, which before Midac had come in had burned with a lovely clear flame and filled the room with a sweet scent, now filled it with a foul stinking black smoke that hung round them in sooty clouds. The smooth and glistening walls of the fine hall that had shone with all the colours of polished wood, were now become hard, raw poles and planks fastened securely together through which the winds and the elements could travel without let or hindrance. Gone were the seven great doors of the proud castle that followed the course of the sun; and instead there was one small, narrow, bolted black grille facing straight north. Gone too were the soft couches, the rich rugs and the furs on which they had reclined; and they found themselves sitting on the bare, damp earth which, as Conán Maol said, was 'as cold as the first snow of winter'.

As calmly as he could and subduing his understandable surprise, for he was a man of remarkable self-control when the mood was on him, Fionn said 'There's something strange going on here.'

'That's a fact,' agreed the others, 'and it's not very nice.'

'What's more,' said Fionn, 'as you all know, my friends, for all the obvious reasons I never stay in a house with only one door – and there's only the one opening in this place, and that's shut! So would one of you ever go over there and smash open that bit of a grille so that we can get away out of this dark, smoky place?'

'No sooner said than done,' said Conán Maol, who found that his mouth was full of old bits of dirt and dung. 'I've changed my mind about this place too.'

He picked up his spear and planted the butt of it on the floor to give him leverage to get to his feet. But, to his astonishment, he found he couldn't move. Turning to the others he roared in confounded anguish: 'Glory be to the gods if that black divil hasn't put some kind of a spell on me the way I'm clung by the arse to the floor of this place and can't move!'

There was a general rustle amongst the others as they tried to get up, but they found that they were as immobilised as Conán Maol. Astonishment overwhelmed them until it was replaced by anger and alarm.

Goll looked at Fionn and said: 'You can't say I didn't warn you. That unspeakable son of a mangy, pox-ridden, foul-smelling, worm-eaten, flea-bitten, misbegotten cur! *Cruch árd gaoithe chuige* (a high, windy gallows to him)! *Maldacht a gaiscid air* (the curse of his weapons on him)! *Go ndamnaí an diabhal síos go leac na corónach duit, nó go tobar na luaithe seacht míle taobh thíos d'ifrean* (may the devil damn him below the flagstone of dirges or the well of ashes seven miles below hell's bottom)! 'Twas he planned this treachery. You may be sure he has more in store for us. Let you put your thumb under your tooth of knowledge, Fionn' – which was the method by which Fionn practised divination, resulting from the powers he acquired through tasting the Salmon of Knowledge – 'so that we will know the truth and consider what's best now to be done to get ourselves out of this fix that you got us into.' He gestured at Fionn and 'twas easy to see they didn't have a whole lot of regard for each other.

Fionn put his thumb in his mouth anyway and sat for a while with his eyes fixed on the floor, for all the world like a baby contemplating some new thing that had caught his interest. At the end of that time he took his thumb out of his mouth again, sank back on the ground as far as he was able – and it wasn't too far the way things were – and groaned. The look of him now was less like a baby and more like that of an old man having been given his death sentence.

'With the help of the gods,' said Goll Mac Morna, ''tis the way that you bit your thumb and hurt yourself that made you groan like that and not anything that you learned from your tooth.'

'With all my heart, I wish that that was the case. But it is not,' said Fionn. 'I'm sorry to have to tell you that, according to my tooth, we are doomed men.' He looked down at them, but they said nothing, only looking back at him and waiting for him to go on. 'Midac has been plotting against us for the past fourteen years and I can tell you I'm the sorry man I didn't consult my tooth about him before.'

Nodding his head like a willie-wagtail Goll looked around and said: 'There! What did I tell you?' The others glared at him.

Fionn went on: 'I must tell you that at the present moment there is a clatter of Lochlannaigh warriors not too far away and they're here for no other purpose but our own destruction. Chief of them is Sinsear of the Battles, the King of Greece, and there are sixteen warlike princes under him and countless others of lesser note, but nearly as bad and as dangerous. Besides that, Sinsear's son, Borba the Proud, is here with another host to make sure of the job. And as if that wasn't enough, there are three kings from the Island of the Torrent, as bloodthirsty as dragons, who never yielded to an enemy in battle before now. And you might as well know that 'tis these three ruffians have us in this fix, for it's their cold clay is stiffening our limbs and clinging to our backsides the way we can't move off of it. They brought hither with them some magic soil from the Island of the Torrent and scattered it here with four spells. That's what's holding us. What's worse, that spell that has us clung to this floor will never be broken until the blood of the same three kings are sprinkled on it. And now,' said he, raising himself a bit, 'I might as well tell ye the worst bit! Sinsear's warriors are even now on their way here from the Palace of the Island beyond, which is Midac's real castle, to stretch us cold and dead where we're fixed here, helpless and unable to defend ourselves.'

Well, of course, the others weren't too pleased with this and they grumbled and complained amongst themselves at having been brought into that fix.

After a while Fionn had had enough of that and he said: 'Will you hold your noise and not be going on like a clatter of women? If we have to die we might as well do it with dignity and a bit of defiance, so you might as well join me now in singing the *Dord-Fiansa*, and we'll let them know what we think of them, even if we can't defend ourselves.'

So together they sang this sweet, plaintive chorus which was at once a lament, a challenge and a death-knell.

A good while had passed as all this was going on and Oisín, who had remained behind on the hill of Knockfierna, was getting worried that he hadn't heard from Fionn as arranged. 'I don't understand why he hasn't sent us word,' he said to his companions. ''Tisn't like him at all. Something must have happened to prevent him, and before the rest of us go after him I think we ought to scout out the situation for ourselves to be on the safe side. Let you, Fiachna, and you, Innsa, go away off down and see what's to be seen.' (Fiachna was one of his brothers and Innsa (Eensha) was his foster-brother, one of Fionn's foster-sons.) They turned to go and Oisín called after them: 'And be careful!'

It so happened that as they arrived near the Castle of the Rowan Trees, dusk was drawing in just as the prisoners inside started to sing the *Dord-Fiansa*. Innsa said: 'Well, they must be all right if they're singing the *Dord-Fiansa*.'

Fiachna wasn't so sure. ''Tis a thing,' he said, 'that I never heard Fionn, or any other of the Fianna sing it as a lament if there wasn't trouble.'

They discussed this between themselves, Innsa saying that Fiachna was putting too much emphasis on something he had no proof of, and Fiachna insisting that they should be cautious. They argued; and in spite of themselves, their voices grew louder and, as luck would have it, weren't they right outside the place where the prisoners were held and Fionn (who had great hearing) heard them and held up his hand to stop the others singing, which they did. And

Fionn cocked his head and listened. But, if the singing stopped, didn't the two outside stop too when they heard the silence, if you understand me. So there they were, the two outside and the men inside, sitting and standing, with their heads cocked to one side, listening and making no sound at all. Fionn listened for a while and then he couldn't stand it any longer.

And he shouted: 'Is anyone there?'

Fiachna looked at Innsa and at the same time shouted back: 'There is. Who's that?' For he couldn't hear well enough to distinguish his father's voice (though, God knows, 'twas distinguished enough).

'Is that yourself, Fiachna?'

''Tis!' cried Fiachna.

'Come closer,' cried Fionn, 'and listen to me, *avic*. And be careful of this place whatever you do, for 'tis destroyed and poisoned with the divil only knows what sort of spells and enchantments that wouldn't do you one bit of good at all if you fell a victim to any of them. Like we did.'

'You did?'

'We did, surely!'

'Is that a fact?'

'It is,' said Fionn, 'so let you be careful. Midac has us trapped and we're held by the magic of the three kings of the Island of the Torrent.' With that Fionn told Fiachna the whole treacherous story from start to finish, ending with the information that nothing could free them but the blood of the three kings sprinkled on the clay on which they sat.

When Fionn learned that his foster-son Innsa was with Fiachna he urged the two men to fly before the foreigners arrived as they would surely kill the two outside as well as the prisoners inside if they found them. Moreover, he put it on his son to protect his foster-son, which was a very proper thing for him to do. But Innsa wouldn't go, saying that he refused to fly away leaving his foster-father in danger, and Fiachna said much the same thing.

Pleased and concerned at the same time Fionn said: 'If your minds are made up there's nothing I can do. But listen to me. I consulted my tooth and, as you have no doubt noticed yourselves, anyone coming from the Palace of the Islands across the way must pass by the ford beyond. And it's a difficult and a hard crossing. One good man standing in the narrow way might hold up an army for a time. That's where you had better make your stand and, with a bit of luck, the others might come up in the meantime.'

So Fiachna and Innsa went down to the ford, and after they had inspected it Fiachna said one could defend it as well as two. 'Let you stay here and guard the ford and I'll go and scout out the Palace of the Island and see how these intruders might be attacked. With any bit of luck at all I'll meet them on the way and decoy them, or harry them a piece.'

So Innsa took up his position and Fiachna set out for the Palace of the Island, where, while all this had been happening, a lot had been going on.

When Midac returned there after he'd imprisoned Fionn and his companions and told the foreigners what he had done, they were pleased enough about it as you might imagine. So pleased that they feasted and drank throughout the evening and the more they ate and the more they drank – and they did rather more of the latter than of the former – the louder and the noisier they became. At last one of the earls, who was with Sinsear of Greece, whispered – or thought he did – to his brother and said: 'I – I (hic), I'll go now over beyond to the Castle of the Rowan Trees and bring hither the head of Fionn Mac Cumhail, so I will, and I'll get a boost from the king for my reputation.'

So off with him and a good number of his own knights laughing and singing (once they got clear of the palace), through the darkness of the night, until they arrived at the ford leading to the Castle of the Rowan Trees where Innsa was guarding. That must have been the crowd Fionn's tooth told him about! They stopped there because they had to cross in single file (and 'twas no easy crossing either, as we know) balancing from rock to rock and stepping in swift flowing water with a great thrust to it on slimy boulders beneath the surface, the way if a man slipped, he could easily fall into a deep pool and hurt himself maybe, or knock his head or some other part of him off a rock in the fall, and drown or do himself some other serious mischief. Anyway the earl decided he'd go first and, peering across in gloom, what did he think he saw, but the shape of a warrior on the other bank. '*T'anam and diabhal* – soul to the devil,' he thought. 'What's this?'

It could have been a rock or a bush even, but 'twas too dark for him to be sure, so he called out to know was anyone there and, if so, whether he was a nobleman or something else not worthy of note. When Innsa called back that he was Fionn's foster-son, the earl, drunk and all as he was, pulled himself up and shouted out: 'Well, I'm going to the castle to bring Fionn's head to the King of the World and let you stay where you are to guide us to it.'

'Well, now,' called Innsa back to him, 'wouldn't that be a strange way for Fionn's foster-son to behave, and he after sending me here to guard this ford? But I'll tell you what I'll do. You come over here to me and I'll keep you here with me comfortable enough, and send your head back to the King of the World for you to save you the trouble of carrying it all that way yourself.'

When he heard that, the earl had second thoughts about being first across the ford and he said to his knights: 'There now! Did you hear that? Blackguardment! Are you going to stand there and let the likes of him bully and threaten us the like of that?'

They looked at him, and although most of them thought it there wasn't one of them who spoke out, and said: 'It was you he threatened, not us,' for they were only knights and he was an earl.

'Force the ford!' he cried.

So as many of them as could fit or find a footing, rushed through the water from rock to rock towards Innsa. But only two of them could attack at a time and Innsa struck them down, right and left, as fast as they came on until the ford was encumbered and inconveniently obstructed by bodies. After this had been going on a while, the knights realised that they couldn't dislodge Innsa, and retired back to their own side again. Innsa leaned up against a rock to take a bit of a rest – which he badly needed – for he had had a few knocks and cuts and bruises himself from all the fighting.

The earl wasn't one bit pleased that Innsa had disposed of so many of his best men and, like the dangerous man he was, he snatched up his sword and his shield and attacked the young hero across the ford without giving Innsa time for any kind of rest at all. Well, whatever start he gave when he saw the earl coming at him, didn't Innsa slip and fall to his knees and drop his sword. 'Twas long enough for the earl to stab at him treacherously while he was down, and cut off his head, which he carried back to his own side of the river.

Now Fionn and his companions were near enough to hear the shouting and the clash of arms at the ford, to say nothing of the groans and the cries of the wounded. But when all became still they wondered how matters stood, for they had no means of knowing. They were to remain in doubt for some time too, for the earl, having got to his own side of the river and not knowing if there mightn't be another of Fionn's warriors – or more – still guarding the ford, decided, as they say, that discretion was the better part of valour, and that he'd return to the Palace of the Island with Innsa's head to show it to the King of the World. While it wasn't Fionn's head, it was the head of his foster-son; and while that wasn't good, it was good enough. Accordingly he made his way back the way he had come and, lo and behold, who did he meet on the path but Fiachna, who had been scouting the Palace of the Island and was now on his way back to the ford knowing nothing at all of what had happened there while he had been gone, and expecting to find Innsa still there before him? The earl, on the other hand, didn't expect to find anyone on that side of the river except one of his own. So when Fiachna hailed him, of course he thought he was one of the warriors of the King of the World and answered him accordingly.

'Haven't I just come from the ford beyond in front of the castle where I was going to take the head of Fionn Mac Cumhail and bring it hither to the king?' he shouted. 'But weren't we met at the ford by the divil's own giant and monster of a warrior who killed half of my men until I tackled him myself and parted his head from his shoulders. Come here and have a look.'

Fiachna went up and in the gloom peered at the head of his foster-brother that the earl was holding up by the hair so that it dangled from his fist and the blood dripped from its severed neck down to the ground.

'Did you ever see a finer head?' asked the earl.

'Never in my life,' said Fiachna, 'did I see a finer head than that.'

'That's what I thought too,' said the earl. And then a new thought struck him. 'And where are you bound for by yourself? Don't you know 'tis dangerous to be abroad on your own? There might be more of Fionn's men about.'

'Indeed,' said Fiachna, ''tis true for you. There might.'

'Well, wouldn't you take some kind of a precaution,' asked the earl, 'and not be wandering around loose the way you are for fear you might meet a hero the like of myself on the other side who'd take a fancy to your head?'

'Many a man has taken a fancy to my head before now,' said Fiachna.

'Well, you still have it,' said the earl, 'and I suppose that's a good sign and speaks well of you. But you mightn't have it long if you go wandering around in the night by yourself. But who are you at all and what is your name? Are you with Sinsear or Borba or what?'

'I'm not with either of them,' said Fiachna. 'And I'll tell you something else.'

'What's that?' asked the earl.

'From this out,' said Fiachna, 'you won't be either.'

And that was when the earl realised his mistake. He reached for his sword at the same time that Fiachna drew his and they fought and stamped and cursed and swore and struck mighty blows at each other there in the darkness until the earl fell at Fiachna's hand and his knights vanished in the dark. Fiachna took his head and then carrying it and also that of Innsa went back to the ford. There he found the body of his foster-brother and made a grave where he stood the body and the head together facing their enemies while grief over his loss and contentment over his revenge filled his mind and his heart.

Having done that he went to the Castle of the Rowan Trees carrying the earl's head and called out to Fionn – who, of course, was only dying to know what had been happening. 'For the love and honour of the gods, Fiachna, would you ever tell us who was fighting at the ford a while ago and what was the outcome? Where's Innsa?'

'The way it is,' said Fiachna, 'I have good news and I have bad news.'

'Give us the good news,' said Fionn.

'Well,' said Fiachna, 'after we left here it was decided that Innsa would defend the ford and I would go out scouting across the river. While I was gone didn't they come and attack Innsa. He put up a fierce defence, I can tell you, for dark and all as it is I could see the bodies of the enemies he had slain piled up beyond in the stream like a dam.'

'That's good news all right,' said Fionn. 'Where's Innsa?'

'Innsa's dead,' said Fiachna.

'That's bad news,' said Fionn, 'and did you, my own son, stand by and see my foster-son killed?'

'Indeed and I did not,' said Fiachna. 'Sure wasn't he attacked at the end of all by the foreign earl when he was tired and wounded, and killed by him who couldn't have bounced his sword off his shield in safety when he was in the whole of his health?'

'And where were you?' asked Fionn.

'Didn't I tell you I was scouting the other side of the river?' asked Fiachna. 'Sure if I had been there there's no way the earl could have killed him. But don't fret too much for didn't I meet the earl soon after and I brought him back to prove it – or at least all you'll want to see of him.' And with that he held up the earl's head as high as he could by the hair and turned the face so that Fionn could squint out through a crack in the wall and see it. 'Besides that,' said Fiachna, 'didn't I bring the two parts of Innsa together again and bury him standing up and facing his enemies as is right and proper?'

Naturally Fionn was very grieved to hear of the death of his favourite foster-son, but at the same time he was pleased to know that his son had carried out his vengeance and his duties. Thinking about that and the fact that he would probably be dead before the morning, he did what men in such a fix often do if they have the chance; he praised his sons and daughters, and said to Fiachna:

'Little enough I had until my children grew up around me, and it is they who have made me happy and prosperous until I fell into this fix that I'm in now. What you'll do is go back and guard that ford, and if the gods are good to us maybe the rest of the Fianna will come up before we're all destroyed.'

So Fiachna went back and sat down on the near side of the ford with an eye over to the west.

Back at the Palace of the Island, the Earl Chiron, a brother of the one whose head Fiachna had tucked up and tied to his belt by his hair, was beginning to feel uneasy. 'That brother of mine should have been back long ago with Fionn's head,' he said. 'I wonder what's keeping them? I think I'll take a rove out and see would I see him coming.'

So off he went with a company of his own knights; and when they came up to the ford the first thing they saw was the pile of bodies jamming the river and they recognised some of them as their own people. They were a bit put out by that, and then they saw Fiachna sitting at the far side chewing on a stem of grass and they called out to him to know who he was. Fiachna took the stem of grass out of his mouth carefully so it wouldn't blow away in the night wind, for 'twas a nice, sweet, juicy piece, and holding it in his left hand he said: 'I'm Fiachna.'

That answer didn't suit Chiron and he roared across at him: 'And who the divil is Fiachna and what force conducted that slaughter there?'

239

Fiachna stood up slowly, loosening his shoulders, and when he was straight he took the stem of grass out of his mouth again. 'I'll tell you who Fiachna is. I am one of the household champions of Fionn Mac Cumhail. And his son. And I'm here to guard this ford. And as far as that crowd is concerned,' and he gestured towards the bodies blocking the river, 'you shouldn't have asked me that question. It vexes me when I think of what happened. And I'm warning you now, if you come over to this side of the ford, I'll give you an answer you won't like.'

When they heard this, Chiron and his men rushed through the water with rage to strike at Fiachna. But of course there was room for only two men at a time and Fiachna was well able to deal with them. One after another they fell beneath his blows until only one man was left and he, having more sense than courage, ran back as fast as he could to the Palace of the Island to tell them what had happened. When he was gone, Fiachna sat down on his side of the ford weary from the battle in order to tend the wounds with which he was fairly covered.

When Midac heard what had happened at the ford, the rage mounted up in him the way he might have exploded in bits like a mountain in Iceland that you'd hear about if he was a mountain instead of being a man. 'The divil blast it!' he roared. 'Those men should not have gone to the ford without telling me! I know the Fianna well and let me tell you there weren't half enough in it to go and meet these two men, and I'm not surprised they died the way they did. What does surprise me,' he said, glaring at the man who had come back from the ford, 'is that one of them should have returned here to tell the tale.' He paused and glared again at the messenger, who trembled before him. And with good cause. A few moments later wasn't he taken outside and made to sit on top of a high pointed stake, and he didn't like that very much before he died.

'What we'll do now,' said Midac, 'is to head off for the ford with enough men of my own to do the job. Guard or no guard, I'll cross that ford and then we'll make short work of Fionn and his companions in my Castle of the Rowan Trees.' He paused for a moment and a smile spread across his face. 'And I'll tell you what we'll do,' he went on, 'we'll have some sport while we're at it. There's one of the Fianna there, a man of venomous tongue who frequently slapped it in my direction and to whom I owe being banished from Allen, namely Conán Maol. In addition to his poisonous mouth, he is noted for numerous other outstanding habits of an unsavoury nature, among them his great cowardice and his great gluttony. He's been in there in an uncomfortable situation nearly a whole night without a bite or a sup, and he must be suffering by now. So what we'll do is we'll bring with us the choicest of food and drink and torment him with the sight and smell of what he can neither touch nor taste.'

They all thought this was a good plan and so they set off with the finest of food and drink in a strong body of men. And when they reached the ford, of course they saw Fiachna on the other side.

'Well, glory be to the gods,' said Midac. 'Is that yourself, Fiachna?'

'None other,' said Fiachna.

'Well, well, well,' said Midac, "tis the sorry man I am to see you in this fix. You know and I know that I must cross that ford, and I won't let anything stand in my way. And I'm a man of my word and do what I say. When I was at Allen and living in Fionn's castle you were the one man of the family who treated me well and never lifted a hand to either man or dog of mine and I'd be sorry to see you getting hurt.'

'Your lies are as big as your treachery,' said Fiachna. 'Dam' the few words I ever had with you when you were living in my father's castle and were treated well by him that you repaid with ingratitude and treachery. And whatever dealings I had with you I have good cause to regret now. And as for your word, 'tisn't worth a curse,' he said – and that was strong language for him. 'If you come across this ford, no one is getting hurt except yourself.'

Midac didn't care for this speech much and it made him angry. A scowl came over his face and his true nature burst out of him. He ordered Fiachna with threats and bullying to leave the ford.

Fiachna only laughed at him and said: 'It should be no trouble to you, Midac, to dislodge one man so what difference does it make to you whether I stand here or not? Come on then, the lot of ye, and I'll stand fast, and all I can say to you is I'm dam' sorry you didn't come sooner when I was fresher so that I could have given you a livelier welcome.'

Midac ordered his knights on and they charged across at Fiachna, but, like a kestrel or a goshawk in a flight of sparrows or a wolf in a flock, he scattered the lot of them powerful and all as the rush was. When Midac saw this he buckled on his own shield and took his sword in his hand, for whatever else you might say about him he was no coward. Making his way over the rocks and the slippery places and the dead bodies that were lodged in them, he confronted Fiachna on the trampled rise of the ford from the water and they attacked each other with deadly hate and fury. This lasted for a while with each of them striving to best the other with thunderous blows and sweeps and slashes and cuts and parries and blockings and stamping and sweating and panting and grunting and clanging and clashing and smashing and banging until the blood flowed and tiredness crept up their arms and their legs and their backbones in a painful weakness and the heat behind their eyes grew hotter and their teeth clenched in their jaws and exhaustion overcame them. But of the two it was Fiachna who became exhausted first for he had been in combat many times already that night and wounded many, many times until at last he fell on his knee and sheltered behind his shield hardly able to lift it or his sword to ward off the flailing blows of Midac.

Now, as luck would have it, Oisín and the others who had remained behind on Knockfierna had been getting uneasy when their two companions hadn't returned, and they decided to go on themselves towards the Castle of the Rowan Trees to find out what was causing all the delay. But Diarmuid O Dyna and Fatha Conán said they would go ahead rather than have the rest of them fall into some trap, and as they were approaching the ford what did they hear but the clash of arms and the drumming of Midac's sword on Fiachna's shield. When they first heard it in the distance, they paused.

Then Diarmuid held up his hand. 'Whisht! Listen! That's Fiachna, for I know his warcry. Come on,' he cried, 'run!'

And the two of them ran as fast as they could until they reached the brow of the hill above the river and, looking down, what did they see in the fading darkness but the ford heaped with bodies and Midac and Fiachna locked in their death struggle beside it. From where they were they could see that Fiachna was in trouble and might be killed at any minute.

Then Fatha Conán shouted at Diarmuid: 'For the love of the gods fire your dart and save Fiachna!'

But Diarmuid paused, thinking to himself, ''Tis a long cast with the danger of striking the wrong man; and if I do, or I miss both of them and he sees me, won't Midac work the harder to kill Fiachna?' And he said to Fatha: 'What'll I do if I hit the wrong man?'

But Fatha knew that Diarmuid was the best javelin man in the Fianna and he urged him to fire. So Diarmuid put his finger in the loop of his javelin cord that was wound tightly round the weapon and, reaching back, hurled it with all his power and deadly aim so that it whirred and twisted through the air and the head of it went through Midac and out the other side of him the span of a hand. It struck him as his sword hand was raised to deal the final blow down at Fiachna who was crouched beneath his shield. And, with his two hands still lifted and grasping the hilt of his great sword, Midac looked down at the head of the javelin protruding from his side in wonder, and then looked up again for he had no idea where the cast had come from, and around, still holding his sword aloft, and then back again at the javelin head. 'Oh – oh!' he groaned. 'I'm done for, for that is Diarmuid's spear.'

And with that Diarmuid's battle-cry reached him from the hill down which he was racing. But, as Diarmuid had anticipated, instead of turning him aside, Midac's fury increased with the imminence of his own death and he struck down at Fiachna as hard as he could and more fiercely than before even as his own life's blood pumped out of him. Diarmuid shouted at him to stop and not to kill the son of Fionn as he ran down the slope and across the ford to save his friend, but the dying Midac snarled at him as he approached: 'If you wanted to save his life you should have spared mine. Fionn will never see his son alive again.' And he struck down through the shield and killed Fiachna as Diarmuid arrived and grasped the butt of his javelin still protruding from Midac's side. Whirling Midac round by that handle, so to speak, he threw him to the ground. But it was too late. Fiachna was already dead.

Sadly Diarmuid looked down at Fionn's son and then at Midac, and he said: 'If you were dead when I came up I would have left you to go to the Other World in one piece. But now that you are alive I must take your head as compensation to Fionn for his son.' With that he drew his heavy sword and whipped the head off Midac with one blow of it.

Diarmuid then ran to the Castle of the Rowan Trees leaving Fatha Conán to watch the ford until he came back. Arriving there he struck the doorpost with his great spear in fearful anger, but the huge, bolted door grille remained closed and silent. However, Fionn heard him and shouted out to him: 'Stay where you are, Diarmuid; don't try to come in. If you do you'll become a prisoner too for this place is full of magic that none of us can break.'

'Is that a fact?' asked Diarmuid. 'In that case I'll stay here.'

'What was all that noise and battling below at the ford?' asked Fionn. 'Where's my son Fiachna?'

'Fiachna fought like a lion against a multitude of foreigners,' said Diarmuid, 'and they're all dead, except for those who didn't come.'

'And where is Fiachna?' asked Fionn.

'He's dead too,' said Diarmuid, and he told them what had happened. Finally he said: 'Though I came to the ford too late to save him, I killed Midac – and here is his head as some kind of compensation for you.'

Poor Fionn grieved greatly at the loss of his son following on the loss of his foster-son and, for a while, Diarmuid heard nothing. Then Fionn, in a quiet voice, said to him: 'That you may be always blessed and victorious, Diarmuid. You're a man was often relied on before when the Fianna was in difficulties. I'll never forget this for you.' (And there was great irony in that in the light of what happened later on over Grainne – but that's another story.) 'And I can tell you,' went on Fionn, 'we've never before been in such straits as this. The fifteen of us chiefest men of the Fianna inside here are clung motionless to the floor of this place by magic, unable to move and doomed to be killed if those blackguards beyond have their way. The only thing that can release us is the blood of the three, large, bloodthirsty, furious, horrible Kings of the Island of the Torrent if it is sprinkled on the clay that binds us.'

'I'll get that so,' said Diarmuid.

'Good man!' said Fionn. 'But moreover and in the meantime unless the ford below is well defended the Lochlannaigh and the other foreigners beyond will make their way in here and kill us without mercy while we're unable to defend ourselves. It's up to you, Diarmuid, to prevent that and we put all our trust in you. Go out there now and defend that ford until the sun rises; for then, as sure as I'm sitting here' – and strange as it may seem the situation was so serious that none of them raised a laugh at that – 'if you can last that long the Fianna will come with the rising of the sun.'

'Fair enough,' said Diarmuid. 'Fatha Conán and I will hold the ford that long, at least.'

He was about to turn away when the voice of Conán Maol, groaning and moaning and wailing rose up from inside the castle. 'Oh, wasn't I the foolish man to allow myself to be brought down here like this. Cold and comfortless,' the voice rose into a kind of a chant, 'is the clay on which I sit that has me locked onto it. What did I do at all to deserve punishment like this that you wouldn't dish out to a beast of the field or your own worst enemy? And worst of it all,' he went on, his voice getting angry and addressing his companions who were in just as bad a plight and who were hard put to it to keep from laughing at him, bad enough as it was, 'is that we have neither food, drink, nor bite nor sup nor divil the dam' bit of a thing to ease the cramps and pains of hunger. Oh, now, Diarmuid, wait 'til I tell you; while I sit here tormented and destroyed with hunger and thirst, over there beyond' – and you could imagine him wave an expansive hand as he bellowed the word through the wall – 'in the Palace of the Island, isn't there food for an army and more, the finest and best to be had? I can't stand it no more, let me tell you. Didn't you tell me yourself, Diarmuid, that you have killed Midac? Will you, for the love and honour of the gods, have pity on my dreadful plight and slip over as far as the palace – 'tisn't too far away by all accounts – and bring me the fill of my belly of food and a drinking horn of wine?'

'Well, the divil fire you and your hungry belly,' said Diarmuid, 'with the foreigners down on top of us and only Fatha and myself to defend you. Isn't that work enough for the two of us without adding to it? And you want me to abandon my post and go haring off to the palace of the foreigners themselves in order to fill your belly.'

'Ah, Diarmuid, my darling,' said Conán Maol wistfully, 'if 'twas a little golden girl with shining eyes and gleaming hair who asked you, wouldn't you fly off without counting the cost? But you refuse me quick enough and we all know the reason. You crossed me often enough when I was courting women before now and you want to get the competition out of the way by seeing me die of hunger in this dungeon.'

Bad as their plight was, the other members of their Fianna could hardly keep the laughter in when they thought of fat, bald, cowardly Conán as a rival to Diarmuid *na mban*, or 'of the women', as he was sometimes called because of his success with them for the affections of comely maidens. But the bitter words of Conán stung Diarmuid's pride and he said: 'All right. Will you hold your whisht and I'll see what I can do? I'd rather face any danger than the spite of your tongue.'

244

With that he went back to Fatha at the ford and when he had told him how things were he went on: 'I must go to the Palace of the Island to get food for that fellow and let you guard the ford 'til I come back.'

Fatha tried to persuade Diarmuid to bring Conán Maol some of the food that Midac had brought and which lay scattered around on the other side of the ford; but Diarmuid refused saying that Conán Maol would never let him forget for the rest of his life that he had tried to fob him off with food from the hands of the dead. For Conán Maol, for all his bluster and cowardice, had a satirical power that could raise blisters of shame and disgrace on the best of men and it wasn't one or two had died in the past because of that. So, leaving Fatha at the ford, Diarmuid set off for the Palace of the Island.

He slipped like a shadow through the trees and from cover to cover until he got close enough to the walls of the palace to hear the sound of revelry and laughter inside. He squirmed up to the walls and, peering through one of the open doors, managed to get a view of the lords and knights. The whole gathering – well, the chiefs anyway – was inside in the great hall, sitting at tables and enjoying themselves eating and drinking (and more besides) with Sinsear of the Battles and his son Borba sitting at the head of all. Servants and slaves were going in and out with unknown quantities of food and drink and of course the large, ornamented drinking horns were filled with wine and the food was presented on plates of bronze and silver no less. Oh, a banquet without a doubt. And women! The finest . . . but, maybe the less said about that the better . . .

Anyway, silent as you like, didn't Diarmuid slip in through the door and stand quiet in a passage where there was plenty of shadow with his sword drawn, but close by his side where you wouldn't notice it? And, of course, after a while didn't one of the servants pass close to him? Well, with a blow Diarmuid removed his head for him and, believe it or not as you like, didn't he whip the drinking horn from his hand before the body fell, so that not one drop of the wine from it was spilled. That took some doing! He put it down carefully where he was and, walking straight into the hall, picked up one of the dishes near where Sinsear himself was sitting and out with him through the open door, picking up the drinking horn as he went. And remarkable as it is, divil the one in the crowd, with all the drinking and noise, took the smallest bit of notice of him, so he was able to return with the food and drink without let, hindrance or harm of any kind. Imagine that!

When he reached the ford beyond where he had left Fatha, he went on up to the Castle of the Rowan Trees with the stuff for Conán Maol, and when he came up he called out: 'Conán, here's the food and drink you wanted. But will you tell me how I am supposed to get it in to you, because I can't go in or I'd get trapped like the rest of ye and I have no intention of doing that?'

Conán hadn't considered this; but, looking up, what did he see but a small, small window high above his head and he called out to Diarmuid: 'I'll tell you what you'll do, let you throw it in through the little window above and I'll catch it myself.'

'Fair enough,' said Diarmuid, glad to be finished with it and not worried too much if Conán Maol caught it or not, or how he was going to do it. So Diarmuid began to throw it in through the little window and, as fast as he did, Conán Maol caught it in his huge hands and gobbled it up hungrily without offering a bite or a morsel to any of his companions.

When 'twas all gone, Diarmuid called out: 'Now I have the drinking horn. How will I get that to you?'

'Drinking horn?' enquired Conán.

'What else?' asked Diarmuid.

'What's in it?' asked Conán.

'Horse-piss!' snarled Diarmuid, fed up with him. 'What do you think they were drinking? Wine, of course. What do you want me to do with it?'

That puzzled Conán a bit. But then he had an idea. 'Let you climb up the wall,' he called, ''til you reach the little window and then let you put your arm in as far as it'll go and pour the wine down to me. I'll catch it in my own mouth.'

So Diarmuid climbed and struggled up the wall with the huge drinking horn in one hand; and when he reached the window he poured the wine down to Conán who opened his great gullet and caught and swallowed most of it without a word to anyone except the 'glug, glug, glug' of his throttle going like an I-dunno-what, and the splash where a fair share of it missed. After that Diarmuid went back to the ford in disgust and waited with Fatha.

By this time, the news of the slaughter at the ford had reached the Palace of the Island. And, of course, the three most important people there were the Kings of the Island of the Torrent who, when they heard what had happened, said amongst themselves: 'That young fellow of Lochlann had no business trying to attack Fionn without telling us. We have the right to behead Fionn and his companions as it's our magic is holding them, and maybe we'd better go now and do that before anyone else gets the same notion to prevent us.' So they went out with a good force and soon reached the ford with Diarmuid and Fatha on the other side.

One of the Kings called out: 'Who's there?'

'Diarmuid O Dyna,' came the answer, 'on Fionn's orders to guard this ford. And whoever you are I'm warning you now not to cross.'

'Diarmuid!' exclaimed the eldest of the three Kings. 'Is that yourself? Well, bedam' if that's not the fine surprise! Do you know who's in it here? Your three fellow scholars from arms school, the Kings of the Island of the Torrent. Your friends and companions. Aren't we well met now? Let you just move off from the ford now and we'll go over and talk about old times.'

'Talk, my foot!' growled Diarmuid. 'I remember ye well. Ye were no friends or companions of mine, and ye were dam' bad scholars too. Go on off about ye're business now and let me here to defend this ford in peace!' he snapped, scowling across at them.

A few of the foreigners then rushed across at him, but Diarmuid stood as firm as a pillar-stone might stand against the onrush of waves on the seashore, and felled them as they came. When Fatha joined him not only did they halt the onslaught, they drove the enemy back before them. At last the three ferocious Kings of the Islands of the Torrent, seeing so many of their men dead and dying and falling back, slowly advanced on Diarmuid who stood out to meet them. And the fury of that battle was beyond description as they raged and tore at one another 'til at last the three terrible Kings fell one by one in that red ford of slaughter under Diarmuid's sword. Overcome as they were by weariness at this stage, Diarmuid and Fatha struck off the heads of the three kings and carried them as fast as they could to the Castle of the Rowan Trees so that the blood would still be wet when they arrived.

Of course Fionn had been listening to the noise of the battle below and was by no means certain what the outcome had been since the tumult was so loud and fierce. So he called out to know who was outside.

Breathless from his exertions Diarmuid said: ''Tis me!'

'Me who?' snarled Fionn, in no mood for levity.

'Myself and Fatha,' said Diarmuid; 'and we have killed the three Kings of the Island of the Torrent.'

'Sound man,' said Fionn, 'that you may enjoy living 'til you die. So you have killed them! Where are the heads?'

'We have them here.'

'Well,' said Fionn, '*nac bfhuil tusa an fear i gcéad* (aren't you a man in a hundred?) What you'll do now is sprinkle the door with their blood.'

Diarmuid did so, and in an instant, with a crash, the door, that none of them had been able to budge up to then, flew wide open. Inside they saw the Fianna heroes in a sad and sorry condition, seated on the cold clay which had them fast bound unable to move. Holding the heads by the hair Diarmuid and Fatha sprinkled the earth under each of them with the blood that dripped from the severed necks, beginning with Fionn. One by one they were freed and as they came loose and the spells were broken they climbed to their feet – stiffly to be sure – but delighted with themselves. Thanking the gods and the two heroes who were their instruments, they embraced them and each other.

But they were still very weak and they couldn't understand why. So Fionn put his thumb under his tooth of knowledge again and after a moment took it out again and said: 'Ye won't be too surprised, I suppose, when I tell you that these spells have withered our strength so much that we won't be ourselves again until sunrise. That being the case,' he went on, 'ye'll have to guard the ford 'til then when we'll come and relieve you.' So Diarmuid and Fatha went back to the ford.

Now, while this had been going on those who had escaped from the last battle made their way back to the Palace of the Island to tell Sinsear and Borba that the three Kings of the Island of the Torrents were now also dead at the hands of those guarding the ford. When he heard this news, Borba the Haughty, Sinsear's son (who considered himself to be the mightiest warrior in the foreign host apart from his father) rose and said to Sinsear: 'I don't know what sort of warriors they were at all who went out against these men at the ford. But they can't have been up to much. Well, I'm going now to avenge them and I'm going to bring back Fionn's head and throw it down there at your feet.' What he did not know, of course, was that Fionn and the others were now free, or he might have sounded a more cautious note – if he hadn't packed up altogether no matter what he thought of himself.

So, anyway, Borba came on to the ford while it was still dark with a large body of men. Naturally he had selected the best armed and the best fighters to go with him so that as they marched through the pre-dawn dusk their heavy tread and the clank and rattle of their arms frightened the sleeping birds and the small animals and reached out to where Diarmuid and Fatha were waiting. And even though they had never before shown fear, when they heard this ominous, great noise coming at them, they were nervous of being dislodged and overpowered, leaving Fionn and the others helpless and unprotected beyond in the Castle of the Rowan Trees. And in his heart each of them longed for the dawn to break and light the eastern sky the way the others would get back their strength to defend themselves, even if they couldn't save themselves, if you follow me.

This time there was no discussion. The foreigners came straight on to the ford, as many as could, stamping and trampling and forging forward. As they came on Diarmuid said to Fatha from the side of his mouth, without taking his eyes from in front of him where the noise and the glitter of points of light from weapons and armour were advancing towards them: 'Strike carefully, *a chara* – my friend. Defend yourself as best you can and don't waste your energy trying to kill. A wounded man is as much of a loss to the enemy. Nurse your strength. Prolong the battle. Dawn can't be too far off.'

The enemy attacked in great numbers and again they were forced to try the ford two abreast and thus fell victim to Diarmuid and Fatha. At long last the sun splashed the broad plain with a faint light that strengthened and broadened with each passing second. Suddenly the withering spell lifted from the Fianna nobles in the castle and they leaped to their feet and snatched up their weapons. One of them was sent flying to Knockfierna to Oisín to bring up the rest of the Fianna and the others raced down to the ford, Fionn at their head, to help their two comrades. They came down on the attackers and a fierce struggle ensued in which Goll Mac Morna killed Borba, and with that the foreigners retired.

When Sinsear learned of the death of his son he summoned his whole host and, in full battle formation, they advanced on the ford for vengeance. But if he did, the Fianna under Oisín, alerted by the messenger sent by Fionn, arrived on the brow of the hill overlooking the ford just at the very moment that Sinsear and his army came up from the opposite side. The Fianna formed up in four battalions of three thousand men each and marched forward with their banners fluttering and cracking in the breeze, their helmets and weapons glittering and their drums and trumpets sounding battle music.

Now at last the battle began in earnest. It would be impossible to describe that dreadful, murderous, slaughtering battle in which thousands of men took part and struggled and swayed over the landscape, many hundreds of them dying or falling wounded and helpless until the earth itself groaned and the dogs of battle slipped round the edges of the fighting to feed on the bodies of the slain and, snarling, drive off the carrion birds of reddened beaks and raucous cries already doing so.

'Twas Fionn's grandson, Oscar, who brought an end to the fighting when, pausing for a moment in the struggle he looked round and saw Sinsear's battle standard on a small hill where he was guarded and protected by a fence of spears. Seeing, too, that the Fianna, outnumbered, were falling back under pressure before the king's standard, Oscar charged through the struggling ranks like a roused beast until he met up face to face with Sinsear. When Sinsear saw him coming he ordered back his guards. He had a fierce, deadly smile on his face expecting to avenge the death of his own son by killing Fionn's grandson. So these two great heroes fell on one another and the battling ranks around them let their arms fall to watch the outcome. At one stage it seemed as if both would fall – they were so torn and wounded. And Sinsear's rage was boundless when he discovered he couldn't so easily vanquish Oscar who was so much younger and inexperienced and looked like a stripling against himself. He made a fierce onslaught on Fionn's grandson. But, in spite of his appearance, Oscar was a great warrior and seizing his opportunity he struck an almighty blow that laid Sinsear dead before him and with that a great roar went up from the Fianna and their enemies instantly gave way. They were pursued and slaughtered on every side. Some threw their arms away; some escaped to the shore where they unmoored their ships and sailed swiftly away carrying with them tidings of the death of their king and the slaughter of their armies.

That is the story of 'The Castle of the Rowan Trees'.

FOOTNOTES

1 See 'Deirdre and the Sons of Usna'.
2 See 'The Contrary Mercenary'. Also *Crucible* Donal O'Neill (Macdonald/ Futura)
3 See 'The Death of Oisín'.
4 Newgrange was a ritual sanctuary, possibly associated with death and rebirth.

An Giolla Deacaire:
The Contrary Mercenary

Third Period: Fianna Cycle

This great story also belongs to the Fianna Cycle and that would seem to place its origin about the third century AD. It belongs to what we might call the saga/legend type of story and is pure entertainment, elaborating on, rather than manipulating or adjudicating in any supernatural sense, essentially human virtues and vices, however enhanced by poetic licence or the 'aesthetic illusion'. There are some thinly disguised 'historical suggestions' which appear to be intrusive and of later origin, perhaps as late as the tenth century. Quite a number of the Fianna tales contain this element, a clear indication that they were popular in every sense of the word. It is sometimes not appreciated that these stories and those from the older Cycles, or the versions of them that survived, were the popular literature of the people well into the eighteenth and possibly the nineteenth centuries.

As this story belongs to the Fianna Cycle it does not possess the 'heroic' and supranatural character of the older Cycles – at least not to the same extent. The characters and events in the Fianna Cycle, magical though some of the occurrences may be, generally and recognisably belong to the human time – place-scale. The stories are 'earthier' than those of the older Cycles. The occasional restructuring, perhaps to provide an enhanced contemporaneity, may, for instance, explain the apparent anomaly of the *Giolla Deacaire* and the army of the King of the World, markedly resembling eighth- or ninth-century Norse Vikings in what purports to be a story from the third century.

The appellation *Giolla Deacaire* does not translate well. Literally, it means 'slothful or troublesome servant', but this does not convey the meaning in Irish in this context with its suggestion of truculence, laziness and contrariness. Moreover, also in the context, while *giolla* means 'hireling', it does not mean either 'servant' or 'slave'. A closer rendering, in this case, would be mercenary warrior. Accordingly I use the title 'The Contrary Mercenary' as being close to the intent of the original.

251

Cormac Mac Art was King of Ireland at that time and a mighty fine king he was too. And what else would you expect from a man who was a grandson of Con the Hundred Fighter himself? During his reign Ireland was known throughout the western world – and the eastern world too, for all I know – as a land of peace, plenty, and good government where, 'twas said, a virgin with a golden fillet and her purse full of gold along with it could walk unmolested from one end of the country to the other, and from side to side too, I suppose – though what a virgin would want to do anything so foolish for 'tis hard to imagine. She wouldn't do it today! She'd have more sense. But, sure, they say the same thing about a lot of places. Don't times change too?

Cormac was noted for his wisdom and his learning and was a profound law-giver. As a matter of fact, he wrote a book of laws for kings called the *Teagasc Rí*, not even, if you don't mind, considering the likes of them to be above a bit of wise instruction when the need arose. It started like this:

> Do not deride the elderly, although you are young;
> Nor the poor, though you are wealthy;
> Nor the lame, though you are swift;
> Nor the blind, though you have sight;
> Nor the sick, though you are strong;
> Nor the dull, though you are clever;
> Nor the foolish, though you are wise.
>
> Be not too wise, be not too foolish;
> Be not too conceited, be not too diffident;
> Be not too haughty, be not too humble;
> Be not too talkative, be not too silent;
> Be not too harsh, be not too feeble.
>
> If you are wise, they will over expect from you;
> If you are foolish, you will be deceived;
> If you are too conceited, you will be thought insufferable;
> If you are too humble, you will be without honour;
> If you are too talkative, you will not be heeded;
> If you are too silent, you will not be regarded;
> If you are too harsh, you will be broken;
> If you are too feeble, you will be crushed!

That book is still there today for anyone with the desire to find it, the wit to read it, and in a position to apply it – and maybe 'tis a pity that more of them in that position don't go to the trouble.

Cormac also had the laws and records of the land collated and compiled in a book called the *Psalter of Tara*. What's more, he founded three university schools at Tara: one for law, one for history and chronology, and one for military science. And, in the latter connection, he built up the Fianna, the standing army of the *Rí Eireann* that was in relation to him as the Roman legions were in relation to Caesar – the force behind the law – to maintain the peace and prosperity for which his reign was distinguished.

No, of course, I needn't tell you that the general in command of the Fianna at that time was Fionn Mac Cumhail. And Fionn was dam' near as popular a man as Cormac himself. More, some would say, but, of course, he wasn't a king. Cormac was the king; and whatever about popularity, Cormac had the renown and the respect. The way it was with the Fianna was that each of the provinces had its own battalion of militia – and there were three thousand men in a battalion – under its own captain, all under the command of Fionn who had his castle on the hill of Allen with its fine flat top below in the heart of Kildare.

Anyway 'twas the heyday of the Fianna and Cormac Mac Art. It all started as the winter was coming to an end with the summer in sight and spring bursting out here and there (but, mind you, like the rest of the people and their fathers before them the Fianna took little account of spring or autumn, 'twas only summer or winter for them). With the end of winter in sight Fionn held his usual feast for all the chief people of Ireland and when that was over the Fianna were to go off for the first big hunt of the season. 'Twas some occasion, I can tell you. Food and drink, the best in the world, were to be had for three days, and no man went to bed sober or alone, with the Fianna assembling and guarding the lords and nobles while it lasted. When that was over, they got themselves ready; they packed up and spent a last night in their winter quarters – for they liked to spend the winter with the generous women of Leinster – and the next day they set off for Munster where this first hunt of the season was to take place.

Men, horses, dogs, servants and slaves – they all set off to the south. Across the wide flank of the Slieve Bloom mountains they swept, along the reaches of the river Brosna that they followed under the twelve mountains of Ebhlinn until they reached Coill Cill, or Knockainy as 'tis called today, in the county of Limerick. From there they broke up into bands and scattered across the broad plains of the two provinces of Munster. Down over Ardpatrick and Sliabh Caoine they hunted, and over the rich valley that comes down to Fermoy; across the river Blackwater in the district of Lehans and Castlelyons and through the marshes of Cork. From there they went south and west into the territory of the ancient Tuatha de Danaan chieftain, Curoi Mac Dara, and past his grim, hillbound fortress of Cahirconree. South again then to Loch Lein at Killarney, only to double back east and course along the blue, streamy banks of the river Suir on the plain of Femin near Clonmel beneath the breasted mountain of

Sliabh na mBan; east and west, north and south they chased and hunted so that there wasn't a plain or a valley nor a wood, a mountain or a wilderness in all Munster that they didn't hunt and start up the deer and the boar and the wild things of the forest from their resting places. And that was the fashion 'til they returned again to the plain of Cliach where rises the hill of Knockainey, or Coill Cill.

And there what did Fionn do but decide to rest himself and the Fianna for a few days? They were tired and in need of a rest, I suppose, and I daresay they had to do something about all the meat they had too, before it went off on them.

Accordingly, they built a camp after the Roman fashion with a ditch and a bank and a fine pallisade – though who it was they were protecting themselves from 'tis hard to say, but, sure, it showed a bit of discipline. When that was built and the tents of the Fianna pitched inside and their shelters erected and the cooking pits and steam houses and baths dug and built and heated and working, they all rested, well contented with themselves, playing hurling and practising as you'd expect.

Naturally they had a few sentries, responsible men, put out here and there around the camp. One of these was a man by the name of Séan Bán Mac Breasil (Shawn Bawn Mac Brazzil), a Galwayman, and his place was on the crown of a bosky hill – but not too wooded, birch and holly and the odd oak – from where he could see in most directions for a good distance. Well, anyway, there he was above on this hill leaning on his spear if you please, and he looking off to the west where the sun was concealing itself beyond in the western ocean – but, of course, he couldn't see that – thinking about this and that and maybe a bit of the other, an occupation sentries in the western parts are prone to, when what did he notice advancing towards him out of the oncoming night but a giant of vast size? And behind him this warrior, if anything so ugly, disreputable, misbegotten and shapeless – to say nothing of being as dirty and as untidy as you can imagine and of such a monstrous size – could be called a man, dragged and hauled a horse of similar proportions – if such a scraggy, hairy and disjointed carcass could be dignified with the name of so noble an animal – by means of a rope as thick as your arm that he used for a halter.

Moreover, besides being the queerest looking creature you ever saw, the giant was also fully armed – after a fashion. He had a garment thrown over his shoulders that might have once been a fine coloured cloak, if only you could get a look at it under the dirt, mud and other things encrusted on it. Over that, on his left side, dangled a shield, so hacked and splintered the wicker sallys stuck out like the spines of a hedgehog, and its leather cover hung in tatters and slivers like the pelt of an old boar had fallen into a staked pit and been skinned by a blind blacksmith; all thumbs! Under that he had a sword, chipped and rusty from one end to the other, and in his left hand, the one with the halter, he had two spears that came out of the same stable. With his other hand he pulled along an iron club and it was that heavy it made a furrow in the ground as he trundled and lumbered down. And, wait 'til I tell you, every so often wouldn't he turn and give the unfortunate creature behind him a belt of encouragement with that same instrument?

Well, anyhow, when Séan Bán Mac Breasil saw what was coming on towards him his jaw dropped, and his spear along with it. He picked them both up and then, concluding it was a situation that would be better handled by his superiors – which shows he had his wits about him, whatever else – he took off towards the camp to tell Fionn what was coming. He ran so fast that when he reached Fionn he was that out of breath, not to mention being overcome with what he'd seen, that 'twas a full half minute before he could speak at all, and then all he could do was make a class of a squawk like a duck and point back the way he'd come. No way, I needn't tell you, for one of the Fianna to act, and it didn't please Fionn one bit.

'Will you speak up, you eejit!' he said not unkindly, noticing immediately there was something the matter with him.

'I – I –' gulped Séan Bán, pointing.

'You, you!' growled Fionn at him. 'You, you what?'

But, in the event, as they say, there was little need for the bold Séan Bán to be any more explicit than 'I – I –', for at that moment the giant and his old nag came into view of the camp and the gasp that went up from the Fianna was heard over beyond on the river Shannon.

The giant came on down the hill with his horse and when they got used to the sight the men of the Fianna couldn't restrain their laughter. More and more of them came up and joined in until the pallisade and the gate and a considerable space outside it were lined with men all roaring their hearts out. And it got worse. But it had no effect on the giant only to make him glower all the harder as he came up and stood in front of Fionn, looking down at him. Fionn looked back up, and he had quite a distance to look because, tall and all as he was – and he was no midget – the newcomer was as near ten and a half feet tall as makes no difference, and that's tall whatever way you look at it.

Fionn looked at him anyway, up and down for a minute; and then, with his fists doubled on his hips (which was a normal way for his class of a man to stand) said politely enough: 'Is there anything I can do for you, my good man?'

The giant looked down at him, opened his mouth to show great, black stumps of teeth and said: ''Tisn't so much what you can do for me, but what I'll do for you. And I'm not your good man.'

With that there was more laughter from those nearby who could hear him. Fionn turned to look at them a moment surprised at their poor manners – he was a terrible stickler himself for the proprieties – and then turned to the other.

255

'Well, where might you be from?' he asked, politely as you please.

''Tis none of your business where I'm from,' said the other, 'but I'll tell you anyway. I'm a Lochlanner. And that's about all I'll say except I'm here to join your army, the Fianna.'

Even Fionn had to suppress a smile as best he could when he heard that. 'I see,' he said.

'That's right,' said the giant. 'I'll join up with you for a year; and at the end of that time I'll decide my own wages according to my own custom.'

Fionn's eyebrows went up, but he passed no remark. 'Well,' he said, ignoring the smirks and the titters of the men behind him, 'I give every man a fair crack of the whip. But I like to know who it is I'm talking to, to say nothing of who it is I'm hiring. Have you a name at all, or what?'

The giant looked round. 'I have,' he declared, 'and I'm well named. They call me the *Giolla Deacaire* – the Contrary Mercenary.'

At that the roar of laughter that went up from the assembly drowned out everything so that he had to wait until 'twas finished before he could go on. 'And I can tell you now,' he went on, as if there had been no interruption at all, 'a lazier, more ill-natured, indifferent, careless or bad-tempered individual you won't meet this side of the other place.' And he gave a sort of sideways look down at the ground and kicked a sod the size of a stook of barley out of it with his *crubín bathlach* (clumsy flat foot).

'Well, there's no doubt,' said Fionn, 'and you're not giving yourself much of a recommendation. But sure you mightn't be as bad as you make out.'

'Worse!' said the Giolla Deacaire. 'You don't know me at all!' He spat out between Fionn and Séan Bán, who had to jump out of the way to avoid the glaucous missile as it whistled past, struck the ground, picked up a coating of dust, and killed an innocent frog sitting in a clump of grass minding his own business stone-dead. 'Amn't I the worst person in the world to deal with? No matter how good or noble the man I work for, or how well he treats me, dam' the thing he'll get from me only hard words and harder reproaches. And it takes what'd feed a hundred men to keep me going.'

Fionn didn't know what to say to that so he changed the subject. 'I see,' he said. 'Eh – what had you in mind to join? The cavalry or the infantry?'

The look the Giolla Deacaire gave him was thick with contempt. 'I'm surprised at you,' he said, 'asking me a question like that. Are you blind or what? Can't you see my horse?'

Fionn's eyes narrowed, but he said nothing. But those near him could see the knuckles on his fists go white. Hospitality has its own paymaster. 'Isn't it obvious,' went on the Giolla Deacaire, 'that someone as lazy as I am would never keep up with an army if he had to walk? What else, but the cavalry? Why do you think I keep a horse at all?'

'Well,' said Fionn mildly enough, but the eyes were hard. 'If 'tis the cavalry you're bound for, how is it you have no servant to take care of your horse?'

If there was contempt in the last look the Giolla Deacaire threw at him, 'twas nothing to the look he gave now. 'For an intelligent man,' he said, 'you ask very stupid questions. Didn't I tell you I eat as much as a hundred men. What master would want to feed a servant as well?'

Fionn's jaw hardened, but he held his peace and nodded. 'I've never refused any man who was able yet,' he said, 'provided he could pass our tests, and you'll have to do those tomorrow. We'll give you a try anyway.' Which wasn't as foolish a statement as you might think, for Fionn knew well, and I suppose the Giolla Deacaire knew too, though he was saying nothing, that there was no way he could pass the Fianna's tests: run through a wood in his bare feet with his hair flying without picking up a thorn or getting tangled in a tree or a bush; jump a spear his own height; to say nothing of knowing twelve books of poetry and having the qualities of grace and courtesy! Small chance!

The Giolla Deacaire didn't reply, but he looked out sort of blankly over Fionn's head at the skitting men of the Fianna and then he said: 'Well, I can tell you I'm hungry now!' He opened his mouth and let go a belch out of his belly. And it was so foul that it wiped the laughter from the faces of the Fianna as it swept over them and, indeed, was the cause of giving a weakness in the stomach or the head to nine of them, if you don't mind! That stopped the laughter.

Fionn was lucky. He was standing so close it went over his head. But the irritation was inside him as much from the bad manners of the Fianna in laughing at the stranger as anything else, and he was glad 'twas stopped. He thought he'd get his own back and invited the Giolla Deacaire inside. 'Come on in,' he said. 'Things mightn't be as bad as you say. We'll see what we can do about giving you something to eat.'

At the mention of food, a noise resembling distant thunder was heard as the Giolla Deacaire's stomach rumbled. And the next thing was he turned himself a little sideways, stood on his toe to raise his right hip, and farted. The blast of it! It flattened three yards of the pallisade, knocked thirty men of the Fianna head over heels in a heap, quenched forty cooking fires and blew away the ashes and scattered the manure heap in the corner of the horses' paddock a good hundred yards away to the four winds. Two crows thrown up like black rags from what had been the pile of dung looked down at him in astonishment, cawing indignantly. ''Tis the hunger,' said the Giolla Deacaire, looking at Fionn with a bleary eye.

Fionn was lucky again for he ducked the moment he saw the Giolla Deacaire's manoeuvre, guessing what was going to happen after the rumbling that had been going on beforehand. Now he straightened up and looked at the destruction behind him and the men of the Fianna picking themselves up. A hint of a smile clutched the corner of his mouth, though his eyes were still hard, and he said: 'The standards of the Fianna are very high.'

'High or low,' said the Giolla Deacaire, ''tis all the one to me.' He shrugged and gazed over Fionn's head with a bleary eye, but said no more.

Fionn nodded, indicating he'd take him on; whereupon the giant turned his horrible horse loose, whacking it on the rump with his club, amongst the horses of the Fianna – which it promptly attacked with tooth and hoof so that the poor animals were sent flying in all directions, neighing and galloping and bewildered. As it happened, it scattered the horses of Fionn's own clan, the Clann Baiscne, first. Having injured them all it headed towards the horses of Conán Maol (Conán the Bald) of the Clann Morna, between whom and the Clann Baiscne there existed a fragile and uneasy peace. When Conán, who had been amused at the plight of Fionn's horses, saw the monster charging towards his own he roared at the Giolla Deacaire to take it away. But the Giolla Deacaire, who was gazing on the scene with as much amiability as you might expect from one of his disposition, replied without bothering to look at Conán Maol that if he wanted to remove the grotesque animal he could do it himself, though he didn't put it quite like that, and he held out the end of the halter. Conán angrily snatched it from the giant, threw it at the horse's head and with a mighty leap reached the animal's back with the intention of riding it into the ground. But, far from galloping, trotting, or even walking, for all Conán's pummelling, thumping and striking with fist, elbow, knee and heel, the horse now refused to budge at all. It just stood there, gaunt, gigantic and bony, twenty-two hands high, with a circle of injured and wounded animals all round it and Conán Maol perched on the ridge of its back, thumping and pummelling – and even standing up and jumping – to try to make it move. But move it would not!

The rest of the men of the Fianna had been watching this with interest. They were concerned for their horses, naturally, and therefore as anxious as anyone else to remove the nag of the Giolla Deacaire from where it was doing such damage. 'I know why he won't go,' said one of them. 'He's used to carrying a much heavier weight and he won't budge until he has the same weight up.'

'That makes sense!' And without more ado, fourteen more of the Fianna climbed or were hooshed up. But in spite of their thrashings and whackings the horse stayed where it was.

The Giolla Deacaire watched this performance in silence. Finally, looking at the men belabouring his horse to no avail, he turned to Fionn angrily and said: 'Now I see the kind of crowd you have, Fionn. Look at what these people of yours are doing to my fine horse. Why should I put up with that class of carry-on? I haven't been in your service very long and I won't stay in it another minute. You can give me my wages and I'll go.'

'Oho!' said Fionn. 'Your wages is it? They are payable at the end of the year like everyone else's. Stay until then and you'll be paid as promised.'

'Not another minute!' said the Giolla Deacaire.

'Well,' said Fionn, ''tis up to yourself. Stay or go, but if you're going, go now,' he went on, 'and take your horse with you before there's more damage done.'

'Damage!' roared the Giolla Deacaire looking around in perplexity. 'What damage? Sure he's only having a bit of fun; getting to know the other animals.'

'Well, you better get him out of here before the men of the Fianna get to *know* you,' said Fionn, now thoroughly angry.

'Oh, that's the way of it?' shouted the Giolla Deacaire. 'I see. Faith! I swear,' he roared, 'that if it was the last hour of the last day of the year I wouldn't wait until morning after this insult. Wages or no wages I'm off and I know what to think of you, and your Fianna along with you.'

So saying he grabbed the end of the halter rope from Conán Maol and off with him out of the camp, the horse following with the fifteen men still on board who, try as they might, found there was no way they could dismount. And slowly and all as himself and his horse came over the hill towards the camp, this time giant, horse and the fifteen men of the Fianna all vanished in a flash like the wind to the west. When they recovered from the shock of seeing this, as fast as they were able – and none were more able – the Fianna followed in pursuit. But fast and all as they were, they could not catch up with the giant before he and his horse and the fifteen men on its back plunged into the ocean where it spread before them to the limitless boundaries of the world. As they watched from the hilltop they had reached, the men of the Fianna saw the waves of the sea divide before the Giolla Deacaire and his horse and close behind them so that they ran and galloped dry-shod, like the story from the eastern world about the King of Egypt, they thought – or was he drowned? Anyway, the Fianna ran and raced to the beach, but nothing was to be seen but a small moving turmoil on the surface of the heaving ocean where the Giolla Deacaire and his horse and its cargo thundered forward along the dry foundations of the billowy sea.

As they milled about in groups helplessly talking to one another, bewildered and bemoaning the fate of their companions, they were approached by a couple of fair young men in respectable dress who claimed to be the sons of a king in a faraway land. Not only that, they also claimed to have magical powers, which didn't much surprise Fionn who was accustomed to that sort of thing. One of them announced that he could, in the twinkling of an eye, and with the use only of his magic sling, manufacture a ship from any old piece of timber that happened to be lying about. Under the circumstances it was a claim – however unlikely it seemed – that impressed Fionn and the Fianna greatly. The other brother recommended himself by saying that there was neither man nor beast, fish nor fowl – or anything else for that matter – that he could not track over land or sea, or, if he was pushed, under them as well. In a moment they had entered Fionn's service; and in another both the ship (a convenient piece of driftwood lay adjacent to where they were) and the navigator to follow the Giolla Deacaire and his horse were available, the one in the other which danced lightly in the shallow water a few feet from the shore where they had thoughtfully placed the driftwood before asking the foreign prince to exercise his magical skill.

With these two young princes and fifteen chosen men, Fionn securely traversed the seas in pursuit of the Giolla Deacaire in this magic vessel. At last they were guided to the cliffs of a great rocky island at the pounded and wave-beaten feet of which the track ended. Diarmuid O Dyna, who later on would achieve even greater frame and renown as the hero who eloped with the bride of no less a person than his lord and master, Fionn himself, was the first to offer to climb these forbidding cliffs and scout whatever territory lay above. With the skill and daring only to be expected of a senior member of the Fianna, he inched and wormed his way to the top of those great cliffs where, to his surprise, he found before him a green and attractive plain studded here and there with trees and meadows of a comfortable and enticing appearance. Going forward, he saw a well which was obviously in use for it was carefully edged and protected, and, being thirsty after his rigorous climb, went to drink from it.

He was within ten feet of it when, seemingly from nowhere, appeared a *grúagach* (a knight who was also a wizard) of a tall, thin, daunting aspect who forthwith challenged him to combat. For three days they fought and struggled with each other from dawn to dusk without respite, as they say (well, that's what they say, but 'tis hard to credit as any man who has been in battle, or swung a scythe, or hurled for an hour, or that kind of thing, will tell you; but that's what they say anyway). As each day of battling drew to a close the wizard leaped into the centre of the well and disappeared. But on the third day Diarmuid grabbed the *grúagach* firmly by the ankle and leaped into the well with him. Holding tight to the wizard he found himself descending down and down through the well.

As they turned and tumbled dam' the bit Diarmuid could see around him but dim shadows. But, marvellous to relate, what did they do but touch dry ground as gently as if they had floated down to it and not fallen. Instantly the *grúagach* tore himself from Diarmuid's grasp and ran off at top speed across beautiful rolling countryside towards a city of towers and walls that gleamed in the distance. He vanished through a huge gate in the outer wall and Diarmuid, who had run after him as fast as he could, was challenged by a group of armed defenders who rushed from the gate to give him battle. After a fierce fight that lasted all of ten minutes, Diarmuid had killed or wounded two, and the others turned and went off taking their wounded with them. Retiring to a little wood some distance away Diarmuid lay down in the shade and fell asleep.

A blow on his foot awakened him and he looked up to see a young man of commanding appearance standing over him and holding in his right hand the sword with the flat of which he had smacked Diarmuid's sleeping foot. However, this young man turned out to be friendly and identified himself as the Knight of Valour and brother of the king of the country, which, somewhat to Diarmuid's surprise, turned out to be Tír fa Thonn (the Land Under the Waves, sometimes known as Ui Breasil). The young man sat down beside Diarmuid and, sticking a stalk of sweet grass in his mouth, proceeded as he chewed on the stem to tell Diarmuid his story. The *grúagach* was known as the Knight of the Fountain, as well as being King of Tír fa Thonn. But – need I tell you? – he wasn't the rightful king, having usurped the throne of the Knight of Valour who was inclined to be a bit easy-going, maybe. After he had explained the position to Diarmuid, all the while chewing on his stem of grass, he asked him for help to recover his kingdom.

Now if Diarmuid had one weakness, it was, as he was to prove over and over in the future, that he could never refuse an appeal to his sense of honour; and so, although Fionn, fourteen other members of the Fianna, and the two magical sons of a far-distant king waited for him below in a boat at the foot of the cliffs, he responded to the Knight of Valour's appeal and made a covenant with him to do battle for his rights or take what might come in the way of consequences. That was Diarmuid – hot-headed!

But Fionn and his men hadn't been idle in the meantime. Having waited below in the boat for Diarmuid to return to no avail, they clambered to the top of the cliff themselves and emerged eventually on the sunny plain across which they tracked Diarmuid to the well-head where he had fought with the Knight of the Fountain. Here, to their mystification, the tracks ceased in a welter of signs clearly indicating that combat had taken place; but scratch their heads though they might they could come to no conclusion other than that Diarmuid had fallen or been thrown into the well and was drowned. Not long after they had reached this conclusion, while they sat round eating what they had brought with them, which wasn't very much, and drinking from the well (though with some misgivings in view of what they thought might lie below – but they were that thirsty!), what did they see coming towards them but a majestic young man riding an equally majestic horse, as unlike the Giolla Deacaire and his nag as it was possible to be. He told them that he was king of that country, which was called Sorcha, meaning the bright and cheerful land. Hospitably he invited them to his palace where he entertained them and they told him why they were there. The king listened to their story with interest, and more, for when they were done he pledged himself to help Fionn in his search for the missing members of his band. Fionn was in the middle of thanking him when a breathless messenger burst in past the guards with the frightening news that a foreign fleet, so big that it seemed to cover all the sea, had arrived on their coasts and that the battle hosts landing from these black ships were so numerous that they could not be counted. Shortly thereafter another messenger arrived to announce that this terrible host was ravaging the land with fire and with sword. Immediately Fionn offered to help the King of Sorcha and, indeed, could go further because, from the description of the messengers, he recognised the enemy as the forces of the King of the World, an old adversary of his own, and he advised Sorcha not to fear as 'many times have we met these foreigners on the shores of Ireland and they have always yielded to us in battle'.

The King of Sorcha summoned his troops and they advanced on the enemy so that the brilliant spear-points of the army of Sorcha danced in the sunlight like the radiance of a sparkling sea and the black helmets and spears of the army of the King of the World advanced ominously across the plain like a host of bats until they mingled and meshed with one another in violent combat so that the noise rose above them like the crash of multitudinous thunderstorms and the swords and the spear-blades flashed like lightning. Black ravens screamed over the battling hosts and the dogs of war filled their bellies for two nights. On the third day, the King of the World took what was left of his army and sailed away, leaving many ships and many dead behind him.

Fionn and the King of Sorcha celebrated their victory with a great feast and as they sat at it before their tents above the battlefield they saw coming towards them a great host with banners and standards and arms glittering in the evening sun. At first they feared it was an attack, but as the host came closer they could see that it was led by Diarmuid and beside him rode the Knight of Valour, who was no longer the Knight of Valour only, but also the King of Tír fa Thonn following the defeat and death of his brother, the Knight of the Fountain, at the hands of his army under Diarmuid's command. The two Kings and all their people, the men of the Fianna, and the two magic princes celebrated their victories and successes and the two Kings did much to try to persuade Fionn and Diarmuid to stay with them as their chief advisers and generals. But Fionn explained that he was already the general of the army of Cormac Mac Art; and Diarmuid that his loyalty was to Fionn and that, in any case, their immediate concern was to locate the Giolla Deacaire and his awful horse and Conán Maol and the fourteen members of the Fianna who had disappeared on his back.

Now it so happened that the Knight of Valour who was now King of Tír fa Thonn was also a wizard and could command magic in his own right. What's more, his particular talent was divination and Fionn didn't have much persuading to do to persuade him to try the exercise of it to locate his missing men. The Knight of Valour stood up and went in front of the table and between it and the fire. He drew himself up so that he became tall, then taller. He became thin and thinner, and green and almost transparent. He looked up at the tumbling stars of the massy night wheeling through the archways of time. He raised his arms to them, but – or so it seemed to Fionn and the others – the stars were visible through him. He was an outline – but when they sought his delineation they could not find it. Showers of sparks flew up from the fire to mix and mingle and be absorbed by the stars, and the Knight of Valour seemed to have done a similar mingling. And yet he had not left them for his presence alone bound the entire together, the finite and the limitless void – and it was a peaceful presence. It seemed to them that he began to bend slightly, a movement as elusive as that in the blackest night when one must look for it with peripheral vision, as if he moved with the winds. There came a low moaning sound, but where it came from or how or even why, was more than any man there could tell. After a while the Knight of Valour resumed his own shape and, as if nothing had happened at all in the interval, was able to tell Fionn that the Giolla Deacaire who had taken the men of the Fianna was none other than Abharta of the Tuatha de Danaan who had brought them to Tír Tairnnge, the Land of Promise. Unfortunately he could not tell them why Abharta had done such a queer thing when the Fianna had no quarrel (or none that they knew of anyway; it was always possible that someone disliked them without their knowing it) with him.

After resting a few days to recover from their battles, Fionn and his men set out again to track their companions across the plain and over the sea from island to island, from shore to shore, until, at last, they reached the Land of Promise. And it is an interesting thing and an indication of the cleverness and cunning of the Giolla Deacaire that, while he came from and returned to the west, the Land of Promise, known as Mann, was in the east, so that they had to go halfway round Ireland in their little boat to reach it. But if that was an obstacle and a hurdle to them there was a compensation in it too for Diarmuid had been fostered there by no less a person than Mananaan Mac Lír himself, whose home it was and who, indeed, gave to the island its lasting name. Accordingly, Diarmuid knew both the place and its god-king.

For that reason he persuaded Fionn against the burning and pillaging that Fionn, in his natural irritation, was inclined to do. And it was no easy task either persuading him. Fionn's dander was rightly up, and he was deaf to all persuasion and blandishment. So, when his arguments didn't seem to be working too well, Diarmuid added in the heel of the hunt: 'Eh, Fionn,' he said.

'What?'

'There's another thing I forgot to tell you which maybe you should know.'

'Dam' the thing you could tell me would make my change my mind,' said Fionn. 'Burning and slaughter are too good for them.'

'Agreed,' said Diarmuid amiably, 'and I'd be the last man to argue that with you' – which only goes to illustrate that there is a logic extremities which has nothing whatever to do with reason, for he had been doing nothing else for half an hour. 'But you should know it all the same.'

Fionn growled, and it was the species of growl that was neither assent nor dissent, but left to the 'growlee' the choice of interpretation – and woe betide him should he decide wrongly.

'The fact is,' went on Diarmuid, ignoring the baleful and warning glare in Fionn's eye, 'that the men of Tír Tairnnge are almost always druids and wizards.'

Fionn pursed his lips. 'Is that a fact?' he asked.

''Tis,' nodded Diarmuid, 'and what's more,' he went on, 'they're fierce good at it. You saw yourself what the Giolla Deacaire and, God knows, he mightn't have been the best of them.'

'Druids, you say?' asked Fionn.

'The best,' said Diarmuid.

'Hmmm . . .' said Fionn.

'Do you know what I'm thinking?' asked Diarmuid.

Fionn shot him a look sideways, and Diarmuid went on quickly. 'I'm thinking,' he said, 'wouldn't we be better off having the like of them for friends instead of enemies? Maybe if we sent heralds looking for the release of our companions instead of the old fire and sword bit . . .'

'Just the very thing I was thinking myself,' said Fionn, remembering the Giolla Deacaire and the manner in which he had stolen the fifteen men of the Fianna.

Fionn looked at Diarmuid and reflected that it was, after all, a noble and goodly thing to be forgiving and magnanimous. That decided, he sent heralds to Abharta's castle, and you'd hardly credit what they saw before them when they reached it. There were their missing companions, dam' the bit the worse for wear, enjoying themselves and being treated with courtesy and consideration with the finest of food and drink and comely maidens to wait on them. Beat that, now. But, wouldn't you know it, with all that they were mad anxious to return to Ireland and the Fianna and the life they knew as fast as ever they could. But that wasn't all. Picture the surprise of the heralds when they met Abharta, as handsome and cordial a man as the Giolla Deacaire had been ugly and offensive – and they the same man. Nevertheless they did what they were told and delivered Fionn's message. Having consulted with his chief man, and now he was uncovered, Abharta agreed to return Conán Maol and his companions and also – and this was the sign of a proper nobleman – to allow satisfaction for the injury he'd done the Fianna.

After that Fionn and Abharta made a compact friendship and they all feasted for three days and three nights. During the course of that feasting Abharta told Fionn the reason for his assuming the disguise of the Giolla Deacaire and behaving as he did. 'Twas the simplest reason in the world and one Fionn understood well: what else but to win renown for himself in his own land by demonstrating his superiority over Fionn and the Fianna? He hadn't counted on their being clever enough to track and follow him and now he acknowledged them the better men. When the feasting was over on the fourth day an assembly was convened to decide on the satisfaction to be provided by the Giolla Deacaire, of which there were to be two, one to Fionn as leader of the Fianna and one to the men who had been taken.

So far as Fionn was concerned the matter was easily decided. Abharta had acknowledged him to be the better man (which he was), and Fionn wouldn't be less magnanimous. 'I'll accept no award, Abharta, because of our new friendship,' he said. 'And because of that I'll give you instead the wages we agreed on when you came in the disguise of the Giolla Deacaire – a *taurcrec*[1] – and, from this out, you'll give me your friendship and allegiance.' Everyone was pleased with this generous statement, particularly the Fianna who felt that Fionn's reputation had been enhanced.

But when it came to Conán Maol it was a different matter, for he was not so easily satisfied. 'It's all very well for you, Fionn,' he said. 'You didn't have to put up with much,' which, looking back on it, seemed less than accurate. The men of the Fianna looked at each other uneasily remembering the old enmity between the Clann Morna and the Clann Baiscne since the time of Fionn's father who had been killed by the Clann Morna, and Fionn himself banished and hidden for fear of being killed too. Conán Maol went on: 'You didn't have to endure the sharp bones and the monstrous buffetings of that outlandish animal or you might think differently.' So vehement was he in remembering it that both the Fianna and Abharta were hard put to it to keep from laughing at the look of him. But Conán Maol was a truculent and short-tempered man at the best of times so they disguised their mirth as best they could, but it was a rare fit of coughing that overtook most of them there.

Then Abharta said: 'Well, Conán, whatever you might want me to do I'll do it, for,' he added, 'I've heard of your ability to poke fearful insults and taunts at a man and I wouldn't want to draw down the power of your ridicule on my own head.'

Conán grunted in acknowledgement of what he considered to be a compliment. 'Very good,' he said, 'give me a minute now while I think.'

When they heard this, Fionn and the Fianna became very anxious in case Conán Maol, whom they knew to be well endowed with meanness and concupiscence, would bring disgrace on them all by claiming gold or silver or women maybe from Abharta. But, for all his meanness, Conán Maol was neither a fool nor entirely dishonourable – though he could have come close to it at times.

After a solid minute, during which he screwed up his thick and globular features into the simulacrum of a bloated walnut and flashed his small eyes out of that perplexed and wrinkled rotundity from one side to the other with the effort of his thought, and while the sweat broke out on the baldness of his head with concentration, Conán said: 'I would not demean you by asking what is unfair, or myself by asking what is less than my due?'

There were murmurs of cautious and dubious assent, but Abharta said nothing. He only smiled and nodded.

Conán went on: 'That being the case, this is my award. You must choose fifteen of your noblest men; recover from whatever bleak and unendurable place you have pastured it that unspeakable animal you miscall your horse; mount them on it; and, with ourself holding onto the tail, follow the self-same track back to Ireland you made us take coming here to the destruction of our bones and our muscles; through the same surging seas, the same thorny woods, over bleak islands, through rocks and dark glens.'

When the men of the Fianna heard this they laughed as much in relief as anything else and agreed it was indeed a just award. Then they took their farewells of Abharta and returned directly to Ireland. They went straight to Knockainey and scarcely had they reached it when what did they see coming towards them at great speed but the same mighty horse with fifteen sorrowful looking nobles of Tír Tairnnge clinging to its back for dear life and the Giolla Deacaire, holding fast to its tail where he was subject to numerous unmentionable afflictions consequent upon his location and the usual activities, internal and external, associated with that end of a horse in motion, trundling and galumphing along behind. They made a melancholy and hilarious sight and the Fianna laughed, and cried with a single voice that Conán Maol had a right good award.

On came the great nag and the Giolla Deacaire until they stood before Fionn and his men as gloomy and doleful as ever, with the fifteen miserable nobles on board. The Giolla Deacaire came round to the front – and a woeful sight he was too, covered from head to foot in this and that, if you follow me. But he said nothing. He stood for a moment, then suddenly pointed above and behind the Fianna so that they all looked round to see what it was he was pointing at. When they did there was nothing there; and when they looked back again to where he had been, the Giolla Deacaire, his great horse and the fifteen noblemen who had been clinging to its back had vanished. They had gone from their sight in the twinkling of an eye, and remained so forever – which goes to show that Diarmuid might have been right about their wizardry and to speak up to Fionn about it, and that Fionn had been wise to listen to what he had said; two commodities, forthright speech and the wisdom to act on it, in short enough supply these days.

That is the story of the Giolla Deacaire.

FOOTNOTE

1 The gift of an overlord to a subordinate king or noble.

The Death of Oisín

Third Period: Fianna Cycle

This remarkable story is evidently a Christian synthesis of an older model. Clearly and deliberately it sets out to bridge the gap between the historical and the proto-historical periods. It also reflects, perhaps intentionally, the third of the three great traditional achievements of Saint Patrick: the conversion of Ireland; the codification of its laws; and the preservation of its literature. In recent years, the latter two have tended to be overlooked. But it is very largely thanks to the wisdom and foresight of the early Christian missionaries in Ireland, no less than to that of their successors who were scribes, that we can still enjoy these ancient tales from pre-Christian Celtic Ireland. It was they who, firstly, decided that these old tales should be preserved and, secondly, wrote them down – albeit, perhaps, laundered here and there – in order to ensure this. The Fianna Cycle seems earthier and less 'heroically' outsize than the earlier Cycles, and the treatment used here is intended to reflect this in, I believe, a manner that is true to the spirit and intent of the original. The essential theme, which reflects aspirational values both understood by, and part of, the expectancy of the pagan Celts, nonetheless – and, in the circumstances, very understandably – places the emphasis on an exchange of worldly pleasures for the greater promise of heaven.

Well, unlike every other story, this one begins *both* before and after, for when Patrick, who became the patron and saint of Ireland, reached here in the year of Our Lord 432 on the command of Pope Celestine to bring the Word of God to the Christians of the west, he was fifty-six years of age, it wasn't his first visit to Ireland, and Oisín had been living in Tír na nÓg – but here I am finishing my story before 'tis started at all. Very good! Back to a beginning.

When Patrick was a youth of sixteen by the name of Sucatus – and 'tis just as well he changed it for I don't think the other would have gone down too well with the Irish people; St Sucatus, patron of Ireland hasn't the same ring to it at all, and he might have had to give way to some other individual with a tidier handle – wasn't he captured by Irish raiders and brought back to be sold as a slave, which was his fate until he escaped about four years after? Understandably he was therefore knowledgeable – if not exactly enthusiastic – so far as Ireland and the Irish people were concerned. So when the Pope sent for him and told him he had to go back to Ireland to convert the Irish people to Christianity, he wasn't exactly jumping up and down with enthusiasm, as you might suppose. But, sure, what could he do? Celestine was the Pope! But his reluctance made him cautious and that caution served him well. So did his knowledge, for didn't it make it possible for him, besides his great work of conversion to the faith, to do a powerful number of things in other areas besides, notably the law and the literature?

Patrick was no daw, and he knew well that the soul of a people was in their work as well as in their spirit inside – 'By their fruits shall ye know them'. He was always eager to seek out and talk to poets and *ollamhs* and other wise men whose stories and histories, passed on from one generation to the next by word of mouth for countless hundreds of years (or maybe written down in the secret language of the druids on wooden books like fans), he carefully wrote down himself in the Latin tongue for their safer preservation.

One day news was brought to him of a very strange and old man, a giant, if you please, who seemed likely to die and mystified all who spoke to him by his extraordinary stories. Now it so happened that Patrick was at Tara as a member of a royal commission set up by King Laoghaire to regulate and codify the laws of the land when he heard the news of this remarkable old man. Divil a one seemed to know who he was or where he came from and many dismissed him as soft in the head. (As a matter of fact hadn't he come to the royal city itself and camped himself on the road not too far away, lamenting the past and telling stories to anyone who would listen in a ragged crowd of all ages who didn't know whether to laugh at him or cry. Very few of them stayed to listen for long anyway, except the children, and some of them teased the old fellow, but more sat wide-eyed listening to what he had to say to the end.) I needn't tell you that Patrick set off as soon as he could to see this phenomenon.

When he arrived, the old man, a giant indeed, no doubt about that (eight feet tall if he was an inch), raised a bony hand in greeting and made the following poem before he said anything else:

> These hands you see are withered;
> These deeds have long been stilled:
> The tide has passed, the sands have come
> And all my strength have gathered.
>
> Yet, thanks to the Almighty
> My years were rich and free,
> But now my wretched days are long.
> And I was fair to see!
>
> Of all was I the treasure,
> Once women filled my pleasure:
> No weakness that I leave the world,
> My spring has filled its measure.
>
> These little bits you crumble,
> This fasting wretch to fumble:
> A little for stone, a little for bone
> A little for this hand, now humble.[1]

The old man, clearly some class of a beggar, thought Patrick, reclined on a huge cloak against the bank, sheltered slightly from the sun by the old and rickety four-wheeled chariot he had somehow acquired. The two hacks which pulled it grazed heedlessly on the long acre, *súgán* (hay) ropes spancelling their hind legs and long leather reins, which they would be less inclined to chew, tethering them loosely to a blackthorn that sprouted from the bank bordering the road. Having introduced himself in response to the greeting from the old man, Patrick said: 'And who might I have the honour of addressing?'

The old man looked at him from very deep-set blue eyes, almost studying him, measuring him as it were against what he was about to say before saying it. Then he replied: 'I am Oisín of the Fianna, son of Fionn Mac Cumhail and Poet of Ireland.'

Patrick looked back at him with no change of expression. Obviously the poor man was deluded. Equally, Patrick had no wish to give offence. So instead of answering directly or casting doubt on what the other said, he observed: ''Tis a long time since the Fianna were heard of.'

'So they say,' said the old man, looking back at Patrick from those deep-set eyes.

'Two hundred years or more,' said Patrick.

'So I'm told,' said the old man.

'That's a powerful long time,' said Patrick.

'A long time,' agreed the old man. 'Is it the way that you don't believe me?'

''Tisn't that I don't believe you,' said Patrick, 'for I have no reason to disbelieve any man 'til he makes me, but 'tisn't every day you meet a man who, by his own account, must be getting on for two hundred and fifty or maybe three hundred years of age. Would you agree with me?'

'Indeed,' said the old man. 'And I would agree. And I can tell you 'tis no comfortable thing to be that old and have the memories to go with it and dam' the one to share them with, and be the butt of ridicule and laughter if you try. I'm telling you 'tis a sad thing to be a fish out of water and yearn for your own kind and realities that are only memories now; histories wrapped in the mists of time to . . . them!' He waved a mighty arm around, encompassing the world.

'Uncomfortable,' agreed Patrick.

'Will I tell you about it?' asked Oisín.

'Indeed,' said Patrick in his turn, 'there's nothing I'd like better.'

'First,' said the old giant, 'I must tell you about the fearful battle of Gabhra which, as everyone knows, is in the vicinity of Garristown (near Dublin). When the great Cormac died,' he went on, 'he was succeeded by his own son, Cairbre, who wasn't the same man at all. Not at all!' he repeated emphatically. 'It was bad enough,' he went on, 'to have Fionn succeeded by his son when there were plenty of others to choose from, but this particular individual was credit neither to himself, nor to his father, nor to much else for that matter. But, if you'll excuse me, you'll appreciate that I speak with some prejudice, for the first thing he did was to terminate Fionn's leadership of the Fianna. Indeed, he went further and banished Fionn and myself and the whole Clann Baiscne from the Fianna and appointed instead our sworn and vengeful enemies, the Clann Morna, headed by Gall Mac Morna. Wasn't that a fearful and woeful thing for a man to do?' he asked Patrick, glaring at him.

'Well,' said Patrick judiciously, 'splits and divided interests are still common enough, I must tell you, and I daresay,' he went on, 'things will stay that way for some time to come.'

'Well, whatever,' growled Oisín, 'that's what the blackguard did, and Fionn and his followers, myself included, went south and we allied ourselves with Fearcorrib who was King of Munster at that time and who also chanced to be Fionn's grandson – my own nephew, if you don't mind – and we rose out against Cairbre and the Fianna because of the injustice he'd worked on us.'

Wisely Patrick held his peace and nodded at the old man to go on.

'This,' said Oisín, 'led to the battle of Gabhra where the two armies met and slaughtered one another. ''Twas a bad day's work,' he said, 'for it brought about the end of the Fianna and much else that Cormac had built up and established so far as government and education were concerned. Cairbre was killed in it too,' he added as an afterthought.

Patrick coughed, but prudently, for while he did not want to indicate impatience at an old man's ramblings, he was also anxious for him to stick to the main story.

'Anyway,' went on Oisín, 'shortly after that fearful battle, what was left of us were below near Killarney hunting – and remember,' he went on looking at Patrick with fierce eyes, 'hunting was all that was left to us then. Dam' few palaces or castles, and those that were left weren't up to much. Oh 'twas a different story to when Cormac was alive, I can tell you. Reduced to hunting for what we could get to fill our bellies, no less, for a living! That was our condition.' He leaned over, cleared his throat, and spat delicately beyond the hem of his cloak. 'Anyway,' he went on, 'there we were, when what did we see one day but a rider coming from the west and, since the sun was setting at the time, 'twasn't until they were close that we could see it was a woman, a maiden, and she on a white horse, the grandest animal ever you saw. And I can tell you now that never was seen anyone so beautiful or fair, with the finest clothing and the most beautiful golden hair. The caparisons were to match.'

He paused; remembering, I suppose.

'She rode straight up to Fionn who asked her who she was. She looked down at him (and the strange thing was she never got down from the back of the horse; and the reason for that will become clear later on) and said, "I am Niamh of the Golden Hair and I am the daughter of the King of the Land of Youth (Tír na nÓg) that you sometimes call Tír na mBeo (the Land of the Everliving) or Magh Mell (the Plain of Pleasure)."

'"Well," said Fionn, "you're a long way from home and what brings you here so far across the sea?"

'"Easily answered," she said. "I have never been betrothed or married to a man for all that I am what you see" – and there is no doubt that no man there had ever seen such a beautiful woman. "But I love your son, Oisín, and that is why I've come."'

'That was all she said,' went on Oisín, 'and I needn't tell you there was no man there more surprised than myself. But my heart was already lost to her. I looked into her two beautiful eyes and fell into their depths straight off. I crossed over to her and took her hand in mine. 'Twas as if I was lifted up into the bright sky and I told her that I loved her too and added, which was the truth, that she was a golden star of brightness and beauty . . .'

The old man's voice went off with remembrance somewhere and now his eyes followed – and his heart too – for 'twas a minute before he continued. 'Then,' he said, swallowing, 'she said a surprising thing, although 'twas no hardship for me to hear it.

'"Oisín," she said, "I put you under *geasa*, solemn vow, to come with me to Tír na nÓg, the most delightful country under the sun, where you will be my husband and we will live together forever."

'"Willingly," I said.

'But if it was easy for me to say such a thing and my heart already gone to her, 'twas a different matter for my father and the remains of the Fianna to hear me say so. Fionn became very sad and said to me, "I do not expect that I will ever see you again, Oisín, or that you will ever return to me."

'But what could I do? It was a great sadness for me to leave my father and the men of the Fianna, but leave I must with my golden Niamh. I could not prevent my own tears, but I promised to return again after a little while and so I mounted behind my lady and we galloped west, back the way she had come. When we reached the golden waves of the western sea the horse made no pause; but, leaping forward, his hooves barely touched the waves and we moved across the ocean faster than the wind itself, with tumbling billows before us and behind us and on every side. Presently we saw a glittering palace like the morning sun rising over the waves in the distance before us (and that was a strange and wonderful thing since the sun was sinking in the west and the rising sun would appear behind us in due course, but that is how it was), and I asked my lady where was this.

'"It is the Land of Virtues," she said. "Its king is a giant Fomorian who brought my sister away by force to be his queen, but she has put him under *geasa* not to marry her until she can find a champion to fight him in single combat."

'As was only natural, I asked her if this had come about as yet and she said "no" and that her sister remained in bondage because no hero had as yet come. "In that case," I replied, "let us go and I will see if I can defeat the Fomorian and free your sister."

'"If you fail," she said, "it will mean that she will be forced to marry the Fomorian; you will be killed and I will be at the loss of you, my own love."

'"What choice have I?" I asked, "Sure what other hero is about?"

'And so Niamh directed the horse to the Land of Virtues and when the great steed galloped onto the strand the young queen herself came to visit us. She kissed her sister and welcomed me and brought us to her palace, which was the most lavishly furnished I had ever seen. She sat us on golden chairs and gave us the most wonderful of fruits and meats to eat and drinking horns filled with mead and hazel nuts. As we sat there eating and drinking our fill, she told us her story, and, with the tears streaming from her eyes, she said that she feared that she would never leave this place that she hated, or the giant she hated even more, to see her country or her people again so long as the giant was alive. Moved by her plight I swore to her that I would free her and kill the giant. No sooner were the words out of my mouth than we saw him coming towards us, a huge, ugly brute of a creature carrying a monstrous iron club in his hand. Without greeting or other courtesy he forthwith challenged me to battle.

'And I can tell you, although I had fought many battles in Ireland and elsewhere with villains and foreign invaders, with wild boars and wizards, never before did I find it so hard to defend myself. He drove at me with that great club of his and smashed it so violently about that he tore up the countryside and broke trees and branches and uprooted bushes, frightening the deer and the creatures of the forest and the birds of the air so that they all deserted the place where we fought for three days and nights without food or sleep or rest. At the end of that time I was bruised and bloody and my spears were both broken. My shield was in tatters and all that was left to me was my sword; and I was hard put to it with that to prevent him from crushing my skull and breaking my bones or doing me some other mortal damage.

'At last I was on the point of giving up from weariness and exhaustion so that it made no difference to me if I won or lost the battle so long as it was over, when I happened to look across at the two Princesses nearby and saw them weeping as if the sky was about to fall, and with that I rallied and summoned what was left of my strength. Thinking I was finished, the giant rushed in to slay me, but as he raised his club I rolled under it on the ground with sudden speed and hamstrung him with a blow. With an almighty roar he fell and it was like the crashing down of a tree in the forest. The earth shook when he struck and before the reverberations had passed I swung my sword again and severed his ugly head from his body.

'My exhaustion and weakness were such that I was scarcely able to appreciate the ministrations of the two overjoyed Princesses who ran to my side as soon as I had delivered the stroke. Indeed if they had not taken me each by an arm it is likely that I would have fallen where I stood. Gently and between that strange mixture of tears and laughter and practicality common in women when moved by great joy, they brought me into the palace and bathed me and tended my wounds with healing herbs and gentle skill.

'After I had rested a full day I dug a hole and buried the giant. I raised a *cromlech* over him and cut his name on it in ogham and put my name beside it so that the world could see who lay there and who had slain him. Next morning, saying goodbye to her sister who was to follow in due course, my lady and I resumed our journey to Tír na nÓg.

'We galloped again across the tumbling billows of the glorious sea and passed many strange cities and islands and white palaces. A great storm arose; the sky darkened only to be lit by many lightning flashes. But though the wind blew from all points of heaven and though the waves rose up and roared about us, the white horse moved on through the turmoil without turning to right or to left, carrying us safely even though the heavens breached, the seas cracked, and the very foundations of the world shook as we passed.

'When at last this terrible storm had ended and the sun again shone I saw before us a land of beautiful plains, purple mountains, lakes and white waterfalls. Close in front of us was a magnificent palace of gold and glittering precious stones and Niamh told me that this was her home. Like any horse returning to its stable, the white steed trotted towards the shore and we dismounted to be met by a splendid company of knights from the palace. Red and purple and green and white and gold were the many flying banners that fluttered cheerfully above them and their armour glinted in the sun as they rode down to greet us on shining chestnut steeds. They were followed by the king and queen at the head of a multitude. No words could describe their brightness which excelled that of any pair of monarchs in the whole of the broad world.

'They greeted us and made us welcome and after they had kissed their daughter, the king cried aloud to the entire assembly there and then that I was who I am and that I was to marry his daughter Niamh, who had travelled to Ireland because of her great love for me to bring me hither. He took me by the hand and welcomed me before all the people. He told me that I would be forever young in that land and forever happy there and forever the beloved of his daughter, Niamh of the Golden Hair, who would be my wife.

'Then I, too, addressed the multitude, first thanking the king and his queen, but most of all Niamh who had come to fetch me. Then we went to the palace where we were entertained at a banquet, and the feasting and the laughter lasted for ten days; and on the last of them Niamh and I were married. For three years happiness overwhelmed me living with Niamh in great joy. At the end of that time, as I thought, a great longing and desire to see my father and my people again overcame me, and the more I tried to refrain from thinking about it the worse it became and intruded on my every thought until at last it was impossible for me to rest easy and I had no choice but to ask permission of the king and of Niamh to visit Ireland again.

'The king readily granted his permission. At first Niamh tried to dissuade me. However, the yearning and longing in my breast was such that I would not be persuaded otherwise and I asked her again. Again she tried to persuade me, and a third time I asked; and so, finally, she said: "Since you wish to go so greatly I will give my consent, but I am extremely reluctant and I feel sorrow in my heart for I fear that if you go you will never return to me."

'As best I could I tried to dispel her fears, telling her that of course I would return and that I loved her beyond anything and that there was no need for her to feel any doubt or dread of any kind. Then I thought of the white horse and I asked, "Does not the white horse that brought us here know the way? And will he not bring me to and fro safely and well?"

'For a moment she considered this and then, still with a sorrowful face, spoke what I thought at the time were these very strange words: "Although I am filled with fear and grief I will no longer deny you; but I must warn you before you go, Oisín, that you will not find what it is you so long for. This is Tír na nÓg and you have been here a full three years. Ireland is not now what it was when you left."

'I thought that was a strange thing for her to say at the time, but realised that there would, of course, have been changes in my absence. But what she said next was even stranger: "Fionn and the Fianna are gone – no more. Where they were is an army of priests and monks . . ."

'I opened my mouth to interrupt her, but she laid a finger on my lips and continued: "Now, Oisín, remember what it is that I say to you and do not forget it. Above all, remember, if you once alight from the horse while you are in Ireland, allow your feet to rest on the soil of the land, you will never return here. Again I say and warn you: if you stand on the sod of Ireland you will not return to me. And yet again a third time, Oisín, I warn you. If you dismount from the white horse you will never see me again."

'Although I had no idea why she said these things or what she had in mind, of course I promised. But she looked at me knowing that I did so lightly and that I did not believe what she said. And at the great sadness of her face I promised her a second time, and even yet there was a fear and an ache and a pain in her eyes, and so I promised a third time. In no circumstances would I dismount from the white horse while I was in Ireland. Then, with my own tears mingling with hers, I set out on the great horse. My longing to see my father and the men of the Fianna was so great that, although the words she had spoken and the promises I had made rang in my ears, they made no connection with the anxiety and the longing in my mind to be in Ireland.

'It did not take long for the great white horse, moving like the wind and swiftly overtaking the great waves of the sea, to return to Ireland. But I scarcely knew it when I saw it.

> Where I remembered lords and princely halls
> And Fionn's and Cormac's blazing standards flew,
> Now slouched pygmy men by tumbled walls
> All ivy-clad, where weeds and nettles grew.
>
> No armies marched, the triumphs and alarums
> Were lost in dust, like Tara in the east.

Old heroes and their rusted arms
Overthrown by tranquil people and the bells of priests.

'Bewildered, I rode from one place to the next, providing awe and admiration for all the little people who saw me. I saw with amazement the multitude of churches and round towers, and heard the tinkling of bells throughout the land. Nowhere did I see evidence of the work of the great Cormac except on the roads that I travelled and in the fields where men had ploughed and now reaped the harvest. But the battalions and the knights, the castles and the gold, the slaves and the warriors had left the land, which itself was the same, but somehow different. At last I stopped to speak to some of these little men and women – at least they seemed so to me who remembered the heroes of my times. These people were astonished by my great size and majesty and more so when I asked about Fionn and the Fianna. It was they who led me to a true awareness of my situation and a greater understanding of what it was that Niamh had said. And yet when I did understand it, it was so overwhelming that I forgot the warning she had given me.

'What they told me was how much time had passed in Ireland while I had been gone; and it had been three hundred years. They told me more; that Fionn and all my company of friends had been dead for more than two hundred years and there was, indeed, a legend still alive about me and my going to Tír na nÓg, and they looked on me in wonder when I told them who I was. When I heard all this, a great sorrow and wonder overtook me, as was natural, I suppose, and I mourned the loss of my father and all the Fianna. In that frame of mind I turned the head of my great steed away from those little people and wandered through Ireland seeing those places I had known of old, now greatly changed. We passed through Allen in Kildare where my father had had his headquarters, where all was bleak and tumbled and covered in nettles and where once there had been glory and glitter and the voices of heroes. I continued north in the general direction of Tara and on the way came to a place called Glenasmole on one of the great roads that Comrac had built and not too far from the ford on the river Liffey at Ath Cliath.

'A group of men were trying to move a rock which had tumbled onto the road, but they could not budge it. Seeing me approach and because of my great size, as it seemed to them, they asked my help. Indeed looking at it I thought it was a shameful thing that all of them together could not lift or move a stone that my son Oscar would have tossed over his head with one hand had he been alive, so leaning down from the *dillat*, that is the saddle-pad, I grasped it and, putting forth my strength, flung it forty yards or more off the roadway. But with that great strain, the girth of the *dillat* broke and, leaning forward to save myself from falling, I suddenly found myself standing on my two feet on the ground.

'The realisation of what I had done and where I was overwhelmed me and I stood still looking down at my feet planted firmly on the road. As I did, two dreadful things occurred. The great white horse that had carried me so carefully and steadfastly across the boiling ocean from Tír na nÓg and over the length and breadth of Ireland, whinnied and tossed his head and backed a few paces and then turned and bounded off with the speed of the wind, and, as he did so, a terrible change came over me. At first I thought it was a sickness – and perhaps it was in a manner of speaking – but I became dizzy and my eyes grew dim so that I could no longer see clearly. Even my own feet in their boots seemed to shrink and grow weak. My strength failed. My youth and manly beauty departed, and I fell to the ground the old and withered man you see before you. Never again did I see the white horse, which was my only means of returning to Tír na nÓg, nor have I ever again recovered; and here I live and languish sorrowing for my beloved wife, my Niamh of the Golden Hair, whom I shall never again look upon; sorrowing too for my father and the lost companions of my youth whom I will now shortly join in death.'

Patrick had taken careful notes of all that Oisín told him and his heart went out to the old man who, if he was to be believed, had passed from the splendour of a young man to that of an ancient and crumbling one in circumstances beyond the understanding of man. 'There is little I can do for you to ease the pain and anguish you have suffered in this life,' he told Oisín. 'But if you open your heart and listen to my words then I can promise you a new life after death where you may again experience happiness with those you love.' When he had listened carefully to what Patrick had to say to him, Oisín agreed to be baptised and, no sooner was this ceremony performed where he reclined against the bank by the roadside, than he closed his eyes and the lines of care and anxiety faded from his face so that he died in peace and tranquillity.

FOOTNOTE

1   See Eoin Neeson, *Poems from the Irish* (Dublin, 1985).

Saint Patrick, the Smith, and the Swindling Publican

Near Contemporary Folktale

This story is not from one of the mythological cycles. It belongs to folk tradition and is relatively modern, with the distinct evidence of that vibrant peasant culture that reached its full flowering in the nineteenth century, and which developed after the flight overseas of all but the vestiges of the native Irish nobility during the seventeenth and eighteenth centuries. It is meant to be heard and not read, preferably in a Munster accent. The dialect is based on that of Munster, specifically that of West Cork/Kerry. It belongs exclusively to an oral tradition, now all but vanished, though it was still very much alive forty years ago. It clearly has local relevance, but may well be adapted from an older version since it seems too well constructed to have derived solely from the activities of one publican in whatever remote district.

Such stories became the cultural walking-sticks of the *seanachies*, or story-tellers, who also kept alive oral versions (often bowdlerised) of the mythologies when most other avenues of traditional culture had been closed. Stories like this usually translate into colloquial English directly from Irish. In the process they may lose the nuances of Irish and what remnants of classical language they might have originally possessed, but what may be lost from one language is richly compensated for in the other. They bring to English a liveliness of expression and a freshness of imagination and inherent humour which have helped make Irish literature written in English a distinctive and living literary form of considerable importance.

The homely, folksy, impossible Saint Patrick is only all too possible in simple human terms, even if the idea of him sharing a drink with a blacksmith and his companions in the local pub seems a bit far-fetched, although he contents himself with 'the nice little fizzy stuff'. The paradoxical humour was hardly lost on the listeners any more than that of the older stories was on their audiences. I first heard this story as a child in West Cork. I am very indebted to Eddie Lenihan for reminding me of it and kindly allowing me to hear and record his inimitable version which he had from a Kerry source.

278

S aint Patrick was doing a bit of converting one time around Macroom, or a bit west of it, and he had a good crowd got, mind you, given the place he was in. Most of those that showed up were sympathetic enough and didn't vex him too much with awkward questions he mightn't have had the answer for too handy; though looking back afterwards at the baptisms most of them agreed they didn't know in the name of God what was all the water about. The salt was bad enough, but the water was a nuisance, most of them having washed themselves clean in the morning. Be that as it may anyway, scores of them turned out to hear Patrick preaching the good Word.

And, begob, d'you know what, after the day at it, between blessings and saltings and waterings, of course didn't Saint Patrick's hand get a small bit stiff – and coming on towards evening time, I might as well tell you, the temper was getting a bit short with him? So, between one thing and another, whatever cranky rattle he gave the bell, didn't he break it!' Cracked it down the middle! Well, that put the cap on the whole story. Religion was forgotten; the people were sent home and Saint Patrick's helpers packed up all the traps into the box. And very quiet about it they were too because they knew the great man wasn't in the best of form after what had happened. When all was done they gathered around him and said, 'We might as well move on now, so, Patrick, the night is coming on and 'tis a fair ould hike to the hostelry.' They walked in silence!

Now, as luck would have it, before the night fell hadn't they to pass what happened to be a forge. And of course, I needn't tell you, hadn't one of the men the bright idea of going in and saying to the smith: 'Hi! Do you fix bells, by any chance?'

'Well, God blast it, hi!' said the smith, aiming the belt of a hammer at the anvil. 'Will you go on out of here with your "Do you fix bells?". What kind of a fancy shop do you think I'm running in this place at all? Horseshoes is my trade and that's it!'

Well, my man came back to Saint Patrick who was there waiting on the road, not too pleased with himself, and he told him how the story was. Saint Patrick heard him out. Then didn't he draw his robes tighter round him, gather himself and walk to the door of the forge, saying, 'I'll sort this man out.'

And God knows, he wasn't ready either for the kind of view that he met inside in that place, and nothing glowing except the fire above at the top, and this huge, black, smoky man behind it and he hammering away. You know 'twould put the heart crosswise in a man that had less courage than Saint Patrick – but, as he was as far as the door he says he might as well go on. And in he went.

He was just at the anvil when he says to the smith, 'My good man, can you do anything about this bell?'

And the minute the smith saw who was there now with all the green and gold robes didn't he mistake Saint Patrick for a Kerry druid and the manner changed entirely.[2] Man, he began to wipe his hands on his apron and he laid down his tools beside him and came forward and he said, 'Oh, welcome to my humble abode, sir. And, eh, is there something I can do for you?'

'Are you listening to me at all, or what?' snapped Saint Patrick, whose humour hadn't improved much. 'Didn't I ask you could you fix the bell?'

'Oh,' said the smith quickly, 'no bother at all. Show me it a minute.' And he took it and looked at it, and gave it a rattle – but, of course, it made nothing but a kind of cracked sound.

'God knows,' said the smith cautiously, 'that the bell has seen a lot of use.' But, catching Saint Patrick's eye, he went on hurriedly: 'But I'll see what I can do.'

He went over in the corner. Usually he had a heap of iron and that was his stock in trade. But, he had a small little collection of daintier stuff over in the corner for high occasions and accidents and, God knows, after rooting and getting at the finer types of metal he had hidden didn't he roll out a little piece of silver!

And the job that man did! You'd never think, with his big hairy fingers, that he would be so gentle. When he was finished – and 'twas no long time either (with Saint Patrick looking at him all the time like a hawk) – he gave the bell another rattle and, d'you know what? 'Twas as good as new.

Saint Patrick couldn't believe his ears. He tried it himself. And while he was shaking it, 'Hi,' he said, 'd'you know something? Smiths aren't as stupid as they look.'

If 'twas any other man he'd be struck between the two eyes. But the smith liked the look of Saint Patrick. He wiped his hands again – needless to say after the job he had done – as he walked over to him. And Saint Patrick said: 'How much do I owe you?'

'Well, sir, seeing 'tis yourself that's in it,' mistaking him again for a druid, 'I won't charge you at all. But d'you know what we'll do? Did you, eh, by any chance notice the house down the road a small bit?'

'Indeed and I didn't,' said Saint Patrick. 'I have more to be occupying my mind than noticing houses. What kind of a house is it?'

'Well, ah,' said the smith, 'to tell you the truth, 'tis a pub, if I might say so. Do you take a drop yourself, sir? I hope you have no objection to my suggesting now that we'd go down there and wet our throat because, d'you know what, I'm after putting in a hard day in this cursed place and I wouldn't say no to a small dropeen at all.'

'All right,' said Saint Patrick. It wasn't in him to refuse the man after the good job he was after doing on the bell. So down the road they went, and the rest of the men following on behind.

They went into the pub anyway and the smith gave Saint Patrick one look as they were roving in the door, and says, 'Watch this.' They went up to the counter and, God knows, when their eyes got used to the gloom inside Saint Patrick noticed that there were only a couple of very miserable looking customers up against the counter, and not one of them a bit happy-looking with himself.

'Twas the smith called the order and he said to Saint Patrick, giving him a nudge with his elbow, 'What'll you have?'

'Oh, you can get some little thing with a fizz in it for me,' says Saint Patrick. 'I don't like the strong stuff.' So the smith ordered for the two of them and, of course, he ordered beer for himself.

Now, there were a lot of bottles up along the shelves and the smith caught Saint Patrick eyeing them, so he gave a nudge again to Saint Patrick and said: 'Hi – eh! 'tis the same stuff that's inside in all of those: poitín³ of the worst kind: rotgut. Stay away from 'um.'

'Oh, indeed I will,' said Saint Patrick. 'I'm only having the nice little fizzy stuff I asked you for.'

While the man was down behind the counter filling the beer – and in those times of barrels filling a pint was a matter of monstrous skill and considerable dexterity with the barman running from barrel to barrel, the pint glass in one hand and his other on the tap; a large dart from the flat barrel and a squirt from the high one to give it a head, if you don't mind – while that was going on the smith was looking down behind the counter at him.

'Ah, blast it! He's at it again,' he whispered. 'Did you see that?' he demanded, turning to Saint Patrick.

'What's that?' asked Saint Patrick.

'Look,' whispered the smith, who was getting ratty again, 'wait 'til the drink comes and I'll tell you.' He didn't want to be barred for 'twas the only pub around.

Well, when the drink came and the man put it up on the counter even Saint Patrick, who was no seasoned drinker, could see that there was something wrong. God knows high! 'Twas only three-quarters up on the glass, and most of the rest of it froth and black things floating around above inside in the froth.

'D'you know what,' says the smith, 'if 'twas another time and another place I'm telling you that man wouldn't be standing where he is now taking my hard-earned money off me; but, since there's no other pub within twenty miles of this place, what can we do?'

'Do you think,' said Saint Patrick, 'that this is the usual?'

'Huh,' said the smith, 'indeed an' it is. He don't give right measure to any man coming in here. God knows what can we do about it? Sure his father was the same before him.'

'I see,' said Saint Patrick. 'Well, now, I might be able to do something for you here.' And he addressed the barman, 'Eh, my good man! Come here a minute!' The man came up.

'What kind of an animal,' asked Patrick 'is that you're feeding there with the shy eye at him?'

The man inside the counter looked out and there was an old dog thrown down outside the bar, his own dog, that was all skin and bone with a bleary, half-starved look to him. 'Well, God knows,' says the barman, 'he's not getting the best of feeding. But he won't ate it.'

'I wasn't thinking about him,' says Saint Patrick. 'I was talking about the other lad.'

'What other lad?' said the barman.

'The lad under the stairs.'

'The lad under the stairs, is it? Uh-huh! I dunno anything about him.'

'Well, come on so,' says Saint Patrick, 'and I'll show you.'

And with that away with him down the hall as if he knew that house back to front – and he was never there before in his life. (But he had the power!) Down along the flagstones with him, and when they got to under the stairs there was a little door and Saint Patrick says to the barman who was just behind him, 'Open that.'

And of course the barman says: 'There's nothing inside there only things for cleaning out the place. But if you're so anxious to see for yourself, I'll show you,' and he opened the door. But, if he did, he jumped back again quick: the fright of him!

'God knows,' says he, 'where did that fella come from?' Because there, sitting inside on a box under the stairs and right pleased looking with himself, was the craziest looking creature you ever saw; two big shiny hooves on him and hairy legs; plenty and plenty of meat up along him and the belly hanging down; hairy drawers and the big, silky whiskers of him. Oh, a well-fed looking customer right enough! God knows, but the barman was shoving back now towards the wall where he could make a dart for it any minute.

'Where did he come from?' cried he. 'I never put him in there, or I never did put a hand on him.'

'Oh no?' says Saint Patrick. 'Well, I'll tell you who he is.'

'Well, while you do, close the door because I don't like the way he's smiling at me at all,' said the barman.

'Huh, and why wouldn't he smile at you?' asked Patrick. ''Tis well known he'd smile at you or anyone else feeding him nicely.'

'Me?' says he. 'I never saw him before in my life!'

'I'll close the door,' said Saint Patrick, which he did. He shut it in . . . and they went back down to the bar where they had a little bit of conversation with the man of the house.

'Now, look,' says Saint Patrick. 'Every drop of drink you're not giving those men, drink that they're paying for, is going down into that fella's belly and 'tis no wonder he'd be well-fed looking.'

'Well, God knows,' said the barman, 'I – I don't believe you.'

'Well, hi, if you don't, then 'tis you'll have to sleep in the same house as him. And what'll you do when he bursts the door out and bursts the stairs up when you have him fed enough?'

'Mind you, aye,' said the barman thoughtfully. 'I won't take the risk. I'll believe you. What can I do?'

'Well now,' says Saint Patrick, 'I can't take him out for you. You'll have to do that yourself.'

'Me, is it?' said the barman. 'I won't put a hand on the dirty thing.'

''Tis you put him in there,' said Saint Patrick, 'and 'tis you must get him out. No one else can do it for you.'

'But how?' asked the barman.

'The only way is, eh, give every man his due. I'll go on from this house now,' says Saint Patrick, 'but I'll be back in a while – I have a bit of baptising to do up the country, and I'll be coming back this way again in a week, or maybe two; I dunno when. And, eh, if you do mean this now, give every man his due. We'll see.'

He went out – and the smith with him, and God knows no respect for size, he was fairly high. 'You did lovely. Hi,' said he, 'I'd say he'll do what you said.'

'We'll see,' said Saint Patrick.

They went off that night even though the smith had invited them to stay the night with him; but Saint Patrick said, 'I'm promised somewhere else, and I'll have to be there.'

So they set off and they went wherever he was going the following day and days after that. But the day came for going back along that road again and all the men he had with him were in a high state of excitement wondering what would they see, or would Saint Patrick likely work a new miracle, or what.

Of course the first call was to the smith – a kind of courtesy. And the minute Saint Patrick put his head inside the door, the smith cried out to him: 'Hi, welcome! Come on and we'll go across the road and see what's what because I didn't do a right day's work since with nervousness and a shake in my hand wondering when would you be coming back.'

They went across the road and I can tell you the man of the house was very anxious to see them. Didn't he put up drinks for the house? (Mind you there weren't too many in it at the time.) And, no charge! A thing that never happened before under that roof!

'Now,' says Saint Patrick, 'that's a bit of a change.'

'Well, change,' said the smith. 'You wouldn't believe the change that's in this house since you left. Full measures for every man and his every third drink free. Look at the dogeen there on the floor. The bones aren't coming out through him no more.' And that was true. The dog had a happy look on his face, the first time anyone could remember such. 'But,' said the man behind the bar, 'I'm anxious to know about the fella inside.'

'Right,' said Saint Patrick, 'we'll go down and see him.'

And down they went. And God knows there was a different structure entirely. Huh! 'Twas big blocks of stones and they blocking the whole hallway, and every night and that poor man going to bed he had to climb up over them and down the other side at the risk of breaking his neck. But he thought to keep the fella in and was taking no chances. What would he do if the fella came out during the night and took the hand off him? And I'm telling you there was heat coming out of the place where he was.

So! 'Pull back the stones there,' said Saint Patrick, 'and we'll see.' And of course the smith, being the mighty man he was, made short work of the stones . . . which only proves that if the fella inside wanted to, the man of the house was putting his bet on the wrong horse.

They opened the door anyway, and – oh! The sight that met their eyes! 'Twas a different story now entirely. The mildew was on the hooves and the shin-bones were showing under big kneecaps sticking out; and the loose skin where the belly was – the Lord save us! – and the ribs showing also; and only patches of beard on him and a forlorn look in his eye. The minute he saw the light, he made one mad dive out under the smith's legs and, clatter, clatter, clatter, down along the flagstones of the hall, out through the door, and was seen no more.

'God,' says the man of the house, 'he didn't delay! And did you see the cut of him?'

'I did,' said Saint Patrick, 'but I hope you saw the cut of him and I hope you'll take a mark from that, that in future you'll give every man his due that comes to this house; and if you don't that fella'll be back to take up residence under the stairs, or over them, maybe, and torment you, and I won't be here to advise you. What do you say to that?'

The man of the house hadn't a word to say to that. But, needless to say, there was no more trouble in that house; and from then on the custom got better and the customers more plentiful – in keeping with the trade of the place.

FOOTNOTES

1 The use of the word 'rattle' suggests a tongued handbell. In fact the bells used by the early Irish missionaries were tongueless bells struck with an implement of some sort, like oriental temple bells.

2 Green and gold are the county colours of Kerry. Traditional nineteenth-century representations of Saint Patrick invariably depict him as a mitred bishop, usually attired in Gothic vestments of green and gold, earnestly banishing snakes from Ireland, which is wrong in every particular. See *Crucible*.

3 Moonshine; note the diminutive 'ín' (een). Also in 'dropeen', a little drop; 'dogeen', a little dog. Pot – a still.

Select Bibliography

Atkinson, R.J.C. *Stonehenge* (London, 1960)

Bergin, Osborne, and R.I. Best, *Leabhar na hUidhre* (Dublin, 1929)

Binchy, D.A. 'The linguistic historical value of the Irish law tracts, *Procedures*, XXIX (1943)

Bolle, Kees W. *The Freedom of Man in Myth* (London, 1981)

Campbell, J.J. *Legends of Ireland* (London, 1955)

Carleton, William *Tales and Stories of the Irish Peasantry* (London, 1845)

Carney, James, *Studies in Irish Literature and History* (Dublin, 1955)

Caughlan, Ronan, *Pocket Dictionary of Irish Myth and Legend* (Belfast, 1985)

Chamberlain, Basil Hall (trans.), *The Kojiki* (Tokyo, Asiatic Society of Japan, 1885)

Clark, Graham, and Stuart Piggot, *Prehistoric Societies* (London, 1965)

Colum, Padraic, *A Treasury of Irish Folk Tales* (New York, 1954)

Cunliffe, Barry, *The Celtic World* (London, 1982)

Dillon, Myles, *Irish Sagas* (Dublin, 1954)

Dillon, Myles, 'Celtic religion and Celtic society' in Joseph Raftery (ed.), *The Celts* (Dublin, 1964)

Dillon, Myles, *Early Irish Society* (Dublin, 1964)

Ellis, Peter Beresford, *A Dictionary of Irish Mythology* (London, 1987)

Fairchild, H.W. *The Noble Savage: A Study in Romantic Naturalism* (New York, 1961)

Fox, Cyril, *Life and Death in the Bronze Age* (London, 1959)

Fraser, J. (ed. and trans.), 'The First Battle of Moytura', *Eriu*, VIII (1915–17)

Gantz, Jeffrey, *Early Irish Myths and Sagas* (London, 1981)

Greene, David, 'The Celtic languages' in Joseph Raftery (ed.), *The Celts*, Early Irish Society, 1954

Hamilton, Edith, *Mythology* (New York, 1940)

Hawkins, Gerald S. and John B. White, *Stonehenge* (London, 1960)

Herodotus, *The Histories* (London 1954)

Hull, Eleanor, *Cuchulain: The Hound of Ulster* (London, 1906)

    The Cuchulain Saga in Irish Literature (London, 1898)

Jackson, K.H. *The Oldest Irish Tradition: A Window on the Iron Age* (Cambridge, 1964)

Joyce, P.W. *Old Celtic Romances* (Dublin, 1905)

    A Social History of Ancient Ireland, 2 vols. (Dublin, 1920)

Kinsella, Thomas, *The Tain* (Oxford, 1970)

Leahy, A.H. *Heroic Romances of Ireland*, 2 vols. (Dublin, 1905)

Levi-Strauss, Claude, *Structural Anthropology* (London)

MacCana, Prionsias, *Celtic Mythology* (London, 1970)

Meyer, Kuno (trans.), 'The Wooing of Emer', Stowe, M.S., *Archaeological Review*, i, 1906

Mitchell, Frank, *The Irish Landscape* (London, 1976)

Murphy, Gerard, *Duanaire Finn* (London, 1954)
    Saga and Myth in Ancient Ireland (Dublin, 1961)
'Notes on Cath Maige Tuiread', *Eigse*, vii 1953–55
Neeson, Eoin, *The First Book of Irish Myths and Legends* (Cork, 1966)
    The Second Book of Irish Myths and Legends (Cork, 1967)
    Aspects of Parallelism in Japanese and Irish Character and Culture (Tokyo, 1992)
    The Nihongi, W.G. Ashton (trans.) (Tokyo, 1972)
O Duffy, Richard J. (ed. and trans.), *The Fate of the Children of Tuireann* (Dublin, 1906)
O Grady, Standish James, *Selected Essays* (Dublin)
O Faolain, Eileen, *Irish Sagas and Folk Tales* (London, 1954)
O Neill, Desmond, *Crucible* (London, 1986)
    Of Gods and Men (London, 1987)
Powell, T.G.E. *The Celts* (London, 1958)
Power, Patrick, *Sex and Marriage in Ancient Ireland* (Cork, 1976)
Raftery, Joseph, *The Archaeology of the Celts in Ireland* (Dublin, 1964)
Raftery, Joseph (ed.), *The Celts* (Dublin, 1964)
Rees, Alwyn, and Brinley Rees, *The Celtic Heritage* (London, 1961)
Rolleston, T.W. *The High Deeds of Finn* (London, 1910)
    Myths and Legends of the Celtic Race (London, 1912)
Sansom, G.B. *Japan: A Short Cultural History*,
Smith, Margaret, 'The limitations of inference in archaeology', *Archaeology Newsletter*, VI 1955
Stephens, James, *Irish Fairy Tales* (London, 1924)
Stokes, Whitley, The Second Battle of Moytura, *Revue Celtique*,
Sutcliffe, Rosemary, *The Hound of Ulster* (London, 1963)
Tierney, James J. 'The Celts and Classical Authors' in Joseph Raftery (ed), *The Celts*,
Wheeler, R.E.M. *What Matters in Archaeology*, 1950
Yadin, Yigael, *The Art of Warfare in Biblical Lands* (London, 1963)
Xenophon, *The Persian Expedition* (London, 1949)